ACROSS THE BIT

ACROSS THE BITTER SEA is a compulsively
readable novel in the great tradition of the
historical saga. Set in Ireland, it covers the
period from 1885 to 1916—a time of terrible
poverty and political unrest. The heroine is
Alice, a passionate woman of peasant ancestry.
When a landowner, Samuel, falls in love with
her, Alice's mother agrees to the union. She
has had to send two of her sons off across the
bitter sea to America in search of prosperity
and knows this could also have been Alice's
fate. During the turbulent years that follow,
Alice is able to observe the dramatic political
events from both sides. She follows the career
of a man of her own class, Morgan Connelly,
whom she also loves, with interest. Alice's
fortunes and those of her children are
inextricably linked to the Irish Movement in
this widesweeping and absorbing novel of
ideals and love.

THE ROSE TREE

'O words are lightly spoken,'
Said Pearse to Connolly,
'Maybe a breath of politic words
Has withered our Rose Tree;
Or maybe but a wind that blows
Across the bitter sea.'

'It needs to be but watered,'
James Connolly replied,
'To make the green come out again
And spread on every side,
And shake the blossom from the bud
To be the garden's pride.'

'But where can we draw water,'
Said Pearse to Connolly,
'When all the wells are parched away?
O plain as plain can be
There's nothing but our own red blood
Can make a right Rose Tree.'

W. B. Yeats

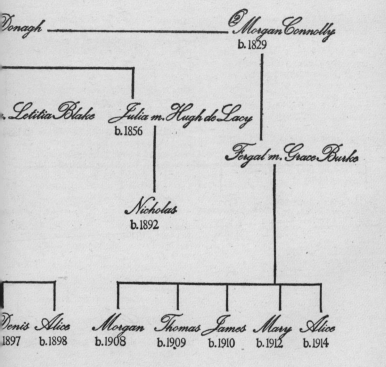

Donagh ———————————————— Morgan Connolly
b. 1829

Letitia Blake   Julia m. Hugh de Lacy   Fergal m. Grace Burke
                 b. 1856

                        Nicholas
                        b. 1892

Denis   Alice   Morgan   Thomas   James   Mary   Alice
1897   b. 1898 b. 1908 b. 1909 b. 1910 b. 1912 b. 1914

To the memory of my husband,
Cormac O' Cuilleanáin

'The Rose Tree' by W. B. Yeats,
from *The Collected Poems of
W. B. Yeats* is reproduced by
kind permission of Mr M. B.
Yeats and Macmillan & Co.,
London, and the Macmillan
Company of Canada

First published in Great Britain
by Hodder and Stoughton
Limited 1973

Coronet edition 1975
Seventh impression 1989

Printed and bound in Great Britain
for Hodder and Stoughton
Paperbacks, a division of Hodder
and Stoughton Ltd., Mill Road,
Dunton Green, Sevenoaks, Kent
TN13 2YA (Editorial Office: 47
Bedford Square, London WC1B
3DP) by Richard Clay Ltd.,
Bungay, Suffolk.

ISBN 0-340-18802-2

PART
ONE

1

On a warm June day in 1851, a week before her eldest son's wedding, Mary MacDonagh was out in the far potato field in the morning. She moved slowly along the edge, by the wall, looking at the ground as if she were searching for the nest of a renegade hen. She knew the hen was dead and gone; ten days ago she had found the carcass in a field, well chewed by rats or foxes, but she had provided an alibi for those terrible compulsive trips to the potato field by asking the neighbors if they had seen the brown one laying out. She was entitled to search the fields for her, while she eyed the crop of potatoes. The flowers were fine and white. The leaves were glossy and thick. There was no sign of withering, no brown spot, no smell of rot, that ghastly smell that all Ireland had breathed in with death for what had seemed like a lifetime.

She was sheltered by the shoulder of the hill from the mountain wind and the scents of summer floated all around her, compounded of salt and seaweed and grass and potato flowers and roses, with a strong addition of manure from the nearest neighbor's pig shed. That was a comforting smell, showing that the pig at least was alive and well.

Mary knew that the neighbors were watching her, and she imagined their conversation with extraordinary accuracy. In every house except hers, there had been so many deaths that no one was in humor for a wedding. Yet they would feel obliged to come, out of gratitude for all the favors she had been able to do them. She fully realized her good fortune. If she lifted her eyes to look up the hill, the dead walls of many little houses were visible, where only six years ago children had played and men and women had worked in the adjoining fields among the accursed potatoes. Now the fields had gone back to grass and the pyramids of the gables were high-piled with fallen thatch and rotted rafters. A dark-brown stain of turf smoke would remain where the chimney had been, for as long as the gable stood. The lucky ones had gone to America, wailing along the desolate, unfriendly roads to Galway and Limerick and Cork. Of those who stayed at home, many had died of the famine fever.

Households of women were everywhere, and Mary knew

how she would have hated that. The women had proved tougher. She was afraid to count the men of her house, since this was said to bring bad luck, but she was not really superstitious. In a way, the removal of the terrors of superstition was one of the great blessings that old George Flaherty had given her. He had changed her attitudes utterly, making an insurmountable barrier between herself and her neighbors. They might in time have accepted her as a returned sinner. Her years as old George's tallywoman had to be forgiven, especially as she could be seen going to Confession and Holy Communion every six months. But the rift caused by her mental experiences was impossible to forget. Try as she would, she could not succeed in returning to the passive state.

Mary had been respectably married for twenty-four years now. She loved her husband, Thomas, dearly, as God knew, and yet the seven years during which she had been old George's mistress had never drifted to the back of her mind. She had learned not to refer to them in speech but almost every action, certainly every important one, was measured against her experience in that time.

She had been more successful in her marriage with Thomas but that was obviously only right, since God's blessing was on it. Every one of their ten children was living but the one daughter of herself and George had died in infancy. The pain of that still stung her sometimes, more rarely every year. At first it had been agonizing, so that she felt surrounded, shut in, cut off by it almost beyond bearing. Five years she had lived with old George before she had found she was pregnant. At first she had been terrified but old George had said, "What could be more natural? If it's a girl, we'll call her Mary."

Still he had not offered to marry her, and Mary even after so many years had not had the courage to suggest it. Old George was a gentleman, a rich man, a landlord with power of life and death. He had the mills in Galway, whose wheels were turned by the wild, swift Corrib river, which seemed afraid of him too, afraid to pause for an instant in its work for him. He had the great stone warehouses by the docks, where ships could bring in coal and timber to store for him. He had a yacht on Lough Corrib in which he could visit his own islands. Mary never called him George. To her he was always Mr. Flaherty, but then so he had been to his wife until the day of her death. One of the servants told Mary this. On the day she died, she said, "This baby has caused my death, Mr. Flaherty, but it meant no harm."

A very odd woman she was, they said, but kindly. Moycul-

9

len was a strange, wild place to bring an English lady. Old George was always promising to take her to Bath or London for the season but he never did. There she sat, day after day, doing her embroidery and trying on her hats, until the baby Samuel killed her unintentionally. That was in 1815, the year of the battle of Waterloo and yet another end to Ireland's hopes. Old George had made a fortune in the years before it, which was why he had had no time to take Sylvia traveling. Later, when she was dead, he had plenty of time, but he had been put off both marriage and traveling, it seemed.

Samuel was five years old when Mary moved into the big house. In theory she was his nurse but no nurse wears a red silk dress and dines at the master's table. George had looked so old—to an eighteen-year-old girl he became old George at once—but he was only fifty then, tall and thin and athletic, with dark weather-beaten skin and iron-gray hair. He treated her like a lady, so successfully that she could refuse him nothing. After her first night in his bed, she ran home to her mother, trailing her red dress in the grass and ruining her London shoes.

"Didn't you know that was what he wanted?" her mother said. "You're spoiling your good dress. Now that it's done you may as well go back. You won't mind the next time. It's like that always."

"But it's a sin."

"And what are we to eat?" her mother asked tersely.

"You fixed it with him!" Mary said in horror.

"I did," said Mrs. Hogan. "We're alive and we'll stay that way if you have sense. He won't see us in want. He's a decent man. We're the one age. I know him all my life. He'll treat you right. Don't let him know you got such a fright. Men don't like that. Was he rough?"

"No."

Mary felt ashamed, for some reason, and could not look at her mother.

"Then you're all right. It's not in him to be rough. He'll never marry again. He won't risk another of his own class after that Sylvia and he's a strong, healthy man that needs a wife."

"You know a lot about him," Mary said sourly.

"I do. I'm the one age with him, I tell you." She stopped suddenly and then said fiercely, "Get back at once. The child might come to harm while you're gone."

So Mary had never complained to her mother again, though seven years later she had had satisfaction in hearing her uncle, her mother's brother Andrew, tell his sister that she had acted disgracefully.

"You sold your own daughter," he said. "You gave her to that landlord as a tallywoman when you should have been fighting to your last breath for her."

"We're not all fighters," Mrs. Hogan said, but sounding frightened, as well she might since Andrew was standing over her with his fists clenched and his face like thunder.

"You're no fighter, though all belonging to you were," Andrew said bitterly, sounding all the stronger because of the slight American intonation that he had picked up. "Hadn't you any respect for the rest of us that you saw striking a blow for Ireland in '98? Don't you remember that we had to clear out for fear of the likes of George Flaherty?"

"George Flaherty is a decent man," Mrs. Hogan said faintly.

It was her last protest. Andrew withered her with a blast of words in which he accused her of betraying the whole country as well as her own daughter. In the end Mrs. Hogan was in an agony of tears and agreeing that Mary must be got out of old George's clutches at once. Her child was dead, and Andrew had the delicacy not to say that this made things easier. He had a fine man eager to have her, Thomas MacDonagh of Cappagh, whose brother had traveled all the way to Chicago from Boston to tell Andrew of Mary's position and to make an offer for her.

So Mary had left George and Samuel, half bewildered with grief, for though she knew that they represented the sins of lust and luxury, still she loved them both with all her heart. George had aged a lot in the seven years and had developed a few old-mannish mannerisms that were a warning of coming decay, but still she hated leaving him. She was used to his ways and afraid of what she would encounter with Thomas, whom she had seen only once. He had come over from Cappagh to a funeral in Moycullen and had met her with Samuel at the edge of the lake.

"Mary Hogan." He repeated her name when she had said it to him. "And you're nurse to George Flaherty's child."

Samuel was too far away to hear. He was skimming stones very skillfully on the smooth water of the lake. Mary cast her eyes down. Anyone could see that Samuel was too old for a nurse. Thomas had heard the whole story, of course, as it was a scandal in the parish.

He said delicately, "I'd like to see you again, Mary."

She said, not more than half meaning it, "I'd like it too."

11

He sent a message to his brother in Boston and got her for himself. Such decisive action was frightening. It might denote a bully, or at least a man who would always be congratulating himself on having rescued her from a sinful state.

Thomas had not turned out like that at all, however. He treated her like a piece of valuable china. She was amused at this, and also at the fact that he respected her knowledge achieved in George Flaherty's bed. He took it for granted that she would be used to delicate ways, as indeed she was, and whatever he felt, he never once taunted her with the manner in which she had acquired them.

Thomas was twenty-seven, two years older than Mary, when they married in 1827. The relief of leaving Moycullen and its whisperers, and the traps and pitfalls of the big house, was good for Mary, so that she stopped resenting her Uncle Andrew's interference. He had given her a dowry of fifty pounds, a huge sum, and old George had added a chest of sheets and blankets, and a bed and chairs and a table so that the two-room house in Cappagh was like a palace. Not only that: he had sent Samuel riding ten miles over the mountain regularly to keep him informed of how Mary was progressing. This was a joy to Mary, who had feared that she would never see Samuel again. George never came himself, however, and she was glad of this.

So Mary had a houseful of fine men and the makings of men, as well as four daughters. At first she had watched her eldest son, Dan, with fascinated fear, until he reached the age of five months, at which her first child had died. She told Thomas about it over and over, and he listened with patience.

"I was just holding her, and she was laughing at me, and then suddenly she went soft on me, and I knew she was dead. Can you imagine that?"

"Yes, I can imagine it," Thomas said. And he poked Dan with his hard finger and said, "She must have had something from birth, the poor child. It won't happen again, you'll see."

Years afterward Mary recognized how heroic was his sympathy. She must have filled him with fears for his son, too, but Thomas was a man who believed in keeping certain things decently concealed. In fact he was always privately a little ashamed of the truth, which was that he cared more for Mary than for all his family of children put together. He bottled up his black jealousy of old George too, and his ugly triumph over the dead child. Mary sensed this, and knew it was something to be glad of, but still she wished he were as concentrated on their children as she was herself. It would have emphasized the good as well as the bad things that happened, so that they could be more deeply felt.

She stretched to her full height and looked down the hill toward the sea. The weather was settled. The water was like pale satin, with an elliptical flaw here and there. The pale-blue mountains of Clare flowed upward out of the far side of the bay, with darker patches where the valleys were. In toward Galway, the blue merged into dark green, flecked with the white of the bare rocks. Mary could see several currachs lying still and black on the surface of the sea. The men were fishing for rockfish, fat and dirty but wholesome to eat. Three would barely give a bite to everyone in the MacDonagh house and Thomas hardly ever brought home three. Little Mary would not eat fish, which was a saving. Born only three years ago, when Mary was forty-six years old, she had not the bloom of the other children. The neighbors rightly called her the scrapings of the pot, predicting that she would be the last child, but her mother was determined to rear her for all that.

As Mary speculated about the number of fish that might be caught, she saw a new movement on the sandy road that ran out from Galway. Over the hill, a little procession was coming, a donkey drawing a flat cart on which a crowd of people sat like a heap of old clothes, and several men walking. She did not pause for a second but gathered up her red petticoat and ran down the green boreen to the house. Alice was there. She would give away everything in the house if the tinkers reached it before Mary did.

She scuttled around the side of the house and flew into the kitchen as the tinkers turned into the lane. Alice looked up from the fire, holding the potlid in her left hand and the fork with which she had been prodding the potatoes in her right.

"What's on you, Mother?" she asked, but not in alarm, since Mary was always in a flutter about something.

"It's the tinkers. Will we shut the door? They're in the lane."

"Then we can't shut the door."

They looked at each other. They were remarkably alike in appearance, both with jet-black hair, though Mary's was going gray, both tall and thin and straight, both white-skinned with a luminous wild-rose bloom, which Mary still retained after eleven pregnancies. The most remarkable feature was their eyes, dark blue and with a deep and steady intelligence.

The half door darkened and a tinker's voice said aggressively, "God save all here!"

Alice opened the door and said, "Come in, let ye, though ye won't all fit."

The three smallest children crouched against the back wall of the kitchen. Then feeling the solidarity of common danger they began to punch and nip one another and give little shrieks of mock terror.

Mary turned on them fiercely and said, "Be quiet or I'll warm your bottoms!"

They crouched closer and watched her with caution. She kept a switch on the mantleshelf and often let fly with it when they annoyed her too much. They had noticed that she was especially touchy when the tinkers were around. This tinker was a new one, a tall, strong red-haired man with a powerful voice. He ignored the rest of the family and addressed himself to Alice.

"We heard there's a wedding."

"That's right. My brother Dan. But it's in a week's time."

"We'll be here for it," the man said quickly. "We'll bring him luck and a fine family. Why isn't it for a week?"

"Sure, a day has to be fixed for a thing like that," Alice said with amusement.

"We heard it was tomorrow." He blocked the doorway. Behind him, his family and relations had climbed down off the cart and were clustered to peer into the kitchen.

One of the women said softly, "That's a fine pot of potatoes you have there."

Mary turned away, but Alice said, "Would there be enough in it for the whole lot of you?"

"There would, *agrá*, and plenty. But what about yourselves?"

"There's time to boil more. The men aren't home yet."

And Mary saw Alice drain the potatoes and give the whole potful to the tinkers to eat outside on the grass. They ate them skins and all, grabbing for them and guzzling them like animals. Then the same man came back and thanked Alice for her goodness.

"There's talk of famine and more fighting," he said. "We came up through Limerick and we heard it. Houses knocked and the people out on the roads. It's a pagan country. Why aren't ye all gone to America?"

"There's two boys going after the wedding."

"It's a grand place, enough for all and money flowing like water. I wish I could go but they don't want the likes of us there. Anyway, I'd be afraid. What day is the wedding?"

"Wednesday."

14

"I'll be here and I'll have news. My wife is good to sing a song. Have you a few sods of turf to spare for the fire? The nights are cold."

"Take what you want."

He took a huge armful from the rick at the gable but scrupled to come for a second after such hospitable treatment.

Alice watched the sad little procession move away down the road and said to Mary, "They won't get much out west."

"They'll get as much as anyone else," Mary said but she did not reprove Alice for giving away the pot of potatoes beyond saying, "I hope they won't tell the world the good treatment they got here or we'll have every tinker in Ireland on our floor."

2

Three mornings later, on Saturday, Samuel appeared, as Mary had known he would. She was ready for him. She had sent the three small children with a can of sour milk to a widow who lived two miles distant. That got them out of the way. Dan was over at his Agnes' place doing a bit of whitewashing, as well he might, since he was going to move in with her family. Two of the boys had gone in to Galway to see about their tickets and she had sent another to Peggy Michael's to help her with the outside work, which she had to do since her husband's death—planting and earthing potatoes, cutting turf, minding the pig and the goat—she would find plenty for him to do. Peggy was too old even for spinning, though she still collected moss for the dye when she felt like it. The two older girls were allowed to stay at home, since it would not look well to show a house empty of all except Mary and Alice. Thomas was earthing up the potatoes today, which kept him nicely occupied.

Mary had two eggs ready to boil for Samuel, as well as a loaf of white bread, but that was nothing to what Samuel had for her. She was so overwhelmed that she had to sit down and watch him helplessly while he brought the things into the house. He had come in his gig, the long way around by Galway instead of over the mountain on horseback as he usually came. A whole sack of flour he brought in, from the mill, of course, and a bag of currants to put in the bread on the wedding day. He brought oats, too, to make the hens lay, and a half bag of yellow meal for porridge. He brought sugar and candles and, most extraordinary of all, six bottles of red Spanish wine.

"That's for the old people. Their stomachs mightn't stand poteen," he said. "There's whiskey, too, and a few lemons for punch."

"Punch!"

"And punch can be made of the poteen, too. You'll have poteen?"

"Of course. Jim Black is bringing it on Monday. You'll be coming, Samuel? It's our first wedding."

She glanced upward at him shyly from her place on the hob. Her hands still hung slackly in awe at the magnificence piled on the table and the floor.

Samuel looked directly at Alice and said, "I'd like to. Would it be all right?"

"Why wouldn't it be all right?" Alice said. "Can't a man do what he likes?"

And she looked Samuel up and down deliberately but in a friendly, cheerful way, without a trace of doubt. Indeed he could see her admiration, which she made no effort to conceal. Samuel was tall, like his father, but his features were more angular. He was said to resemble his mother, who had been the thin kind by nature. Old George was thin, too, but from hard exercise, and he had a thin mouth, apparently fixed, like his eyes, in a tense, watchful way from habit or necessity. Samuel had a softer, kindlier look, a little uncertainty in his manner, which made Alice like him. He was well made and clean-looking, which attracted her as a good boat would have done. His well-fitting clothes and polished top boots were seemly. She liked looking at him.

Mary said, "Is your father well?"

"Yes. Riding every day. He complains of rheumatism but no more than usual."

That was the sort of talk they always had about old George, but Samuel kept his eyes and ears open so that Mary's requirements were always dealt with before even she had become aware of them. The extension to the house had been the most remarkable of these. It now had five rooms, an unbelievable luxury. Built in an L shape, from the front it looked like every other cottage in the area. The extension was at the back and was like a whole house in itself, with thatch and fireplaces. Samuel had supervised the building, which was done ten years ago by Thomas and his older sons, who were then only boys but well able to work. It was then, too, that Samuel had instructed Mary in the use of whitewash and disinfectant to keep out disease. The sweeping brush was to stand in a bucket of disinfectant always, he said, and the house was to be whitewashed inside and out every six months. Grandeur, the neighbors called it, and disrespect to the dead who had been taken by the fever, but Mary cared nothing for that. She would have done anything that Samuel told her to do. He had assured her that this was the way to keep her family alive and it seemed to have worked.

Now Dan was going to do the same and Agnes' mother was offended about it. The house wasn't good enough for the tallywoman's son, she had said, but Agnes had quieted her with threats. It had all come back to Mary, of course, and she had spoken to Dan about it.

"How will you ever live with that old hake? She has a wicked tongue."

"Agnes says she'll keep her quiet."

"She won't be able."

"Agnes will be disgraced if I don't go there. Her brother is gone out. There's room for me."

"You can come here, if you want. I wouldn't mind Agnes around the place. She'd be a help to me. She's a good girl."

But Dan would not consider introducing a thirteenth person into the house.

"I said to Agnes that we'll try it for a while. I said we can go to America if we can't stand it."

"God bless America," Mary said sourly.

"Sure, I know, but maybe we won't have to. There's time enough for that later."

Wednesday was a fine day for the wedding. It was in the new church in Barna and the priest came out from Galway for it. Samuel had brought a little money this time, though they had an unspoken rule that gifts were always to be in kind. Now there were three sovereigns for the priest, so that there need be no collection for him, which was just as well since there was not a shilling among all the pockets in the church that day.

The priest came up to the house afterward and drank a fine glass of whiskey, though he had been preaching all the year about the evils of drink. As Mary handed it to him she said apologetically, "A small drop will do you no harm. A wedding is hard work."

He cocked an eye at her but she was quite innocent. The house was shining with cleanliness. The dresser was newly painted and there were ornaments and luster jugs on the man-

17

telpiece. Knowing the source of all this wealth, the priest shut his eyes and sipped his whiskey. In all Connemara, beds and tables and chairs were almost unknown. A bundle of straw, the earthen floor and a few big stones substituted for these things. Some people had a stool or two. Mary's property was the wages of sin. When she came to Confession he made sure she repented but he sometimes questioned her about the presents she still received, to make sure there was no quid pro quo. At last they had agreed that old George was entitled to salve his conscience and that at the time he had made use of Mary he had known no better.

The presence of the priest kept the company subdued. There could be no free-and-easy talk, since apart from religious considerations it was known that he was on the side of the landlords. In the blackest days of the great hunger, he had got up in the pulpit every Sunday and told them that a good Christian will pay his rent even if he dies of starvation to do so. Their reward was in heaven, he said, and many of them were to go there very quickly and find out if this was true.

Morgan Connolly edged into a corner by the dresser and watched the priest chatting to a too-respectful Mary, holding his glass and taking it as his right that a little circle should be clear around him while he drank. Potatoes and fish and sour milk were not his daily diet, Morgan could see, and he hated the bland sheeplike face and the smooth hands of the man. Dress him in any other clothes and you would take him for a landlord's agent.

Alice moved directly in front of him and blocked his view.

"You're glaring at the holy man of God," she said softly with a little chuckle. "If he sees you, he'll turn you into a goat."

"I was thinking he looks like a sheep," Morgan said. "He'll be going soon, I suppose."

"Of course."

He did go, a few minutes later, and until she had to see him to the door Alice kept guard over Morgan and his dangerous tongue. He had had only one glass so far and his voice was still low.

"If we had the priests and the bishops behind us we'd be free long ago, but they're sold out to law and order and that's the landlords—"

Alice watched Samuel to make sure he was too far away to hear. It was early in the day for talk of landlords. She said, "For God's sake, Morgan, keep quiet today or you'll start something. Samuel is here."

"I saw him. Samuel is all right, though all belonging to him are landlords—"

"Wait till tomorrow, Morgan, please. You'll spoil Dan's wedding with that sort of talk."

So Morgan was quiet. The tinkers came, as they had said they would, and the big tinker's wife sang in Irish the song "Young Red-haired Sally" for which she was celebrated all over Ireland. It was a man's song by right but no one minded that. She was tall and thin and fierce-looking, like her husband, and she had red hair like poor Sally in the song. She stood with her back to the fireplace and with her eyes shut, and while she sang, tears forced their way through her eyelids. Mary and old Peggy Michael held her by a hand each to give her moral support. The tune had long lines, extended still further by many decorations and grace notes. It had a painful beauty that tore into Samuel's heart so that he pushed his way gently through the crowd of listeners to ask Alice, "What is this terrible song about? I've never heard anything so sad."

"Don't you know it?" And she began to translate softly as the song went on line by line:

" '*It's I am a pity on my way to Carrigane this holy day,*
Weeping and wailing and making my moan,
Carrying my child in the crook of my arm,
And not even a drop of milk I could give him.
I'm only a weakling, there's no denying it,
I have no more strength than the mist,
And the blood of my heart is shed in drops,
And O God, what wonder, after my red-haired Sally.
I'd rather have her in my own place,
Milking my little cow and minding my house,
Than the wealth of King George that I'd get with a stranger,
And it's under the sod I've left the love of my heart.' "

There were several other verses but Alice did not make any attempt to translate them. Samuel stood quietly beside her until the song was ended, overwhelmed with the pathos of what he had heard and wondering at the strangeness of singing such a song at a wedding. It was part of the attraction that these people had for him, the paradox that mixed heartbreak and tragedy with gaiety. Sure enough, right after the song, while the tinker woman was still being congratulated, the first tuning of a fiddle could be heard in the far corner, where Mary's big wedding chest was. It was Jim Black, called Black because his father was Black Michael, and it was he who

19

had brought the poteen. He came from Furbo, and though he owned no land, so far he was always a little better off than his neighbors. His door was usually shut since his old mother died, and he was out around the county with his fiddle or his poteen or helping with a day's tailoring. Like everyone else, he had found that his living had shrunk almost to nothing since the bad times had struck, but still he had not yet become a tramp.

In no time the floor was cleared and four couples danced a set. Everyone else pressed back against the walls and watched. Some were crowded in the doorway. The little fair-haired bride hopped and skipped about, never taking her eyes off her Dan. When they had finished, another eight took the floor. Samuel asked Alice for this one. A man from the mountain slapped his shoulder and said, "Good on you, for a Flaherty! If we had more like you we'd have a free country."

Samuel was pleased and knew they were watching him benevolently. He knew very little of what they said since most of their talk was in Irish. Because of their proximity to Galway, most of the people could speak and understand English but they did so with difficulty. There was more English around Samuel's home because the land was so much better and the landlords preferred to live there.

Afterward they made him sing, since Mary had of course told that he had music in him. First he sang "Barbara Allen," a great favorite, and then, a little too appropriately, the ballad of Rich Dives and Poor Lazarus:

> " 'Rise up, rise up, Poor Lazarus,
> And come along with me,
> And you'll go up to the heights of heaven
> To sit on an angel's knee.' "

And later:

> " 'Rise up, rise up, Rich Dives,
> And come along with me,
> And you'll go down to the depths of hell
> To sit on a serpent's knee.' "

He had a strong baritone that was much admired, as was his slight English accent, acquired partly in his English school and partly from his aunt whom he used to visit occasionally in Cheltenham.

20

Morgan watched him from every corner of the house in turn, milking the barrel of poteen at every opportunity. In the long, warm, bright evening, there was time for too much. The currant bread was eaten and the punch was made, and at last the bride was taken home in style in Samuel's gig. Her parents' house was on the Galway road, on a little track that led down to the sea. It had two rooms and therefore had possibilities. Dan was planning to build a real chimney instead of the makeshift one that was there at present, consisting of a hole stuffed with brambles, through which the smoke was filtered. He hoped that Agnes' mother would like him better when that job was done but just now he was so excited that he cared nothing for any of them.

When the bride and groom had gone, Mary burst into tears and had to be consoled with a glass of punch. It was her first drop that day. She had kept off it to make sure to maintain order but because of the punch she missed seeing Morgan go out of the house. Alice had just taken old Peggy home so that her daughter-in-law Sally, the young widow of her son, could come back for another few dances. They had taken turns like this all day with the children. Peggy could very well have gone alone but the dark had come down and she had had a drop too much of the punch for the good of her stomach and Alice feared she might fall.

The reward of her good deed was an encounter with Morgan. Like a wild animal he leaped on her and rolled her over on the grassy roadside. At first she was terror-stricken. Then she realized who it was and began to laugh.

"Morgan, you devil! You frightened the wits out of me."

He did not answer but breathed hard, pulling at her clothes violently so that she doubted for a split second if it was Morgan at all. Then anger filled her with a superhuman force. She drew off with her open hand and hit him a sledge-hammer blow on the side of the head.

"You Connemara man! You talk of freedom! You talk of Ireland, old Ireland that you'd like to save! You're no better than the most backward mountainy man in the country!"

She was hissing, in her fear of being heard. Morgan was quite still.

She said, "Do you hear me? Is that how you want to be? A wedding goes to your head—you want another one, quick. God forgive you, and I thought you were my friend."

Then suddenly she was in floods of tears and Morgan was beside her, afraid to touch her at first. At last he got up his courage and lifted her to her feet, and smoothed her skirt and her hair gently, and led her back to the wedding house where the dancing was still going on.

3

Samuel drove home in the heavenly white dawn, first along the hilly road by the sea of Galway and then skirting the town to the Moycullen road. He thought of visiting the mill but it was too early. Besides, he was too exalted and too tired to concentrate on any business. His head sang and his eyes prickled. The poteen had been wicked and the night warm, and now the sun had a painful brilliance that already warmed the air still more. At Loch an tSáile a seal had drawn himself upon a rock and was looking boldly around him. At this distance it was not possible to see him clearly. His watching attitude and tilted round head delighted Samuel and he slowed the pony to a walk, but the seal had heard them. With a slow, deliberate movement he slid gently into the water. Samuel had heard the men talk with anger about the seals, how they ate so much fish and broke the nets of anyone rich enough to own such a luxury. He wondered if Thomas would need a new net soon. It was not so easy to give presents of that kind to Thomas.

Samuel drove through the Claddagh, where turf smoke was already filling the air with sweetness. A solitary man was sitting in his hooker, going over his tackle. The sea was alive with squalling sea gulls taking advantage of the low tide to work the mud for worms. Samuel looked across to where his own big hooker, the *Saint Enda*, was moored to the quay wall. She was safe and sound, in perfect shape. He had not taken her out for a month. Mike Troy, an old Navy man, kept an eye on her for him. Having his pension and nothing else to do, he gave good service to the boat. Samuel wondered if Alice would like the *Saint Enda*.

He jerked the pony to a smart trot and set him to the straight road home, past the stark new university buildings, with their gray limestone walls and their gardens and their little new trees like walking sticks. Dust rose in a cloud behind the gig. To the right were rolling grassy hills that shut out the view of the Corrib river for a mile or two. There were big houses at intervals at that side of the road—Dangan, with its long winding avenue, and the Bates place, with a great smooth grassy lawn, then a mile before the beginning of Jerome Burke's land at Bushy Park.

A huddle of miserable hovels crouched by the roadside, each with its manure heap outside, each with its door shut at this hour. Samuel noticed that two more had been knocked down in the last few days. The mud walls were gapped and the doors were down where the crowbars had struck. They were Jerome Burke's property and Jerome stood no nonsense. Six months' credit was his last word. Samuel knew he was hoping to get rid of this collection of cottages. They were unsightly, being below the level of the road, which gave them a cavelike appearance. Jerome was planning to complete the long stone wall by the side of the road when this lot was gone, but of course he would wait until the people failed in their rent one by one. He would not put them out without reason. He would not have to wait long, as he very well knew.

Soon Samuel was driving past Burke's house, a fine, high, newly painted house half turned to the road, approached by a short avenue that curved between two little hills. It had style, partly because of the angle at which it was set and partly because of the curved flight of steps that led up to its white door. White-painted urns with geraniums finished off the painted iron balustrade. Jerome was a lawyer with a thriving business in Dublin but he always spent part of the year in Moycullen. The Burkes had three daughters, as elegant and as well cared for as the house, and a son. Amy, the eldest daughter, was sixteen now and had already been paraded for Samuel's inspection several times by her mother. Unmarried at thirty-six and sinfully wealthy, Samuel was a temptation to any reasonable mother.

He admired Jerome's house, as he always did in passing, for its neat whiteness. Even the curtains were lined with white, so that now in the early morning they blinded the windows.

After Burke's the road went sharply downhill and curved toward the lake. The pony always wanted to hurry here, knowing that he was near home, but Samuel held him in. Exactly at the foot of the hill, a great semicircle of land had been carved out to make the entrance to the estate. Tall iron gates stood between high pillars surmounted by stone pineapples. The pony turned in toward the gate, which was being opened hurriedly by Billy Thornton, who kept the lodge.

"I was listening for you all night, sir. Was it a good wedding?"

"Fine. I'm nearly asleep."

23

Billy gave a crow of laughter.

"You can sleep all day. That's what everyone does after a wedding."

This morning Samuel was not in humor for bawdy wedding jokes. He thanked Billy and trotted the pony up the avenue, feeling as he often did a thrill of joy in its beauty. On either side, smooth fields, grazed close by the cattle, stretched to where the woods began. The avenue was not fenced off and this enhanced the spacious appearance of the land. At first the house was out of sight and then a curve of the avenue brought it into view.

It was easily the best house in that part of Connacht. Built in 1701 by old George's grandfather, it had an elegance of the kind that can only be acquired at great expense. A short flight of steps led from an oblong gravel sweep to the carved mahogany door. The windows were all framed in mahogany, carved with birds and flowers and fruit, but the work was so complicated and delicate that there was no look of heaviness. The house rose three stories over the cellars. The whole front of the second floor, with seven long windows, was given to the drawing room. When she had first come, Samuel's mother, Sylvia, had put in French brocade curtains and Louis Quinze furniture, and so it had remained, covered in dust sheets, since the day of her death. Mary had been afraid of that room. She would no more have used it to sit in than she would have used a tomb.

Though it was not yet six o'clock when Samuel drove into the huge, cobbled, gray-walled yard to the right of the house, Paddy, the groom, came out of one of the stables. He took the pony and led him into the coach house. Above its wide doorway, the window of Master Fahy's room was open and a shadow crossing showed that he was up and about. He seemed never to sleep, or perhaps he took his sleep in short naps throughout the day and night, like a cat.

Pleased with this new notion, Samuel went into the kitchen, a great, square, flagged room with barred windows that looked out on the side of the house. Fat bunches of blue wisteria cut out the light because Samuel could not bring himself to have it trimmed back often enough.

There was no one in the kitchen and the fire had not yet been lit. He poured a glass of milk from the cool dairy and went upstairs, where he took off his boots and lay on his bed fully dressed and slept for several hours.

Well after noon, the sun beating on his face woke him. He

24

pulled the bell rope that hung by his bed and washing water was brought by Andy Hanlon. Andy was not a Connachtman and he despised everyone west of the Shannon except the Flahertys, the Burkes and the Bateses. Sometimes he included the Frenches and the Martins. He never associated with the other servants but spent all his free time in his little pantry off the hall. Master Fahy he regarded as an intellectual equal but the feeling was not reciprocated.

"Your father is waiting to see you," he said in his cold voice when he had helped Samuel to change into indoor clothes. "I told him you were asleep and he said you were not to be disturbed."

Samuel found George in the mahogany-paneled gun room off the hall. As usual he was oiling a flintlock gun, handling it with gentle precision. He took exercise every day on horseback, always carrying a flintlock and occasionally bringing home a few brace of snipe or plover, though at eighty-one his sight was beginning to fail. George was beginning to move heavily, too, and the hard lines of his mouth had lately taken on a petulant look as he felt himself restricted.

Samuel had long ago learned the folly of taking his father gently. Almost at once, after he had given news of Mary, he said, "I'm hoping to be married at the end of the summer if Alice will have me."

"Alice!" George gave a shout of laughter.

Samuel flushed with anger but said quietly, "Mary's daughter, Alice."

"I guessed which Alice you meant. Mrs. Burke was hoping you would marry Amy."

"Amy is a child. Alice is— Alice is—"

"No need to tell me. She's Mary's daughter."

"You have never seen her."

"No, but you've told me about her. Why do you say 'if Alice will have me'? Haven't you asked her?"

"Not yet."

"Of course she'll have you. Get Mary to talk to her. Get Mary on your side."

"What do you think of it?"

"It's no worse than what I did myself. In a way, you're made very independent by having me for a father." George chuckled as he picked up the gun again. "I see nothing wrong in it. Breed good stock back into the family. Mary was the finest woman I ever knew. I should have married her but I hadn't the courage."

"Was that the reason?"

"No. It was not necessary, really. That was probably why. Times have changed. Yes, you had better marry Alice."

Samuel cut the conversation short there, feeling anger rise in him again. He had found out the essential, that his father would receive Alice well. This had to be ascertained in advance because at times it seemed to the exasperated Samuel that a lifetime of argument could not have convinced George that a tenant or a servant was on a higher level than a good horse or dog. Even if he spent whole days with his coachman or his gamekeeper, they parted at the end of it without warmth. Samuel found a little of this attitude extended toward himself but weighing the matter up he judged it was more convenient to leave it that way.

He had often wondered how his father had felt at parting with Mary. It seemed like the passing regret that he felt when a good servant left him, or died—no more. Yet Samuel knew that he would never understand the workings of his father's mind. The blankness that he encountered at a certain point seemed to have something defensive in it, as if George were determined to keep a part of himself free to enjoy a life without conscience. And after all, he had never forgotten Mary.

As Samuel was leaving the gun room, George said, "Just one piece of wisdom I can pass on. When you have fixed things up with Alice, don't bring her here directly. Send her out to the Husseys for a while. She'll need to learn how to behave so that she'll be able to handle the servants and so that the county will receive her."

He chuckled again and repeated the last two words.

Samuel said in surprise, "Did you do that for Mary?"

"No. There was no need. I was not marrying her, you see. There were lots of things she didn't know but she learned them here. Your case is different."

Though on the surface George's attitude seemed sickeningly cynical, still Samuel found wisdom in it. The Husseys were an inspiration. Alice could easily spend a few weeks with them. They were the caretakers of the Flaherty house on Inishmore, the biggest Aran island. Mrs. Hussey had been lady's maid to Sylvia, and her husband, Tom, had been her coachman. After Sylvia's death, wanting to get rid of both of them, George offered them the Aran house as bait if they would marry. This they did with very small persuasion. For them it was the chance of a lifetime. Well fed and housed, and visited only once a year, at first by George and later by Samuel, they had remained there for thirty-five years, on good terms with their neighbors. Tom Hussey collected the rents for George. Since the potato blight never struck the islands and Inishmore was a good place for rearing cattle, there was no great hardship there and therefore little ill feeling toward him. Of their seven children, four had gone to America and two had married on the island. Their youngest son, Stephen, was still unmarried and living at home.

Since dinner was not until three o'clock, Samuel asked Andy to bring him a sandwich in his study and began to examine some mill accounts. It was irritating work. The manager was a Blake, descendant, as he was fond of saying, of one of the great Blakes who had helped to establish Galway as a commercial town in the twelfth century, but somewhere in the intervening years the family business flair or acumen had dried up. Ironically, in those early days the O'Flahertys had made implacable war on the Twelve Tribes of Galway and it would have seemed impossible then that one of them would employ a Blake someday. Later an O'Flaherty had had the wit to marry a D'Arcy and so acquire the mill and drop the distinctive Irish O' from his name. In those days, wine and salt were imported from Spain, as well as wood ashes and alum for tanning hides, which were a great export. Sheep and cattle were exported, too, and the furs of little wild animals, so that the Galway merchants became rich and powerful enough to build fine limestone houses. Cromwell's army destroyed them. Samuel had often heard the Cappagh people talk of Cromwell as if he had passed by the week before. Perhaps the Moycullen people talked like this too but Samuel was not on sufficiently intimate terms with them to be sure of this. To them he was the landlord, or the landlord's son, to be avoided except in the way of business.

Now he could not concentrate on his work. It was always like this when he came back from Cappagh. There he seemed to be a different person. He was one of a group that could have rejected him but did not. As his father had pointed out, the family disgrace probably helped him to start even. Now being in love with Alice had lifted everything to a different level. It had come to a head last night when she had stood beside him while the tinker woman sang her heartbreaking song. A glow of friendliness and then a shock of intimacy had touched him and he realized that he need never part from her. She need not go to America or be a servant in some big house. She could be his, with him, keeping the feel of Cappagh and its people with her forever.

4

Samuel shut the account books, glad that he had heard hooves on the gravel outside. He glanced up and saw Paddy taking Father Kenny's horse into the yard. This would mean that Master Fahy would come down and that dinner could begin. Sure enough, as he greeted the priest in the hall, Fahy could be heard fog-horning in the kitchen.

"That looks fine, Kate, very fine. Nothing like a roast of beef and a pig's cheek. Either alone is excellent. Together they are a banquet."

Father Kenny said, "Master Fahy is in his usual form."

Samuel led the priest into the dining room, which also served as a living room for this household of men. Andy had placed a tray with whiskey and glasses on the sideboard.

As he poured the whiskey, Samuel said, "I didn't know you were coming until I saw the horse. I've been to Cappagh."

"At the wedding, of course. Did you see Martin Connolly?"

"No," Samuel said in surprise. "Morgan was there but I didn't even miss Martin. Is he in trouble?"

"He's in trouble now, all right," Father Kenny said. "Someone seems to have informed on him. I was told he's on the run. Did Morgan speak of it?"

"No. I doubt if he would trust me."

Then the probable reason for Morgan's dislike of him became plain to Samuel and he chuckled with relief. It was because of Alice, of course. It was stupid of him not to have thought of that before now. Morgan was in love with Alice too. Since he had so often enjoyed Samuel's hospitality and indeed was obliged to him for most of his education, Samuel had taken his friendliness for granted. Last night Morgan's glares of dislike had been unmistakable. They had blighted the night's fun to some extent and Samuel had thought they were political in origin.

Father Kenny said, "Why wouldn't he trust you? He ought to know who his friends are."

"Coming to school here with Master Fahy? He should know. But I don't blame him. He has to be careful."

Then Fahy was on top of them, rolling from heel to toe and sounding his voice with an echo as if he were addressing a huge meeting. Teaching his little school in the attic of Flaherty's house had given him this habit of intoning his words to make them more impressive and memorable. It was a mannerism that belonged to a former age and it caused great amusement to the children; it had, however, exactly the effect he wanted, that his words were never forgotten. A sharpness creeping in could be taken to forecast danger, and from his own days as a pupil of Fahy's, Samuel still retained a capacity to recognize this. The sound traveled down to the hall, so that everyone paused in his work and waited for the short silence followed by sounds of thumping that meant someone up there was being taught to write like a lady or a gentleman, or that Fahy's own son James had failed to recollect a point in Greek grammar.

It was really for James's sake that Samuel kept the school going at all. It was often hard to assemble the few children who were necessary to prime Fahy into a teaching humor. Morgan had come for four years, from ten to fourteen, staying with old Mrs. Hogan and helping her around the place. Samuel had noticed him first at the MacDonagh's house, where his great friend had then been Dan. Morgan was interested in learning, and when Dan had refused to come to the school, saying firmly that he and Michael were needed at home, Samuel had invited Morgan instead. His classmates had been Burkes and Bateses and D'Arcys, as well as one or two bright local boys who had sucked the national school dry and who had had the luck to be noticed by old George. From Fahy, Morgan had learned the rudiments of Greek and Latin and a basic selection of English poetry ranging through Shakespeare, Ben Jonson, Donne, Milton, and Goldsmith, who was represented as being the best of them all. From the traveling teachers he had learned some French and music and drawing but in these last two he had made little headway.

Watching James Fahy slip into the room, Samuel pitied him. He knew that James was embarrassed by his father. There were many small ways and reasons, as for instance his habit of holding up a whole tableful of people at dinner to make the air shake with a quotation in Greek or Latin that he considered apt at the time. Always afterward he looked around with a threatening scrutiny to see how many people had understood him. His clothes were fifty years out of date: a jacket with a velvet collar and rusty black broadcloth breeches that hung slacker every year on his shrunk shanks, as he said himself. He wore his bushy white hair long, tied back with a black bootlace. This was undoubtedly his most peculiar feature. He was tall and broadly made and straight as a rush at sixty. His son was small for sixteen, light and somewhat wizened, probably taking after his mother, who was the sister of a genteel squireen from Cong, and had kept her maidenhead until the age of forty-four, when she eloped with Master Fahy as her last chance of discovering the mysteries of nature. She paid for the experience with her life, and after less than a year of her company in the room above the coach house, the Master was left with a sickly infant to bring up as best he might. The women servants of the house helped, of course, but Fahy made it clear that James was not their equal.

The ambiguity of his position was hard on the child and on the whole he had weathered the situation very well. He was quiet in company but not deferential. To his father he was a genius. To Samuel he appeared intelligent. Usually old George hardly seemed to notice him, but when he did, it was in a somewhat quizzical, conspiratorial way, as if he believed that James had been born on the wrong side of the blanket. James kept well out of his way but he could not avoid him at meals.

Therefore he was much embarrassed now when Samuel began to speak of him in front of all the company. In a glow of good will toward humanity in general, Samuel said, "I think we'll send James to the new university in Galway in October, if he can matriculate. Would you like that, James?"

James was instantly aware that Andy at the sideboard had paused in his carving of the pig's cheek and roast beef, whose aroma was already making him feel a little queasy. He said quietly, "Yes, sir. There is nothing I would like more."

In his father's presence, Samuel and George were always addressed as "sir" but this was quickly dropped when they were alone.

"Then we'll see about it," Samuel said jubilantly. "What would you like to study?"

"The classics, of course," said Master Fahy.

"Medicine," James said firmly.

"Then medicine it will be," Samuel said. He turned cheerily to the priest. "Do you think he should be excommunicated for going to one of the godless colleges?"

Father Kenny said dryly, "No. But I'll have the bishop on my tail for it, you may be sure. They've sent out a directive that we're to dissuade Catholics from going. After centuries of howling that Catholics are denied education, when it comes they condemn it because it won't be under their control. They say they're going to start a university of their own. Never look for logic from a bishop."

"But don't you have to obey them?" George asked. "Won't

you be strung from the yardarm or unfrocked or something? Aren't you supposed to prevent us from educating James?"

Samuel was pleased to see that the prospect of annoying the bishop had conveniently settled George's opinion in favor of the new plan.

"No," Father Kenny said. "A parish priest is very independent if he chooses to be. My brethren of the cloth are all bleating loyalty—not all, indeed, but most of them. A Catholic university for a Catholic country, they say, but I don't agree. Truth is truth, and a truth-seeking university will give good service to the Catholics. James won't come to any harm. It's an excellent idea to send him there."

Andy had begun to carve again. James shivered at the prospect of the ugly teasing he would have to endure later and he was thankful to the priest for speaking so calmly of this controversial question that had been sensational news for the last year. Father Kenny was young, for a parish priest, barely thirty years old. There was a shortage of priests in Connacht and his career at Maynooth had been so brilliant that, in spite of his political opinions, he could not be ignored. The son of a small landowner at the opposite side of the lake, he had a brother who was a bank manager and another a lawyer. Nevertheless he persisted in condemning the behavior of the landlords, using every opportunity for denouncing their inhuman rapacity in the matter of rents and their ferocity in evicting those who could not pay. He visited no big houses except the Flahertys' because in all that district it was the only one whose owners had not evicted a tenant within living memory. Easy for them, Samuel said, since they had the mill and warehouses to live on, and Father Kenny sometimes wondered how George would have behaved if he had been dependent on rents. Not very differently, he thought.

As a curate in Oughterard during the great famines of three and four years ago, Father Kenny had been so angered and appalled that in a very real sense something had broken in him. Too much death, too much pain, too much misery, too much sorrow, had surrounded him at an age when normally a young man's optimism is at its height. His friendship with the Flahertys dated from that time, when Samuel had fed anyone who had the strength to stagger up the avenue, day after day without complaint or self-congratulation. Homeless people were housed in the yard and stables, money was paid out for passages to America, work was found for anyone who could do it. Throughout this, old George's expression had hardly changed. He had gone out with his gun by the lakeside and in his own woods every day as if nothing unusual were happening. Only once he said that he had seen many famines in his lifetime but never one as bad as in '47. He had never by the smallest hint tried to limit Samuel's charity.

After the roast beef and pig's cheek, there was a bowl of oranges and then some port. Master Fahy was twirling his glass happily and had taken only one delightful sip when Andy appeared at his elbow to say, "There's a man outside to see you, Master."

Fahy turned his mouth down impatiently.

"Has he an animal with him?"

"No, except the jennet he's riding and that looks all right to me."

"Do you know him?"

"No, but he said he's a Kelly from Glann."

"That's a long way." He poured the port down his throat in one swallow and got up. "That's no way to treat good port. I'll come now. Where is he?"

"In the coach house."

Fahy gazed at his son and intoned, "Well, James, if you wish to study medicine, now is your chance. Either this man or his beast is needing treatment, no doubt. Will you come?"

James said quietly, "Yes, I'll come." And he followed his father out of the room.

Old George said, "Turpentine and whiskey are Fahy's most usual cures, sometimes mixed, sometimes separately. Amazing how successful they prove, for inside and outside. James's function is to stop him from relying entirely on these things."

"Interesting that he said he would like to study medicine," Father Kenny commented. "He could take over his father's practice."

"Except that Master Fahy is never paid," said Samuel. "He has done some astonishing repairs in his day but I suppose his main value is psychological. He convinces people that they can recover if they want to. He's usually wrong but that's neither here nor there."

"I'd better go out and see if I'm wanted too," Father Kenny said after a moment. "If someone has come all the way from Glann, it must be serious."

George and Samuel sat on for twenty minutes but none of the others came back. At last Samuel went out to the yard and Andy told him that they had left in a body for Glann and had behaved mysteriously about the sick man, who was said to be a cousin of the man on the jennet. Paddy had harnessed Samuel's mare to the gig for James and his father. They had not confided much in Andy and something in his manner showed Samuel that he resented it. He registered this automatically, adding it to his subconscious dossier on this rather odd servant.

While they stood before the coach-house door during this discussion, they heard light, quick hooves on the sandy avenue and a moment later a pony trap trotted into the yard. Its driver was a roundheaded, heavy-faced man with a look of anxious joviality. His soft appearance suggested that he was not a farmer. He pulled up the little yellow pony and sprang to the ground, talking excitedly.

"Ah, there you are. You'd think you were waiting for me. It's the same everywhere I go. Always a welcome for Mike Sherwin. That's Irish hospitality. I'd swear my bed is ready and my pipe laid out as usual. Always the height of hospitality at the Flahertys'. That's how it always was, since the days when they were the great chieftains that ruled the whole of Connemara, from Galway out to the islands and back over the mountains to the Joyce's Country—"

"All right, Mike, all right," Samuel interrupted when he could stand no more. "If you'll go into the kitchen you'll find cold pig's cheek waiting for you. But you'll have to be quick or it will all be gone. Leave the pony. Andy will put him up for you."

"Thanks, Mr. Flaherty, your Honor," said Mike and threw the pony's reins to Andy smartly before darting for the kitchen door.

Andy held the reins with contempt for a moment before chucking at them to lead the pony into the coach house. Samuel was almost sorry for him. He was said to be the illegitimate son of Lord Sligo's English butler but this could have been the invention of spite. Whatever the reason, he had certainly some impediment to mixing with the people who should have been his friends. Even Mike Sherwin, who was glad of any audience, did not spend time with Andy if he could find other company.

An hour or two later, there was Mike established at the dining-room hearth, which was empty because of the warmth of the day. This did not trouble him. It remained the focal point, the gathering place, of every ordinary house, summer and winter, and he knew that old George and Master Fahy at least would gravitate to it later in the evening. He was delighted to see Samuel come in so early and he sprang to his feet with his usual cries of adulation.

Samuel said, "Give that up, Mike, for God's sake. Where have you come from?"

"Mayo," Mike said in an entirely different tone, quite soberly. "It would break your heart to see it. The agents and the landlords will soon have it all between them. A Castlebar landlord sent word from London to his agent that he wants ten thousand pounds at once because his daughter is marrying a Sir, and the people are to pay fines when the leases fall in or else be out on the side of the road."

"Who is he?"

"The agent? Blackett is his name. A Scot that was a captain in the Army—"

"No, the landlord."

"Burke is his name, a kind of a cousin of your neighbor here. He never comes to his place in Castlebar. They say he's afraid of the fever and he's right there. I'd be afraid of that myself. Is there any of it around here?"

"We haven't had it in the house, thank God."

"And there's a good story of Clare Island that I'd say is hard to beat. You know the subsheriff bought it there a while ago—whatever his name is—and do you know what he was planning to do with it?"

"I haven't heard. Go on."

"Sell it to the Government for a convict station!" Mike said. "Did you ever in your life hear the beat of that? He put it up to them that if they had Clare Island they wouldn't have the expense of sending the convicts all the way to Botany Bay and Van Diemen's Land. Isn't he a clever one? But he didn't bring it off and he has to make his money somehow, poor devil, so all the rents on Clare Island are trebled this next quarter day."

"Trebled!"

"That's right. You don't want the poor man to starve, do you?"

"For God's sake, mind your tongue, Mike."

"I will that. I'll be up in Mr. Martin's place next week or the week after talking about banshees and fairies and Granuaile and Finn MacCool and anyone else I can think of that's dead a thousand years. I've been in three landlord's places in the last three months and I can tell they'll never see God. They're jumping with joy over the new Civil Bills Act—no more notice to quit for anyone, only out on the road if the agent or the landlord doesn't like the look of you. That used to be only for the poorest but now it's the law for all. Up in Leitrim, my Lord used it to bring in good, honest, reliable Protestant farmers from England and he put the Papists out on the road. He had the Army helping him level a whole

34

village when I left the area for the good of my health. God help us, Mr. Flaherty, what kind of a country have we at all? Have we no fighting men left in the length and breadth of the land?"

"You can tell that better than I can," Samuel said quietly. "Let's have no talk of fighting."

"I don't see Master Fahy about," Mike said after a short pause.

"He went over to Glann, just before you arrived, to doctor someone. A man came to fetch him. I'm surprised you didn't meet them. James and Father Kenny went too."

"I came from the other side, from Galway," Mike explained. "Who was the sick man?"

"I didn't hear any names."

"They'll be late back," Mike said and sighed with disappointment. "Ah, well, time is what I have plenty of. I'll have many a day for talking to the Master, a learned man, indeed."

He watched Samuel anxiously to make sure of his welcome and looked relieved at the readiness of his reply.

"Yes, you have plenty of time, and Master Fahy has been saying he hoped you'd be along soon, that you were due to visit us."

If anyone else had been present, this would have drawn down an avalanche of unseemly congratulations on the Flaherty reputation for hospitality. Now, however, Mike said simply, "Thank you, sir."

To Samuel's mind this was a greater compliment and far more to his taste just now.

5

Two days later, on an urgent message from Father Kenny, Morgan rode over the mountain to Moycullen. He went late, for two reasons. One was that he had to get a day's work done first and the other was that he wanted to be sure to arrive after dark. The long, bright evenings were an annoyance. Everyone in Cappagh saw him go and there was no help for it. Where the sandy road became a track across the mountain, he turned and looked back at the scatter of cottages that dotted the hillside. He knew the occupants of every one of them, and their exact condition both spiritually and economically. He knew which houses had been struck by starvation and the fever and which ones were empty or about to be vacated forever. The beauty of the scene, backed by the calm, pale water of Galway Bay, was an added pain. At the mouth of the bay, above the sea, the sky was streaked with clouds alternating in red and black, suggesting that the weather was going to change at last. That was a bad lookout for the potatoes. A wet July played havoc with them.

Above all, Morgan was angered by the look of resignation on the people's faces when they talked of the long, hungry summer before them. With most people, the old potatoes were just finished. Anyone who had a pig would sell it now and buy some oatmeal to keep the family alive until the new potatoes could be dug. The likelihood, however, was that the pig had already been sold or was being kept to give the landlord his rent. In that case the family starved.

Like Father Kenny, Morgan at twenty-two had suffered more anger than was good for him. He was familiar with the sensation and made a point of relaxing into it so as not to injure himself. Only last Easter he had explained this to Father Kenny.

"To be angry is a natural thing. If you turn a natural thing back on itself you get sick, you block it up so that it will break out somewhere else where it will do more harm in the end."

"What about the idea of self-restraint, self-mortification, silent suffering for the love of God?" Father Kenny asked sardonically.

They were in the presbytery's little sitting room in the late half dusk. There was always an hour of this, to save oil, until at last they could not see each other any longer and the lamp had to be lit.

"I mean you must go part of the way with it," Morgan explained earnestly. "Then gradually you begin to hold back. It's like driving a wild horse."

"You'd never make a priest," Father Kenny said. "Your policy is the direct opposite of the Christian idea of forbearance. Just before turning the other cheek, you would aim a clout at the persecutor's head."

"Just one, for his own good."

"It's not allowed."

" 'Be ye angry, and sin not,' " said Morgan. "You read it out at mass. Davis was right in the song: 'Be sure the great God never planned for suffering slaves a home so grand.' I have no trouble with my conscience. Here am I, that could count the books I have read, and I could teach a sounder philosophy to the whole bench of bishops."

"What you have is humanism."

"It's practical Christianity," Morgan said with certainty. "It's the Christianity of the good Samaritan, and the raising of Lazarus, and the curing of the widow's son and the centurion's son and Jairus' little daughter. Christ cared about the little people—the woman at the well that rightly said she had no husband, and the children that were not to be kept away, and the man that climbed the tree to have a better look at Him, and old Zebedee's wife that thought her sons were going to be big fellows in heaven. It's the Christianity of the eight Beatitudes. If He were alive today He would put a flea in the ear of some of our bishops, you may be sure, with their talk of laws like paying debts even when your family is starving and accepting your lot in life in a Christian spirit. He hated laws. He often said so."

"Hold on, hold on!" Father Kenny said. "Now comes the time to calm down."

"Perhaps I won't, after all," said Morgan.

And now, only a few weeks later, this message came about Martin, Morgan's older brother. The expectedness of it had not lessened Morgan's anger, or the fact that Martin had certainly invited the trouble he was in. When he disappeared periodically, his young sister Nora and Morgan made no comment, since it was known that Martin was involved in many dangerous things and all talk was dangerous. Morgan did not know much about Martin's activities, except that one of them had been to help in smuggling a marked man out of the country to America two years ago. There he was to ask Michael Doheny for help, through the Irish in America. It was probable that the help was to be in the form of money to pay the foreign soldiers who were to be a vital section of the new rising. Martin had mentioned this, and Morgan knew that there had been a plan for a rising two years ago. The Chartist leaders in England had agreed to keep the British Army busy while Ireland made a bid for freedom. Morgan dared not disagree with Martin, but when he looked around at his weak, dispirited, half-starved neighbors, he wondered how much fight there was in them. It was a question whether their poverty engendered their awful patience or their patience brought on their awful poverty.

Father Kenny's message was brought by a slinking tinker called Dara Ward, whom Morgan knew by sight. He often traveled alone. He had a dirty tongue and savage ways, quite unlike the usual run of tinkers, who were merely objects of pity because of their professional homelessness. Long-ago

37

famines had created the whole class. They knew how to live on the road, and by a rather gentle insistence managed far better than the unfortunates who had just been evicted and who were so shocked that they had not the heart even for begging.

Dara Ward offered curses instead of blessings in return for charity. He ran like a broken-winged bird up the lane to Morgan's door and flopped into the kitchen, startling Nora, who was brushing the hearth in the early morning. Morgan came out of the bedroom at her shriek.

Dara said, in his snarling, contemptuous drawl, "You're out of bed, anyway. By God, if I don't get a bite to eat, I'll never give up my story. I'll put a curse on this house. I'll put the curse of Cromwell on the whole seed and breed of the Connollys—"

He smirked at Nora's cry of pain.

Morgan said, "Cut that down. You'll get what we're having and that's not much. Give over annoying the girl."

"When I see the food, I will. What's in the pot?"

"Porridge."

"Good eating enough. Better than I'm used to."

"What's your story?"

"Father Ned Kenny sent me. Martin is shot. Ara, will you stop your bawling, you slut?" he shrieked at Nora, who had burst into tears at the news.

Morgan fell on Dara and lifted him like a little bag of twigs from the hob. He stared into the white, terrified face of the tinker, who gazed back into his eyes with tightened mouth and high-arched eyebrows. He dropped him onto the hob again after a moment and said, "Is Martin dead?"

"No. He's hurted in the leg. Not too badly."

Nora turned away and began to pour the porridge evenly into three bowls.

"Where is he?"

"In Father Kenny's. You're to go over."

"Is that all the message?"

"Yes," Dara said almost apologetically, going to the table for his porridge. "Father Ned has him hidden upstairs. He was over in Glann in a *bothán* of a house belonging to Jamesy Quinn. He's a young lad, about one age with yourself. All belonging to him are dead—father and mother and sisters and brothers and all—and he'll be off to America one of these days if he doesn't break his leg falling over a stone first."

He gave a savage laugh at this prospect. He seemed to have got his courage back.

Morgan said, "Well, what happened? Do you know any more?"

"I do, and I'll tell it in my own time."

Maddeningly he ate a few spoonfuls of his porridge while Morgan and Nora watched, rendered helpless by the obligations of hospitality.

When he had drawn enough satisfaction from this, Dara said, "A couple of mornings ago, they were there in the house when they saw six policemen coming up the hill and they armed to the teeth. It's a handy house—you can see anyone coming a quarter of a mile away because it's clung to the side of the hill, looking down on the lake. Martin went outside and made for the mountain, and he was nearly away with it when one hero up with his carbine and blasted him in the leg. He kept going, though his blood was flowing, and they couldn't find him after, though they combed the whole district for him. What he did was to double back and get into a house that they had searched already. They knew his name, too. Martin Connolly was the man they were looking for but they think he comes from Tipperary."

"What happened to the other man, Quinn?"

"He was taken down to the barracks in Oughterard but they hadn't enough men there to mind him so he got away. He's probably on his way to the Cove of Cork now because he had his ticket for America in his pocket."

"How do you know that?" Morgan asked.

Dara said furiously, "How do I know anything? Haven't I ears? Haven't I eyes? One thing I have for sure is a shut mouth. Someone informed on Martin. Six policemen don't come out in a body to search a house unless they know what they're looking for."

"We're never short of informers," Morgan said bitterly.

"Oughterard is full of them," said Dara. "That's one place I skirt around if I can at all. Wherever you have shopkeepers and tradesmen, you have people that want to be well in with the police, in the hope that a few shillings will come their way, if it was only for mending their boots. It's hard to blame poor people," he added with surprising tolerance. And then he asked suddenly, "Is there any more in that pot?"

"No," said Morgan. "There was enough for two and it did for three. Are you going back Moycullen way?"

"I am not. If I were to appear there twice in two days, I'd have the police on my own tail wanting to know what I'm up to."

"It doesn't matter," said Morgan. "I'll go this evening myself. You're going out west?"

Dara spat into his left hand and said contemptuously, "The west, is it? I wouldn't give that for it. There's nothing out there but starvation and misfortune, though the people are more decent than some. I'm going back into Galway. I only came out here with that message from Father Kenny. You might have a few shillings you could give me for my trouble?" he finished aggressively.

Morgan laughed but did not bother to answer. He knew that Father Kenny had already paid Dara well, else he would never have come so far out of his way. Besides, Morgan had so little money that it would have been madness to give some away. Food was different.

"The porridge wasn't bad," Dara said to Nora directly.

"God's blessing go on the road with you," she said courteously and went to the door with him.

She scrubbed the bowl and spoon he had used repeatedly.

Morgan noticed this and said, "Dara is not the worst. There are things he wouldn't do."

"I'll go down to Peggy Michael's for the night, maybe."

"There's no need, unless you want to. You could ask Alice to come and sleep here." Morgan warmed at the notion of Alice being under his roof. He said again, "Ask Alice to come. That's what you'll do."

"I will, so. What will happen to Martin?"

"God knows. I'll talk to Father Kenny. Martin won't be led, you know well enough. But I think he won't be able to do much more good here if the police are on to him."

They did not discuss this further, but sure enough, when Morgan reached Father Kenny's house, he found that Martin had arrived at the same conclusion. He was lying incongruously in a real bed with sheets and blankets, a luxury he never enjoyed at home. There a heap of straw with a makeshift covering was all the bed he had ever had. Though he was only a little older than Morgan, he looked worn and weather-beaten. Morgan blamed his injury for this and realized also as he looked down at his brother that the hunted life he had been living lately had aged him unnaturally.

Martin said, "I'm suffering partly from Master Fahy's attentions. He dug the bullets out. It didn't seem half so painful before. Poor James was sick."

"Were you?"

"No. Well, this finishes me for a while."

"You'll have to lie up with it."

"That, yes. But I was thinking of something else. When I'm on my feet, I'm for America."

"I thought you might be."

"Kathleen sent passage money from Boston for two. Father Ned says he'll get us the third. He agrees with me, there isn't much more we can do here. America is the place for us. You know they're well organized there. Here the men don't know whether they're going or coming, they're so weak, and the priests are telling them it's a sin to fight for your country. There's none of that rubbish in America. We'll get into the middle of a proper organization there. We'll be back in a year or maybe in two years. Kathleen has a new job in a house in Beacon Street and she'll get a job for Nora there, too. Judge Kelly says we'll have no trouble getting work, especially you with your book learning." He closed his eyes and seemed to suffer intense pain.

Father Kenny at Morgan's elbow said, "That's enough, now. There will be more time to talk. Go to sleep if you can."

He closed the shutters and shut out the last of the daylight. The house was partly screened from the road by the church but still it seemed safer not to show an unaccustomed light upstairs. Martin drank some of the whiskey that Master Fahy had prescribed and seemed to become drowsy. The other two went downstairs. Father Kenny closed the shutters of the sitting room before calling for the lamp. His cousin Mary, who kept house for him, brought it, showing no surprise at seeing Morgan. She was old enough to be the priest's aunt but she never tried to influence him in any way. Morgan found her unpleasantly distant and lacking in the trappings of welcome but Father Kenny assured him that she meant well. She did not sit with them but retired to the back of the house again, where the kitchen was.

Father Kenny said after a moment, "It was lucky that I was having dinner with Samuel when the message came for Master Fahy." He described the arrival of the man on the jennet. "Peter Cooney is his name. He's a good man." By this he meant a reliable nationalist. "We rode side by side to Glann and he was able to tell me what had happened."

"What about Master Fahy?"

"He's as sound as a bell but I wouldn't be too sure of James. With such a young person it's hard to tell. They were together in Samuel's gig so Peter and I could talk as we pleased. James showed no signs of knowing Martin when he saw him. Of course he knows he's here now, and he saw his father take the bullets out of Martin's leg."

"I don't think they have ever met," Morgan said. "Martin didn't come this way very much. He seems sure that we're all going to Boston."

"Don't argue it with him until he's well again. I could see you don't want to go."

"Was it so plain?"

Morgan had not been sure at first about Martin's proposition. The notion of reuniting the four remaining members of the family in Boston pleased him immensely. His mind had even run ahead to details such as that it might not be necessary to put little Nora into bondage in Beacon Street with her sister if he and Martin were fortunate in getting work at once. But along with this thought had come the knowledge that he did not want to leave Ireland. Politically it seemed indeed that no more useful work could be done at home. What affected him most was that he had so often in the last few years seen how violently the emigrants suffered, from the moment of their decision to leave their country. It was an emotion too deeply felt for analysis, too powerful for rationalization or contradiction. Not even the most enterprising or careless seemed to be immune from it. There was nothing to which it could be compared. It denied the notion that familiarity with beauty brings indifference. Morgan had seen young men with unashamed tears walking their tiny holdings, caressing the individual rocks and their stacks of winter turf as well as their few and precious animals with an awareness that made their coming departure seem a crime against all humanity. He had heard them state with certainty that nothing could surpass the splendor of the blue Clare mountains seen from across Galway Bay on a fine summer's day or the glory of a winter storm when the thunder of the waves could be heard up in Cappagh. Things as fine might exist in America, they said, but nothing could compensate for the loss of childhood scenes. Such wisdom in young people was appalling. Not all of them were capable of expressing it in words but the evidence of it was on their faces. Of all who had gone, in Morgan's experience not one but had been driven to it by penury. Greed for money can only exist where there is moderate wealth, and Morgan's neighbors had never enjoyed even adequate subsistence. Yet he knew that he would view the whole question differently if Alice were in the party.

Father Kenny said, "If you can hold on, you needn't go just to please Martin. I'll make that plain to him."

"When Martin is set on something it's hard to change him."

"Martin has to go, of course. Now that they have his name

42

and the Tipperary connection they won't rest until they find him. The Tipperary men are good fighters, he says. I suppose he has told you all about his activities there, and in Clonmel?"

"I've hardly seen Martin in the last six months, more like eighteen months," Morgan reminded him.

"He's full of the idea of having a network of secret societies all over the country," Father Kenny said, "but I don't agree with him."

"On moral grounds?"

"Don't tease me," Father Kenny said calmly. "A just war must have reasonable hope of success, as you know, and I don't believe these secret societies would remain secret or function in concert if they had to. I believe they should come out in the open now. If they do, the moralists and the patriots would be equally satisfied. Have you a girl in Cappagh?" he asked suddenly.

Startled, Morgan replied, "I think so."

"You think so?"

"She's not anyone else's girl, so far as I know. How did you know I was thinking of her?"

"Could she go with you to Boston?"

"I'm not going to Boston," Morgan said with certainty.

6

He wavered once or twice in the succeeding days but he did not discuss the question with Martin until his second visit to Moycullen. Martin had made a quick recovery. The wound was clean and showed no sign of gangrene. Master Fahy came each day to dress it and used the excuse to have trumpeting discussions on philosophy with Father Kenny in the sitting room. His hoots came through the floor into Martin's bedroom, though the words were indistinguishable. Martin, newly comfortable, sat in an armchair and listened quietly to Morgan's explanation.

"You have to go. I can stay. If we all go, we'll never come back. That's how it always is. Our fire will go out. Our roof will fall in. There will be nettles and brambles growing in our kitchen. We won't want to come back to see that. Our land will go to waste and ruin. Our turf won't be cut. We'll never come back."

Martin was silent for a while when Morgan had finished.

Then he said, "We'll come back. I saw the Tipperary men try to fight and I saw the spirit they have there. Sometimes I think we have as many informers as policemen in Ireland. Every policeman seems to have a circle of them that bring them all the news. The Castle knew every move we made in '49. That's why it looked such a failure but I can see signs that we're getting better at it. After '48 we should have been finished for another fifty years but only one year later we made another attempt. In my lifetime and in yours, Morgan, we'll have a free country. As I see it, it's our plain duty to go to America and work from there. When we come back we'll have confidence and certainty. People will be convinced that we're in the right. Poverty has the life knocked out of us here. Even strong men like us can never tell if we'll have a bite in our mouths tomorrow. God help us if we marry. And we're better off than most, with our two boats and our extra bit of land. Was Herring around?"

Herring was the agent for Lord Gough, who owned all the Cappagh land.

"Yes, he came. Folans are to be evicted but it's all the same to them. They were off to America anyway, all except the grandmother. Mary MacDonagh is taking her in. Michael and Roger MacDonagh are going to America from Galway next week so she'll have room. The poor creature is in a bad way at the thought of taking charity at this hour of her life and she wanted to go to the workhouse but Mary wouldn't let her. Mary is a saint."

Martin said after a moment, "Next week's boat is the *Pheasant*. We'll be on that ourselves, you can tell them, to keep them company. They'll be having an American wake." He used the term bitterly. "I'll see them there. They're good boys, though the bad drop is in them, from their mother."

Perhaps it was this comment that stiffened Morgan's resistance. He rode home under cover of darkness with a promise from Martin that he would come over to Cappagh on the day before the boat was due to sail. Martin was still expecting that the three of them would go together, and even if he were to go alone, of course Nora must see him before he went. He could risk one night at home, since there was no police station in Cappagh itself.

Nora and Alice were still asleep when Morgan slipped quietly into the house in the gray dawn. He made up the fire with fresh turf from the little pile that stood against the wall and then sat on the hob and dozed for a couple of hours. When the two girls appeared, they made porridge and listened to the news of Martin.

Then Alice said, "We'll have a houseful for the boys before they go. You'll be coming, of course. Will Martin come, do you think?"

Morgan had noticed before how Alice respected Martin as a man above the foolishness of dancing and singing and similar diversions.

"He'll come," Morgan replied. "He said he would. He'll be on the one boat with Michael and Roger, so they'll have good company."

This was his first mention of Martin's project in Nora's hearing, and now that discussion of it could not be postponed much longer, he wanted to find out first what Alice thought of it. When she left to go home, he accompanied her down the lane and along the road. At the turning to her place, he stopped and faced her. It was only seven o'clock and a nighttime coolness remained. The slow waves struck heavily on the rocks below them, sounding clearly through the still air. Larks sang loudly as they rose and then faded into nothingness in the blue, cloudless sky.

Morgan said, "It's cleared again. They say the sun shines always in America."

Alice gave a little chuckle. "Would you believe that?"

Watching her, Morgan realized that it was for her quick, innocent laughter he loved her most. At once it set up an answering reaction in him, an exuberance and an excess of courage that made him say without further delay, "Martin wants me to go to America with him. I'd go if you would come with us." She said nothing but looked at him with sudden penetration. He went on quickly. "Martin has the tickets for myself and Nora. We could get one easily for you. We could be married in Boston, or in Galway before the boat sails—"

Suddenly he stopped, realizing that he was not talking sense. If Alice were to laugh again he would be thrown down in the dust.

She did not laugh. She said very gently, "Morgan, people can't do things like that, as you know well. What would my mother say, and my father, if I were to walk out of the house without warning? It's bad enough for them to have two boys going."

"Then we can be married here. Why shouldn't we?" Suddenly he was full of this idea, seeing clearly that the sooner he made sure of Alice the better. He could not consider Samuel as a serious rival, since the days of the tallywomen were gone and a landlord who wanted a girl like Alice nowadays usually had to do without her. Besides, surely Samuel was too old to attract as lively a girl as Alice. But Morgan had seen his interest and some instinct warned him that it could be dangerous. He said in a low voice with great urgency, "We can be married in a month or two, whenever you're ready. Your mother will be glad, because you'll be living near her. She knows you won't stay at home forever. I won't go to America without you. I have the land and the boats, and my work is always good." He seized her by the shoulders and said, "Alice, we won't starve. You needn't be afraid of that. Soon there will be an end of poverty in Ireland. The landlords are selling out."

"There's a worse breed buying their land," Alice said. "And there's plenty of the old ones left."

"They couldn't be worse. You need never be afraid with me."

"I know that, Morgan. I know there isn't better than you anywhere. You've always been my friend." She looked at him with such honest admiration that he felt himself grow to fit her opinion of him.

"Maybe you didn't think we need hurry, but why should we wait? If we're poor, we may as well be poor together."

"It's true for you."

Then she went home. Morgan had the sense to recognize that she would need time to consider the question fully. It was another way in which she was unlike most of the girls he knew. With them, quite early they became the acknowledged property of a neighboring boy, who attended them naturally everywhere until the girl's family decided that they could be married. In the old times, before the great starvations, a bargain involving money was struck, but nowadays, in the Cappagh area at least, this complication had ceased to exist. Morgan knew that in this sense Alice was his girl and that he had nothing to fear from his neighbors. Samuel was the only danger, and in a strange way he feared Mary, too, though she had always been friendly to him. She had arranged for him to stay with her mother in Moycullen while he went to Master Fahy's school. He had always assumed that this meant she knew he would marry Alice some day but now it seemed too large a conclusion.

The party for Michael and Roger was very like the wedding. The tinkers were there, a different lot this time, with a tin-whistle player instead of a singer among them. They had come from Cork where they had seen a new development.

"Grand big fields turned over to sheep. Man, it would make you mad to see it. Out near Macroom, on the inch of the Lee, where the best corn always grew and there were strong, proud farmers and fine, high-stepping women—all, all out on the road, though they paid their rent and kept their houses like palaces and their fields fenced and watered and their cows bedded like the gentry. 'Tis the end of the world. Sheep are going to have it all now. 'Tis well for them that are going to America, where they don't put the sheep above the people."

Old Peggy Michael began to wail and Sally had to sit beside her and hold her hand for half an hour before she was quiet. Sally had found that this was the best way to give her comfort, as if the old woman were drawing the life and warmth out of the young one through her fingers.

Morgan avoided Martin, who was in roaring good spirits, very different from his usual gloom. Even at this late hour he had not told him that he must go to Boston alone. Nora would not go unless Morgan did.

She had said, "I can go later, if need be, though I don't want to. Kathleen is in Boston to look after Martin. If I go, you'll have no one. That's not fitting. Our mother would haunt me, God rest her, if I did the like of that." Nora was only eighteen years old and had been her mother's pet until the fever took herself and her husband and two brothers in '47. "How would you manage at all? The place would go to rack and ruin. You'd be better to come with us if Martin and myself are going."

She had sounded so distracted that Morgan had asked, "Would you like for us all to go, then?"

"No, no!" she had said violently. "I'd be afraid. I'm afraid of the sea. I'd be thinking of the *Edmund* and all the other ships that went down. By the time I'd get to America I'd be out of my mind."

In November of last year, the *Edmund* had been wrecked in a gale off the coast of Clare, and for weeks afterward the bodies of the drowned emigrants were being washed up on the shores of Galway and Clare. Many other ships never reached America either, though no more was seen of them or of their crowded cargo from the time when they sailed unsteadily away from Irish shores. Coffin ships, someone had christened them, and in a way it was as easy to die in them as at home or in one of the American clearing stations.

"Martin said we'll be rich in America," Morgan had said. "We wouldn't be starved the way we are here."

"We're better off than many a one," said Nora. "We have the money from Kathleen for meal in the summer and in winter, too, when the blast takes the potatoes. It's little would keep a person alive. Martin can send some money, too, I suppose. He must go, since the police are after him, but we needn't stir. Maybe I'll go when yourself and Alice get married, if you want me to."

Shocked, Morgan had said, "I won't want you to go, and neither will Alice."

Nora left the telling of their decision to Morgan and he had put it off deliberately until after the party, lest Martin might refuse to go to it. He was glad he had done so when he saw how Martin joined in the dancing and even took the tin whistle from the tinker and played "The Blackbird" on it. Morgan was amazed at this. It had been Martin's specialty when he was a boy but it was so long since he had played it that he might well have forgotten the notes. It was a slow horn-pipe, very complicated, with variations and finally a return to the original theme. Everyone loved it and made him do it again.

Thomas MacDonagh said, "That's a great gift you have, Martin. You'll hear plenty of the old music in Boston to remind you of home."

Then he demanded a song from Michael, and since he was half full of poteen by this time, he specified what it was to be. Normally a quiet, soft-spoken man, Thomas became truculent when he was drunk, though he was never known to injure anyone. Now raising his voice, as was his right, he said, "Let you sing 'A Match Was Made' and I'll remember it when you're gone from me."

Obligingly Michael sang, in Irish:

> "'A match was made for me last night
> To a girl I neither love nor like,
> But I'll take my own advice and I'll leave her far behind,
> And I'll travel the wide world over.
>
> Oh, I walked up and I walked down;
> I walked England and Dublin Town,
> But the like of my own true love I never yet did find:
> A dark-haired girl is my darling.'"

It was for this line that Thomas had wanted the song. He kept his eyes on Mary while Michael finished it:

> "'I got up three hours before dawn;
> I got a letter from my own true love;

48

> *I heard the linnet and the blackbird sing*
> *That my true love was on the wide ocean.'*"

Morgan was astonished to see how Michael went through verse after verse of the song without seeming to suffer any pain. When he had finished, however, he pushed his way through the crowd to the door and went outside. Martin left soon afterward and did not come back. Now every singer chose an emigrant song, so the tone of the whole party became more and more depressed and sad. In the dawn, faces looked white and worn and at last people went home in quiet little groups, first silently shaking hands with the two boys who were leaving in the morning.

Morgan and Nora walked home together and found Martin waiting for them in the kitchen of their house.

Morgan said at once, "I'm not going to America, and Nora wants to stay with me."

Martin was not angry. He looked at them as if they were strangers or children, so that Morgan felt almost as if this older brother were divided from him by twenty years instead of three.

Martin asked, "Why are you not coming? You know you have nothing here but hunger. Maybe you won't be turned out because the land is so bad that even the landlord doesn't want it but you'll have an empty belly and rotten potatoes as long as you stay. I've said it all to you before. Is it the tallywoman's daughter?"

"Don't call her that!" Morgan shouted with sudden fury.

"That's what she is," Martin said coldly. "The bad drop is in her, exactly like her mother. You'll find that out. She looks to me as if she's for the same road—"

"What do you mean?"

Morgan leaped on Martin and had to be recalled to his senses by Nora pulling at him helplessly and crying to him to stop. He put down his hands and then absently put one arm around Nora's shoulders so that she could lean on him.

Through a fog of sound, he heard Martin's voice say kindly, "I shouldn't have said it. That was a wicked thing to say, God forgive me, and I leaving you behind. Sit down now and we'll be talking until it's time to go the road to Galway."

And he led Morgan to the hob and sat opposite him and talked of Boston and the work he would have there and his prospects of coming home in a couple of years. When the sun came around to the door they knew that it was ten o'clock.

Martin stood up and said, "Now I'll have to be going."

Nora had a sack full of hard oat bread for him to eat on the voyage. There would be yellow meal on the ship, and salt meat, but by now everyone knew how foolish it was to depend on those, they were so little and so bad. Martin had no other luggage. They watched him down the hill. Neither of them stirred out of the house that day. Neither did the MacDonaghs, nor any of the other families whose members embarked that day in Galway on the *Pheasant*.

7

It seemed to Alice that her mother changed from the day that Michael and Roger went away. Until now she had seemed to concentrate her attention on keeping the family together but now she talked sometimes of providing for their departure. Probably Dan's marriage had something to do with it too. It was not that she seemed relieved at having fewer mouths to feed, for she had quickly taken in old Mrs. Folan as soon as there was room. It was rather as if a long-expected disaster was now obviously about to occur and that she found the tension of waiting for it harder to bear than the misfortune itself would be.

Alice wondered if she had at last accepted emigration as an equal solution with marriage. When Peggy Michael rambled into the house, Mary now listened quietly to her stories of the fine life that the emigrants had in America, where before she would have hushed her up lest the children might be listening. Peggy brought the sock she was knitting and sat on the hob with her bare feet on the warm hearth. The vision she had of America was a kind of fairy tale, of a country where everyone was rich and well dressed and fed like a king.

"They have eggs and meat every day," she said, "and tea whenever they feel like it. The men have as much tobacco as they want."

"Thanks be to God! Glory to God!" said old Mrs. Folan from the other hob, thinking of her own children who had lately set out for this paradise and were still tossing on the ocean.

Alice saw how two of her young sisters, Kate and Eileen, were drinking this in. They never spoke in company but they stood together and seemed to understand each other without words. Kate was fifteen, and like her mother and Alice in appearance, being if anything bolder in style. Eileen was thirteen and had a delicate look that was enhanced by her fair hair. Most of their neighbors thought her harmless but Alice found her inclined to whine, which upset Kate, who felt responsible for her.

Alice said now, "Go on over and see does Sally need anything."

They could do nothing but obey, though clearly they would have liked to stand their ground. Old Peggy maundered on for a while about the beautiful clothes the girls had in America, with all kinds of ribbons and beads on them, and bands of black velvet. Everyone had shoes, and for very cold weather the cloaks were lined with fur. At this bizarre notion, two of the smaller children who were present began to giggle and had to run for it from Mary's onslaught. She gave a little moan of frustration as they skipped outside. She could not endure bad manners in her own children.

Alice said to her later, "Can't you stop Peggy from talking like that? You never used to allow it."

"I should, I suppose, but the poor old creature has so little pleasure in life."

Alice took steps of her own. After their supper of Indian-meal porridge, the whole family knelt down as usual for the Rosary. It was a delicious moment of the day. In winter there was the firelight shining on the oleograph of the holy picture and on the luster jugs. Being better off than most, the Mac-Donaghs kept their pigs outside, which made the kitchen pleasanter to be in. Now in summer it was still broad daylight and the evening scents came more strongly through the open door than they could ever do in the daytime. Thomas led off, in Irish, of course, since it was the family language and well known to be the one used in heaven.

"Lord, open my mouth."

All the family answered, "And my tongue will praise you aloud."

"Lord, lean down to help me."

"Hurry, Lord, to help me."

Then there was the Rosary, the five sorrowful mysteries, since it was Friday. After Thomas, Alice and Joeen and Kate and Eileen each took charge of a decade. Old Mrs. Folan moaned with compassion for the sufferings of Christ, as if they were being re-enacted before her eyes. That part took only ten minutes but Tim was asleep, leaning against Alice, when the droning, rhythmic voices stopped. Now Mary took over for the longer part of the ceremony which was still to come. Every relation, dead and alive, had to have special mention and special prayers, and there were also prayers for the heathens in uncivilized countries, where Christ had never been heard of, and prayers for George and Samuel Flaherty, who had always been so good to this family, and prayers for the potatoes and for the two pigs that were fattening in the shed.

Knowing that they were coming near the end, Alice said, "I think we should add on a new prayer for the unfortunate people that have to cross the stormy sea in rotten ships, in terror of their lives, and land on a hungry shore far from their friends and work themselves to their death in the height of their youth in the houses of strangers."

"That's a good thought, Alice," her father said. "From now on we'll have that prayer too."

And in spite of Mrs. Folan's tears he gave out the intention almost in her words and followed up with three Hail Marys for it. Alice almost smirked to herself as she imagined how the impact of the repetition of this every night would work on the minds of her two sisters. Once added to the family Rosary, that trimming would stay for good.

The new spell of dry weather took the family out on the bog cutting turf. Even the small children went and worked at footing the turf when it was dry enough to handle. Four sods had to be placed upright with their tips leaning inward against one another and a fifth was placed across the top so that the drying wind could blow through them. The children liked the bog because everyone was in good humor there and any mischief they did was looked on tolerantly.

This was why Mary was at home alone when Samuel appeared one morning in the middle of July. His horse had whinnied as he topped the last hill on his way down to Cappagh. Mary heard him and had time to sweep the house and hang the kettle on the crane before Samuel appeared in the doorway. She knew that old Mrs. Folan had gone off as usual to ramble around the wreckage of her home, felled by picks and crowbars a week ago. Mary did not try to dissuade her from it yet, though she intended to do so later on.

The sight of Samuel was a comfort. In her pleasure at seeing him, she spoke to him in Irish, which was the language of her thoughts.

"You're welcome, Samuel, my son. Come in and we'll be talking."

Samuel answered her in Irish. "How are you, Mary?"

This brought her to her senses and she chuckled. In English

she said, "That was well said. We'll have you pouring out Irish yet, as good as the next."

"I wish I could talk it properly," Samuel said, "but I'm afraid it's too late now."

"You won't be needing it anyway," Mary said. "You have enough to understand it, and they say that when the old people are gone, there won't be a word of Irish heard in the whole country."

"Do you believe that?"

"There's better than me believe it and I suppose they know what they're saying. Tell me now, how is your father?"

"He's very well, the same as usual," Samuel said. "The boys went off all right?"

"They did, sure, a big company together. Martin Connolly was with them. I hardly know yet that they're gone. I hear a step outside sometimes and I think 'That's Roger, the light one' or 'Michael is back early.' Then it comes to me that it couldn't be. Thomas feels it worse, I think, because he never makes that kind of mistake."

"They had the address in Boston safely?"

"Yes. I wrote it out twice and gave one to each of them. They promised they'll go straight to Judge Kelly when they land."

"I hope he'll go to meet them," Samuel said. "I asked him to, but sometimes the ships are late and people don't know when to go to the docks. He's a good man, John Kelly. He'll do what he can for them."

"I'm sure anyone would do what you would ask them, Samuel," Mary said in admiration and gratitude.

It was too good an opportunity to miss. He waited while she made tea and brought two mugs from the dresser. When she was sitting companionably opposite him he said, "Mary, you can do a thing for me."

"What?" she asked in delight at this unusual reversal of affairs.

"My father said 'Get Mary on your side.'" Samuel paused to let this sink in and then he said evenly, "I want to marry Alice."

Mary felt a sickness go through her, leaving her weak and without speech. It was like being savagely bitten by a pet dog. On the first breath that she could use, her thought expressed itself.

"Oh, Samuel! And I thought I reared you a Christian!"

It took Samuel a moment to understand where the error lay. He gave a short, bitter laugh.

"God help us and our reputation. I said I want to marry Alice and I'd like you to help me. Can't you believe that?"

"I can, I suppose," she said reluctantly. "You mean, really to marry her?"

"Yes."

He had thought he was hardened enough but he could not look at Mary now. It seemed that he had never before been truly aware of the depth of the injury that had been done to her. Physically, financially, it had been repaired many times over but this seemed a triviality. To condition people to accept the inevitability of injustice and misfortune is, after all, the final achievement of a tyrant. Samuel had always felt a loathing for his father's whole class but it came to a head now as the effect of its attitudes touched him so closely.

Mary was apologizing for her discourtesy. "Samuel, sure I meant no harm. I didn't think you could mean that. Alice is only a country girl. It couldn't be right for her to marry the like of you, a gentleman with a fine house and land."

"That's got nothing to do with it. Why shouldn't I have a wife, like everyone else?"

"Of course you should," Mary said eagerly. "A lady of your own kind—"

"There aren't any ladies of my own kind," Samuel said, "and you know it well."

"I do, I suppose," Mary said helplessly, and then she was afraid she had been uncivil again.

"I ask you, Mary, what lady would put up with my father and Master Fahy and James and myself, with the way we live in Moycullen? There are hardly any parties, or any reason to dress up. The fear of fever keeps people at home, as well as the dismal thoughts we all have. Going to Mass on Sunday is our most exciting outing and that's a glum business enough, with all the empty seats. If I were to marry a lady, as you call them, she'd be crying all day, like my mother."

"How do you know that?"

"I heard. Anyway, I want Alice and I don't see why I shouldn't have her. She hasn't a boy of her own."

"She has not. There's no one in Cappagh or Barna good enough for her. They'd be afraid of a girl like Alice, that she'd have high notions of herself and maybe think herself above them."

"Then you'll talk to her about it?"

"Give me time," said poor Mary, almost weeping in her confusion. "How do I know she'll listen to me?"

"Of course she'll listen to you. Surely she never thought to marry her own choice, without asking leave. No girl does that. Alice would never think of doing it. Where is she today? The house is very quiet."

"They're all on the bog. Samuel, love, I'd be in heaven if you could marry Alice but it's such a strange thing for you to want. No one does the like of that. Or if they do," she corrected herself hopefully, "they go away to America and start up in a place where no one knows them. I've heard that Lord Sligo's daughter did that. Maybe you're thinking of doing the same."

"No. Why should I? I have a better living than I'd ever have in America. And who would look after the mill? And the people on the land? You know my father can't, now."

"He said 'Get Mary on your side'?" Mary asked. "He didn't try to stop you? You told him what you're planning, I suppose."

"Yes. He was very pleased. He would welcome Alice."

He would have liked to repeat his father's remarks about Mary but delicacy forbade it. In any case there was probably no need, since she could very easily build on the implications of old George's advice.

She said, in a firmer tone, as if she were pinning down a difficult proposition, "Then Alice would live with you, in Moycullen, the way I did myself."

"No," Samuel said sharply. "Not the way you did. Alice would be my wife. She'd go everywhere with me. I'd make them all bow to her."

Mary was silent for a while. Samuel watched her, well aware that she was not in the least dazzled by his proposition and was considering it on its merits.

At last she said, "Why don't you ask Alice yourself?"

"It's not the right way to do things. I wouldn't have asked her without your leave."

"You have my leave."

"Mary, please help me," Samuel said. "Alice is very young. You'll know how to put the idea to her so that she won't be shocked or frightened."

"That's true. But you know Alice has courage for anything."

"I know. That's one of the best things about her."

"Those people that are going to bow to her won't do it if they see her on the bog today," Mary said, distressed as the lovely vision of Alice as a lady began to fade.

"My father thought of that," Samuel said and he told her of the plan to educate Alice a little before bringing her to live in Moycullen.

"It's a sensible idea," Mary said, "though I don't know if Alice will think so."

"Alice sees sense quicker than anyone. She wouldn't be insulted. She'd know it would be only like learning a game."

8

Samuel did not stay much longer. When he had gone, Mary went about the house in a state of horrible uncertainty. She could not trust herself to have a clear judgment since old emotions that she had thought dead and buried kept coming at her like vicious dogs from all sides.

She could not get rid of the idea that Alice would be shown the door someday by Samuel, as she had been forced to leave old George. That had not been his fault but he had not lifted a finger to prevent it. The notion that he could have prevented it had always been dormant in her mind and now it came startlingly to life with all its implications. She need never have married Thomas. But then she would never have had Alice. She might have stayed with Samuel. Hatred of her mother rose up in her and almost choked her. Then she was filled with concern for Thomas, who was in a way a victim of the same cynicism and greed. How could she talk to Thomas about Samuel's proposal without reminding him of old George? Yet Thomas had got what he wanted and in this way he was not to be pitied at all. She felt confused and miserable. Alice saw it the moment she returned from the bog.

She had come ahead of the others, leading the donkey whose panniers were loaded with the potato pot that she had cooked dinner in, on the bog, and the leftover potatoes that were to be given to the pigs. Her mother stood at the door and tried to imagine her dressed in silk and with shoes on her feet and her hair brushed smooth. She knew this would be no miracle, since she had gone some way toward achieving it herself. She remembered wryly how she had dropped her eyes before every looking glass for months, in shame at her altered appearance.

With a sharp eye on her mother, Alice lifted off the panniers and turned the donkey loose. Then she asked, "What's the matter? Are the pigs all right?"

"They're fine. Alice, Samuel was here."

"Well? Is his father sick? Is something wrong with Samuel?"

"There is not, faith. I never saw him better in my life."

56

Alice's face lit up with pleasure. She said, "Thank God. You frightened me for a moment."

Mary glanced out through the doorway and saw that there was still no sign of the rest of the party. To have a·private conversation with one of her children was almost impossible. She seized this chance, in fear that she might not get another for a week.

She said harmlessly, "You're fond of Samuel."

"Of course I am. He's a fine man. It lifts my heart to know that there are some like him in Ireland."

"Would you marry him?"

Alice never answered abstract questions if she could avoid it. Perhaps her mother should not have been left alone all day so soon after the boys had gone away. Then she saw by Mary's expression that this question was a serious one.

She said, "How do I know? I've never thought of marrying him."

"He told me to ask you. I know I should tell your father, but as you're here now, you may as well be the first to hear it."

Mary was afraid that Alice would dismiss the idea at once but she did not. She said, "Samuel asked that?"

"Yes. He has it all thought out. God forgive me, I didn't believe him at first but he didn't hold that against me."

"Has he quarreled with his father?"

Trying to see some sense in it, Alice had begun to wonder if Samuel were perhaps planning to come to live in Cappagh. She had long ago seen how much he loved to be there and had thought it a little unhealthy.

But Mary said, "Not at all. He said his father would welcome you."

"But look at me!" Alice said, pointing down at her ragged skirt and her bare feet. "How could I go like this to a gentleman's house?"

"You wouldn't go like that. You'd go to Aran first and stay with some people there that would show you how to behave like a lady."

"It's all worked out."

This was no near what Mary had said to her own mother on the day after she had been seduced by old George that she burst into tears.

"It is not. It is not. You can do as you like. Samuel is decent. He made a decent offer."

"All right. But he's a landlord. I'd be a landlord's wife."

But though Samuel owned land and had tenants on it, he belonged to that small group of generous-hearted landlords who cared for their tenants during the black famine years. Everyone knew this, just as they knew that Lord Monteagle had cared for his tenants in Kerry, and the Duke of Leinster in Kildare, and Mr. Guinness in Dublin. Tinkers and travelers and journeymen had brought news of these and a few others to the west and Alice had always been proud to hear Samuel's name mentioned with theirs. In one sense, it was the thought of these exceptions to the general run of greedy, stupid land-lords that had given the people any fighting spirit they had. Through the horrors of the last five years a glimmer of hope shone, that the hearts of Lord Lucan, Lord Leitrim, Lord Erne, Lord Sligo and Lord Clanricarde might be moved at last by the example of their more honorable peers. They solved the problem otherwise, however, by stopping their ears and remov-ing themselves from the sight and sound of the unpleasant things that were going on, or else by developing a reasonable theory that since events had proved there were too many peo-ple on the land, it was a good thing for as many as possible to leave it. A short choice was offered—death or emigration. Agents and bailiffs, rough persons by nature, spared the deli-cate feelings of the gentry.

Alice knew hunger, of course, because the Flaherty bounty had to be shared and stretched among the neighbors as far as it would go. There was no other source of food when the potatoes rotted. Fifty pounds had to be scraped together, shilling by shilling, for the rent, which had been doubled a few years ago when Herring, the agent, saw the extension that Samuel had helped to build. Thomas never told Samuel the result of his generosity. He had succeeded in paying the rent until now and with the help of the two boys in America he hoped that things would be easier. Wool from his sheep and every grain of oats and barley that he managed to grow were sold in Galway to provide this annual miracle.

From Morgan as well as from her mother, Alice knew of the luxuries of Samuel's house, where she had never been. From Morgan she had learned anger, though she had never acted on the consequent need to do something positive. Neither for that matter had Morgan done much. The time was not ripe, he said, but Alice had seen that it was ripe enough for Martin.

She looked directly at her mother and said, "Morgan asked me to go to America with him."

"When?"

"When Martin was going."

"What did you say?"

"That I would not. Then he asked me to marry him here."

"He has the right to ask, I suppose. What did you say to that?"

"I gave him no answer. Maybe I said I'd think about it. I don't want to marry anyone. I haven't the heart for it. I'm all right here."

"You must marry sometime," Mary said eagerly, seeing Alice's uncertainty. She had noticed at once the lack of enthusiasm for Morgan, which gave her courage to go on. "Samuel is thirty-six. If he doesn't marry now, he never will. Do you think he's too old for you?"

Still thinking of Samuel as a child, this idea had only now occurred to Mary.

Alice said, "In these times, it doesn't matter what age a person is. There isn't one of us that's sure of living a year. Anyway, Samuel is not old. Why didn't he go after a girl out of a big house?"

"I asked him that myself," Mary admitted, "and he said he doesn't want one like that. The times are against it. He hadn't the heart for it either, I suppose. I know he can't stand the landlords and gentry around his own place. There's the Burkes, half a mile away. A while back he was telling me about a dance they had in the house and he went, of course. Christmastime, it was, and all the girls were home from their schools in England, and everyone came from all over and they had a band and dancing and lovely food, and poor Samuel could hardly be civil because he was thinking of the starvation outside. I said to him that a bit of dancing never did any harm and we sometimes have it ourselves in the middle of our worst troubles to keep our hearts up. But he said it was all right for us but not for them."

Listening attentively to this, Alice found her heart warming to Samuel. She had never speculated much about how he lived at home but had somehow assumed that he took part in a round of visiting and entertainment of the kind that her mother had sometimes described, though she knew it only at second hand. Old George's cook used to be lent, the way you would lend a horse, to make ready for a twenty-first-birthday party or a wedding.

Her mother was saying, "Samuel said you'd learn to be a lady the same as you'd learn the rules of a game."

"Is it as easy as that?"

"No, but he would help you too."

59

"Then you think I should do it?"

"I do," Mary said with certainty. "It's a different life altogether. It's I that know it."

Alice longed to ask her mother if she had gone willingly to live with old George but she could not imagine how to word the question. She suspected that it had been arranged without her leave. She wanted to know too how it had felt when her uncle took her away, but this also was an impossible question. Watching her mother's face for signs, she knew that she could not quite trust any advice she might get from her. It would be almost impossible for Mary to dissociate herself completely from Alice's problem, not to feel herself again in her old position. What that position was Alice burned to know but Mary had just enough guile not to tell her.

Mary knew that she would instantly be suspected of behaving as her mother had done, though Samuel's offer was a very different one. She said, "Listen, Alice. What is there here for anyone? When I came here, there was nearly a hundred families in Cappagh. Now there's hardly twenty. All the friends I had, other women like myself, I saw the fright of starvation come on them until they lay down and died. I saw a woman grudge her own husband the bite he ate. I saw people take to the roads to beg like tinkers, people that were always decent. Why in the name of God would anyone stay in this place if there was a way out of it? They're not staying. They're going to America, a place that's only a name to them. There's the hungry look on my Dan already, though he's only a month out of my house."

This was true. Alice had seen it herself. It had brought home to her, more than anything else could have done, the special position of her own family.

Perhaps it was this notion that forced her to her decision. Forced it was, and though she did not intend to retract it, she disliked the lack of freedom that accompanied it. Some new information confirmed her in the rightness of accepting Samuel's offer, however. When she had agreed, her mother said with obvious relief, "That will draw the Whiteboys off Mr. Flaherty."

"What do you mean?"

"Dara Ward told me a short while ago. I had to give him a shilling for it." It was a shockingly big sum but the news had been big enough, too. "You know Samuel manages everything now except the piece of land up in Clonbur."

"I didn't know they had land in Clonbur."

"There was a fine piece there by the shores of the lake,"

Mary said, "and a while ago Mr. Flaherty sold it to a man called Shaw from Claremorris. He thought he was doing no harm, but Shaw is a hound of hell, God forgive me, and he's rack-renting and evicting all over the land."

"But that has nothing to do with Mr. Flaherty. The White-boys can have nothing against him."

"They've been threatening him, all the same. Maybe there's nothing in it. Maybe they just want to make sure he doesn't sell any more land to the like of Shaw. There's some wild people up there in the woods around Cong and Clonbur, and on the islands, too, and they'd kill Mr. Flaherty without a thought if it would frighten off a few more."

Alice knew that this was true, and she knew from Morgan that though the people had nothing against old George they had no love for him either. Times when he could have intervened to save a poor man's house or property, he had done nothing, and an accurate judgment had been reached as to the difference between himself and Samuel. The credit for Samuel was usually given to Mary, accurately enough too. With his habits of solitary wandering, old George would be an easy target. The Whiteboys would be his own neighbors, who knew him well. Morgan had never ridden with them but Martin had, until a few years ago when he had turned against that kind of warfare. A terrifying sight they must be, a band of white-shrouded, malignant ghosts.

Mary said, "I'm thinking that when you and Samuel are married, the people will think the Flahertys are only like ourselves."

"It might make them think we are the same as the Flahertys," Alice pointed out.

"Could it? I don't think it could. It's a lot easier to come down in the world than to go up."

Now Mary wanted to have Alice to herself altogether but there was no possibility of that. The whole family was almost at the door, in high good humor because it had been such a beautiful day and the turf was drying well. Joeen had caught a cock pheasant in his cradle bird during the afternoon. It was a rough trap made of hazel rods, not very heavy, and the pheasant should have been able to shrug it off easily. For some reason it had not succeeded. Joeen had come back to find it struggling, its long tail feathers entangled in the bars of the trap. He finished it off with a blow of a stone. Now everyone was exclaiming at the beauty of its feathers and looking forward to a taste of meat with the evening meal. In honor of the pheasant it was decided to have potatoes instead of the yellow-meal porridge, which no one liked and which often griped because of its roughness.

It was Alice's job to pluck and clean the pheasant but she found the notion unpleasant this evening and she prevailed on Kate to take over responsibility for it. The small children had the lovely feathers to play with and had no objection to their acrid smell.

To get away from it and from the suddenly overcrowded house, Alice took a bucket and said she would go for drinking water, not to the near well but to Colman the Keener's well, where the water was well known to be much better. Colman had been a gifted composer of laments for the dead until his eviction in 1847 when he had foolishly allowed his wife to cook the seed oats as porridge and use the money he had saved for the rent to feed his sickly infant son. Not only that: he had actually urged the people of Cappagh to make a mass stand against paying any rent at all after the potatoes had rotted. The country was full of food, he said, and there was no need to starve. He was read from the altar as a dangerous man and an encourager of dishonesty, and in due course the bailiff and the soldiers in their red coats and brass helmets came out from Galway to throw down his roof and make holes in his walls, showing clearly that defiance did not pay. Alice had not seen this but Martin Connolly had fired a few shots that day and made a speech, which was why he first went on the run. Colman the Keener was in America, they said, but his wife was dead of course. It was rumored that the child was dead too.

None of this story depressed Alice as she walked in the gold sunlight up the lane toward the well. All around her there were similar ruins, each with a somewhat similar story. One cannot live in a permanent state of pity. Even though the heart does not harden, familiarity creates a buffer of resignation or custom that makes toleration of pain possible. Brambles ran wild at either side of the lane, twirling and curling around woodbine and grass-grown walls. A single hawthorn tree shaded the roadway with its complicated shiny leaves. Earlier it had been a heaven of sweet white blossoms. In the autumn it would be bright with haws, like little lamps. Three splendid seasons it had, and even in winter she loved its twisted black branches with their warts and clawlike tips.

Colman the Keener's field was higher than the road so that she had to climb up into it by an easy stile. The well was down from the ruined house. The long flowering grass was trampled around it but only by human feet, since the stone wall kept straying animals out.

Alice let the bucket slide slowly into the sparkling water and watched it turn on its side and fill. Then it sank, and she got it upright and hauled it out onto the grass. Perhaps it was the achievement of this simple operation that cleared her mind. Suddenly she became overwhelmed with a great sense of disaster. She had experienced something like it before, connected with the desolation that grew inexorably all around her, but this had been more impersonal and therefore more bearable. Now she had a feeling of being caught in the whirlpool that had not touched her before, and of having no possibility of escape. For the first time she realized how it must be to be aware of having the fever, or of being arrested after long flight by the soldiers, or of lying on a pile of straw waiting for death from starvation—all things that had happened to people she knew.

It was ridiculous to associate such horrors with dear, good Samuel and in a moment she recovered. She could not possibly envisage being married to him, though she could well see herself sharing his bed. There was reason in that but in marriage there was none. On the other hand, she would not lie in his bed unless she were married to him because it would be a sin for both of them. She could be his servant but it seemed that this was not what he wanted. There was excitement in the notion of living like a lady but it was an outlandish idea and she wondered if there were any hope of talking Samuel out of it.

But her mother had said that if he did not marry now, he never would. Why should she not marry him, after all? She had never felt inferior to him or to anyone. A Flaherty was no better than a MacDonagh. They had enjoyed equality in the old times, not so long ago, before Cromwell. Then Hobsons and Shaws and Smiths had come in, lording it over the people that they should have been serving. Alice would have spurned an offer of marriage from one of these, even if he had owned half of Galway. And she had agreed with her mother to marry Samuel. There was no getting out of that now. A girl married who she was told if she had any sense of decency and gratitude to her parents.

Thomas had not yet been consulted. She expected that he would agree with Mary, as he always did, and this was what happened. As she climbed the stile from the field, carrying the heavy bucket, she saw that he had come to meet her.

He took the bucket from her and said at once, "Your mother said you'll be marrying Samuel."

"Yes."

"Do you want it?"

"It's he that wants it."

"Do you like him?"

"Yes. He's a fine man. You'd have to like him."

"What about Morgan?"

"Morgan has no rights over me."

He looked at her directly for the first time, with sharp relief. This angered her, since its inner meaning was clear, but she made no comment.

He said, "Your mother is all for it."

"Yes."

Thomas laughed suddenly and unconsciously echoed what old George had said. "She's the finest woman in the world. Follow her. She has sense." They walked for a while in nervous silence and then Thomas said, "Samuel would be doing all right for himself."

This was the most intimate conversation that Alice had ever had with her father. She took the rare opportunity of asking what had often puzzled her about him.

"What do you think of all this new talk of fighting?"

"I'd be in it now if I were young again," Thomas said positively. "We were put off with talk, talk, talk. When we got Catholic Emancipation in '29 we were told the good times were here but Daniel O'Connell was only a big, noisy, empty drum, though they called him the Liberator. What did we get out of it? A lot of churches and mighty little else except the same starvation every year since. We lost Mr. Davis and Daniel O'Connell, and an empty drum is better than no drum at all. If I were young now, I'd fight. We'll never get a present of freedom. That's something you have to take. But now we have no one to follow. In all Ireland there isn't a man."

"There's always someone," Alice said.

" 'Tis true, I suppose. But there's too many gone to America. Where would we be without America? We'd have our backs to the wall and that's a good way to fight. A man told me there lately when I was at the fair in Galway that Daniel O'Connell left a queer wish when he died: his body to Ireland, his soul to God and his heart to Rome. So it seems they divided him up that way. Do you know what I thought? A man that would have an idea like that couldn't have much sense. What could he know about dying of starvation, with your wife and children around you? Your heart and soul and body will all stay in the one place then, you may be sure. He was no Liberator, though I'd say the poor man meant well. Maybe he was too old when the time came for fighting. It's the young people are the best for that."

"You can't fight when you're hungry."

"That's true, I suppose. And we'll always be hungry, so we'll never fight."

"We won't always be hungry."

"Maybe not,' said Thomas, but it was only from politeness that he said it.

9

Casting about in her mind for a suitable messenger to go with the good news to Samuel, Mary thought of sending Joeen. Then she decided on Morgan. Thomas would have been better but Mary never encouraged him to go to Moycullen lest he might encounter old George.

Morgan had often taken messages for her on other occasions. Mary was in no way conscience-stricken concerning him. She was utterly satisfied with the present state of affairs, and while she did not wish to hurt Morgan's feelings, still she felt that he had no rights whatever once Samuel had entered the field.

Mary wrote a short letter to Samuel in the beautiful, clear handwriting that she had learned with him from Master Fahy. This literary skill of hers was highly valued in Cappagh by her older neighbors, who had never learned to read and write at all, and she was very obliging about writing to America for them. There had always been some scholars from the hedge schools, and everyone was learning now, in the new national schools, from whose book the children sometimes recited with hoots of derisive laughter:

> " 'I thank the goodness and the grace
> That on my birth has smiled,
> And made me in these Christian days
> A happy English child.' "

"Never mind that," Thomas said. "You're learning to read, aren't you? Mr. Davis said 'Educate that you may be free.' "

And he made Alice, who had a beautiful voice, recite Mr. Davis' poem:

> " 'When boyhood's fire was in my blood,
> I read of ancient freemen

> *Of Greece and Rome who bravely stood*
> *Three hundred men and three men.*
> *And then I prayed I yet might see*
> *Our fetters rent in twain*
> *And Ireland, long a province, be*
> *A nation once again.' "*

Even the small children knew that there was a clear dichotomy between what was in the schoolbooks and real life. Who could be bothered, for instance, with a moral story about the dangers of walking in the park without a hat and gloves? Far more real were the stories Thomas told, when he had time, of the Trojan War and the great voyages of Aeneas. The Aegean Sea was Galway Bay and the islands were Aran and all the islands on the coast. Seals and sharks were witches and sea monsters, and the storms that tossed the little boat could be seen any day in winter by glancing out of the doorway.

When Thomas began on a story, it was usually late in the evening, with the fire giving the only light and everyone sitting in a ring before it to enjoy its warmth. After Dan's marriage, Joeen took charge of the turf and kept the fire stacked up so that all the faces shone. Full of pride, Thomas sat on the left-hand hob and gave out the verses in Latin that he had learned in Mayo when he was young and living there for a time with his aunt.

> " *'Arma virumque cano, Trojae qui primus ab oris*
> *Italiam, fato profugus, Lavinia venit*
> *Litora; multum ille et terris jactatus et alto*
> *Vi superam, saevae memorem Junonis ob iram.' "*

"They believed in those old gods, you see, Juno and Jupiter and Mars, before the coming of Christ." Then he would go on with the story of the great war over Troy and the voyages of poor wandering Aeneas, which were very like the wanderings of Mael Duin, who was an Irishman and a Christian.

Even in the worst of the starvation, Thomas would put on this show, and Mary and all the family loved and admired him for it. He always finished the story with the same words.

"And at the end Aeneas said 'We had a hard time and a hard passage, but it will be a pleasure to us in after days to remember these things.' "

Alice especially liked the sound of the Latin words, which she only half understood. She had gone through Thomas' old Latin grammar, whose pages were black with use and smelled

66

of turf smoke, but she was aware that thousands of other books existed that were denied to her. Thomas' old teacher had taught in a shed near Claremorris, where in bad weather the owner's donkey looked interestedly over the pupils' shoulders as if to join in the class. The law had been changed a few years before Thomas was born so that there was no longer the danger of the school being suddenly raided by the soldiers and the teacher arrested and transported. Catholics were still nervous about learning, however, and though there was talk of secondary schools being started in different parts of the country, Mayo and Galway were still barren of them. Indeed the bond that existed between Alice and Morgan was based to some extent on their common interest in books. When Morgan went to Moycullen he sometimes brought one back, a loan from James Fahy or from the Flahertys and he and Alice would read it together.

Seeing Morgan setting off for Moycullen in the morning, Alice called out to him, "Bring us back a book if you see James."

Morgan waved to her to indicate that he had heard. He was a fine sight on a horse, with his straight back and his head held high. His whole posture expressed freedom and determination. He would be angry when he would discover that she was leaving him for Samuel but he would have to recognize that she must do as she was told. Besides, such a fine man would not be long without a wife. A moment later she was surprised at a feeling of anger and agitation lest Morgan's wife might be some weak slut who would not know how to treat him. But of course as Samuel's wife she would always be in touch with Morgan. Samuel had often said complimentary things about Morgan. They would be able to advise him when the time came for him to marry.

Morgan had no idea of the contents of the letter that Mary had sealed with red wax. Samuel kept her supplied with paper and ink, and she was skilled in cutting pens from sea gulls' feathers which she picked up on the seashore. She did it neatly, without wasting a stroke: first she cut half of the quill on the length for an inch or so, then hollowed the remaining half, then trimmed out two semicircles to leave a point at the tip and finally slit the point slightly to hold the ink. Old George had taught her with jackdaws' feathers, but she found that sea gulls' feathers were just as good.

Morgan knew that as she grew older, Alice would be very like her mother. This was why he paid no heed to his brother's warnings about her. In the last few days he had begun to pave the front of the house yard with flat stones, to make it clean and dry for when Alice would come, and he had a plan to buy two small pots of paint in Galway on his next visit to touch up the stones around the fireplace. Red outlined in white would look best. It would be a great extravagance but Nora had agreed that it would be worth it.

He was glad that Martin was out of the way just now, with his talk of fighting and freeing Ireland—necessary things, of course, but destroyers of the small enjoyments of daily life. Besides, in spite of his apologies, his disapproval of Alice had cut very deep and had cooled Morgan's affection for him temporarily. Now he was determined to have her. His mind shied around the details. He was glad now that he had not raped her on the night of her brother's wedding. All alone, crossing the mountain, he flushed at the memory of it, and then he relaxed gradually as he realized that she did not in the least hold the incident against him.

The sun was shining on Samuel's place when Morgan arrived. The great rolling park that skirted the avenue was a glorious sight, dotted with healthy cows, so different from the rocky, lumpy landscape of Cappagh, where only sheep and goats and donkeys grazed now. It was hard to believe that it was part of the same country. He would bring Alice to see it after they were married. Mary had never allowed Alice to visit Moycullen. It was a kind of revenge on her mother, and perhaps some kind of precaution, too. He was pleased that she had called on him to carry this message for her. It was a further sign of the friendship that she had always shown him, whose greatest manifestation had been in arranging for his schooling with Master Fahy. But for this, he would never have met Father Kenny, to whom he had introduced Martin. An odd notion this: Morgan had joined that strange, nameless secret society that was pledged to gain freedom for Ireland long before he had brought Martin into it. Now Martin had left him behind. It was he who believed in dedication to freedom and regarded Morgan as a backslider. He had not said this explicitly but Morgan could see that he felt it.

He put up his horse in Samuel's stable and noticed with relief that though Samuel's bay mare was in her stall, George's old gray was missing. He had known him from childhood but he was never at ease with George or ever felt any friendship toward him. There was no warmth in him, no trace of humanity that could be seized upon as an excuse for exempting him from the reputation of his whole class. Yet one could see that he was not a cynic. Lazy, perhaps, and this had been Morgan's defense of him when more than once some member of the organization had suggested shooting him. The last time, Morgan had said, "Spare your bullets. He's not worth it."

Paddy Egan, George's own groom, had backed up Morgan and the matter was dropped.

Paddy was forking hay down from the loft into the mangers when Morgan rode in at noon, and hitched his horse to a ring in the wall.

"A grand day," he said, "and bacon and cabbage for dinner."

Paddy acted the clown for the benefit of anyone who might be listening. Morgan made some noncommittal answer and started for the back door. Stout brown hens sprang delicately out of his way. From the ashpit by the side of the yard came the squall of a slaughtered cock, and the flutter, soon still, of great colorful wings. Sure enough, the kitchen was empty, though pots were bubbling on the stove. Kate saw to the hatching, rearing and killing of the chickens herself. Morgan passed through the kitchen to the hall and saw through the open front door that Andy was out on the steps watering the urns of flowers. Samuel's door was partly open and he was sitting at his desk. He was not working. He had not even opened the huge account books that dated back a hundred years.

He looked up quickly when Morgan appeared in the doorway. As usual his expression showed welcome. Morgan had the letter ready in his hand, having taken it out of the front of his jersey as he passed through the kitchen. With Samuel, Morgan was not concerned about his ragged condition, his patched hand-woven tweed trousers and threadbare jersey.

"A letter from Mary MacDonagh," he said and laid it on the table.

Samuel put his hand on the letter but he did not open it. He asked, "How are things in Cappagh?"

"The potatoes look good," said Morgan, "but it's early yet to say how they'll do. Martin went to America last week."

"I know. Father Kenny told me. I wish I had known. I'd have arranged for a friend of mine to look after him in Boston —Judge Kelly, who's going to meet the MacDonagh boys."

"Martin has friends in Boston, thanks all the same," said Morgan.

He did not mention that Judge Kelly was one of them. He was never sure how far Samuel's nationalistic leanings went, or even if they existed at all. All before him had been Unionists, and he had often wondered if Samuel would be capable of kicking over the traces that held him to his family tradition.

Then Samuel smiled suddenly and said, "Morgan, excuse me, but I can't put off reading Mary's letter any longer." And he ripped it open without waiting for any more conversation.

As long as he lived Samuel blamed himself bitterly for what happened then. It came about mainly because he thought of Morgan as a boy. He was only twenty-two years old and Samuel was thirty-six. Morgan had the strength of a man but the innocent eyes of a boy. Samuel had known him almost from infancy, at least from the time when Morgan, with shaved head and long, gray tweed skirt, used to trot down to MacDonaghs' to play with stones and pieces of colored pottery outside the door with the MacDonagh children. Then he remembered him coming, tongue-tied at first, to Master Fahy's school, barefoot and wearing gray tweed breeches that were banded below the knee to be worn with stockings. He had seen him come to the use of his tongue and learn the table manners of the well fed, first in the kitchen and then in the dining room. He had come to respect him for his industry and determination, and for his continued use of such education as he had received.

He read the letter through now and at once said, in a tone of delight, "Mary says that Alice has agreed to have me."

"What?"

"To marry me. I asked Mary to put it to her. I couldn't believe until now that she would."

"To marry you?"

"Yes," said Samuel happily. "It will be a sensation with some people but I don't care. In the present state of the country, a man can do as he likes. If I waited forever, I might not find a girl like Alice." For Samuel, Morgan and the room had disappeared and he was babbling into a vacuum. In all his life he had never acted like this before and probably never would again. "I've been through hell in the last few days, since I spoke to Mary. I've even wished I were poor, so that I'd have a better right to Alice. I thought she'd turn me down and laugh—you know the way that Alice laughs. I thought she wouldn't believe my offer was real. Alice loves honesty above all." He came to himself suddenly and Morgan floated into his view again. "You don't like it," he said.

Morgan sat motionless, as if his heart had ceased to function and his blood stream had stopped bringing life to his body. It was hatred that filled him but Samuel saw only astonishment.

"It's not so extraordinary, after all," he said. "I'm a Flaherty, one of the plain people of Ireland." A sharp look at Morgan showed Samuel that he was a danger. He attempted a

70

cooler tone. "Life will be worth living, with Alice. I don't think I could endure it without her."

He stopped, realizing once and for all that every platitude he applied to himself could equally well be applied to Morgan. Indeed, Morgan had less to live for, except perhaps the uncomfortable adventure of emigration.

They sat in miserable silence and watched each other. They were rescued by the arrival of James Fahy, dressed in his best clothes. They suited him and showed clearly the refinement he had doubtless inherited from his lady mother. Certainly he had little of his great, gangling father about him. His fine hair was smooth and faint side whiskers were beginning to appear. He moved lightly on neat, small feet. As usual he had a book in his hand. James affected an air of calm boredom and carried a book always in case he needed to dive suddenly into it to escape from the pressures of the world. Shakespeare, Dante, Boccaccio, Plutarch—the fatter, the better—had all in their day saved him. He was like a rabbit that had somehow contrived to take its burrow about with it. Absorbed in his book, he could have walked past a murder, an eviction, an armed rebellion.

Today, however, he looked positively excited. His pale face was slightly flushed and there was an unusual gleam in his eyes. Samuel stood up awkwardly, almost knocking over his chair. As he righted it he said, "Ready, James? We're driving in to Galway to register James at the university, if they'll have him. Can you stay and have dinner with my father?"

"Thanks, I will," Morgan said firmly, hating the prospect but seizing on it to hold his own with Samuel.

In spite of his poverty, his position as a former pupil of Master Fahy's gave Morgan a traditional right to eat in the dining room instead of in the kitchen. He would have greatly preferred to dine with Father Kenny today but now he was determined to hold on to his privilege. He even went out into the yard, where Paddy had the gig already harnessed, and watched the pair of them climb in and drive off. Morgan saw that Samuel was discomfited by his continued presence and he took a savage pleasure in this, and in the fact that in his hurry to be off Samuel flicked his whip over the pony's back so that he rocked the gig dangerously as he turned into the avenue from the yard gate.

"What's the matter with him?" Paddy asked, staring after them.

"You'll find out soon enough," said Morgan.

"My lord is going to go to the university," said Paddy.

"He's all right," said Morgan, suddenly pitying poor James. "He has a fancy for learning. He'll take to it like a duck to water."

To escape from Paddy, Morgan went into the dining room and began to take books from the shelves at random. Most of the books in the house were kept in this room, since the other two rooms on the ground floor other than the kitchen were used by George for his guns and by Samuel for his accounts. Samuel had some books in his room, too, local history for the most part, which interested Morgan, but not for anything would he have gone in there today. His feeling for Samuel was not so much of hatred now as of defeat, the inevitable defeat of the poor by the rich. Alice he could not blame. She was a commodity, an article of high value to be sold at her proper price. He felt a fool now for ever having aspired to her and yet he still felt that he had rights like the next.

Finding himself with the letters of Madame d'Arblay in his hands, Morgan smiled sourly to himself. Surely that Paris was a myth, like the story of Aeneas or of Finn MacCool. More real was the world of Thomas Nashe, a favorite of Master Fahy's, who used to give off during the regular famines:

> " 'Adieu, farewell earth's bliss,
> This world uncertain is.' "

And with tears he would intone:

> " 'Beauty is but a flower
> Which wrinkles will devour;
> Brightness falls from the air;
> Queens have died young and fair;
> Dust hath closed Helen's eye;
> I am sick, I must die.
> Lord have mercy on us!' "

"So there is nothing new under the sun. Plague and famine were always the scourges of the world."

Baby James, then only five or six years old, used to look terrified, and for his sake the older children did their sniggering imitations in private.

Wrinkles would not devour Alice's beauty for a long time, Morgan knew well. He had only to look at her mother. With a sense of justice, he took *Evelina* from the shelves and laid it on the mantel to borrow from George. It seemed suitable reading for Alice just now.

Later, when George came home, the book proved useful for diverting his ill-humor against the damned Whiteboys who had cleaned out the snipe from the bog to the north of the house. He found no incongruity evidently in complaining thus to Morgan, who, he seemed to assume, was thoroughly on the side of the landlords.

Of *Evelina* he said, "A pretty fair picture of Bath, I must say, though I found it a useless sort of life. Too much indoors."

10

On the way to Galway, Samuel was careful not to babble to James. He had some idea of what went on in the boy's head, from chance remarks and from a certain kind of determination that he expressed occasionally, as he had done concerning his choice of a university course. Samuel thought the present plan for James a better one than his other idea, which had been to apprentice him at the mill and later make him manager if he turned out well. Vaguely behind this had been the idea that James might be his heir but of course all that was changed now. Alice's children would be marvelous people, much more satisfactory than the cautious James.

He whipped up the astonished pony again and said before he could stop himself, "I'll be getting married this year."

"Good," said James sedately. Then he burst out suddenly, "To Amy Burke, I suppose."

"Good heavens, no," said Samuel. "Amy is only a child."

Noticing something odd in James's tone, Samuel glanced sideways at him and saw his tears. They were silent while the gig bumped and clattered along for a mile or more. Samuel was heartsore for James. In his own happy state, it seemed to him essential that everyone should achieve the girl of his choice. James might as well aspire to a daughter of Queen Victoria's as to Amy Burke, whose silly mother was already on the watch for an established husband for her. A woman of small imagination, she would need to see the color of a future son-in-law's money before she would believe. The acceptance of James, who was the same age as Amy and who had a father who could scarcely be successfully laughed off as a character, Samuel thought, would be quite impossible for her. The best he could hope for was that in a few years' time, if he were to make money, she might let him have one of the younger sisters.

At Galway, dusty and shaken from the drive, they went straight to the gray limestone County Club on Eyre Square. If Morgan had elected to come with them to Galway, Samuel would now be embarrassed because he could not have invited such a ragged figure into the club. James, in his neat suit and with his quiet ways, was another story. Samuel had taken him here before, without opposition, as he thought. The first time he did it, a serious discussion among a group of the members resulted in the conclusion that James had better be admitted without question for three reasons. One, of course, was Samuel's importance as perhaps the wealthiest member, independent as he was of rents, which had become a nightmare to collect. The second reason was that Samuel at thirty-six was unlikely to marry and in that case he might well make James his heir. And James's mother had been a lady, though a misguided one.

The important point was that Samuel was the most solvent landlord in Connacht, though he had given away countless sacks of flour and meal from his mill over the last few years. He had not discovered for a while that he had thus helped the landlords, because when they knew that this bounty had been given, they or their agents made sure to send around quickly for their rent in kind. Samuel's flour had even found its way into his neighbor Jerome Burke's kitchen, before he had got wind of it and advised the people to hide it.

The result of all this was that Samuel entered the club dining room with a curled, disdainful lip and lifted chin and eyebrows. There were several tallyhoes sitting at the tables. No women were allowed in the club so there was no need for the silence and gloom that prevailed. Secretly terrified, James imitated Samuel's expression as best he could. He wanted to learn this because already he knew that it would be necessary to him if he were to achieve his ambitions. In the same spirit he ate sole and roast lamb and drank some hock, noticing beady-eyed how the waiter served the food. He wished he had a better stomach and yet he guessed that he could make a fetish of eating sparingly but elegantly when he was rich. From Samuel he had already learned that mere quantity of food was not a token of gentlemanly living.

James was clever enough to interpret the gloom of the other members today as yet another symptom of their weakness. Though they acted the bully almost to a man, yet they were frightened in a new way. Some were selling their estates at reduced prices under the new Encumbered Estates Act, with help from the Government. James calculated that this would still be the habit when he would be of an age to buy a great house and land of his own. He longed passionately for this. Every day the room over the coach house, which he shared with his father, became more like a rathole. No one ever entered it except themselves. They cleaned it and kept it well enough, and took their laundry down to the washhouse regularly, but though it was in fact a pleasant, sunny room, for James it had become a symbol of poverty and servitude.

This glorious day, when he was alone with the great Samuel, the most wonderful things happened. The university accepted him as a student, subject to his doing a puerile examination in Latin and Greek and mathematics. He sat at the best table in the County Club among the respectful gentry, whose gaiters and tweeds and especially whose faces looked hopelessly bucolic beside Samuel's angular neatness. Best of all, on their way home in the gig, Samuel looked at him sideways after a long silence and said, "I wonder if you would like to move into the house when you're a student. You'll do better if you have a room of your own—if your father doesn't mind, that is."

James said coolly, "He won't mind." He could not trust himself to say more for several minutes and then he was able to add his thanks.

"The big room in the corner where the bees swarmed three years ago—that would be a good one," Samuel said. "There's a fine big window there, and you can see the lake. I'll put in a desk, and we'll get Andy to keep a good fire in winter."

Andy was going to hate that but James did not say so. Instead he asked, "Do you think your wife will mind having me in the house?"

"Alice? Not at all." Again the unfortunate pony paid for Samuel's exuberance at the thought of Alice so that the gig rocked with his fright. "She is generous. She will be glad to have you there."

Her name, then, was Alice. James resolved to be very quiet in that heavenly room, into which he had often peeped on his way up to the schoolroom. If this Alice were English, she might be quiet too, and perhaps away in Bath or Cheltenham a lot, as women seemed to enjoy. If she were Irish, however, she might have grand ideas and not want a studious boy taking up a room that could be occupied by one of her Dublin friends. Never for an instant did the true identity of Alice occur to James, though he knew the old story of George's tally-woman, as everyone did, and that Samuel visited her family in Cappagh.

Then Samuel said, "You'll need the gig every day, too, to go to college. I'll get a new one."

Since he was afraid of horses, James was petrified into silence at the thought of this new obligation.

After a single day spent in arranging for his absence from Moycullen, Samuel set out for Cappagh again. He knew that Mary would be expecting him because he had sent word by the herd's boy. For the crown with which he rewarded him, the boy would have trotted to Dublin, let alone a miserable ten miles over the mountain to the sea.

Alice was waiting, too, when Samuel arrived. This time Mary had the whole family lined up like a little army, combed and clean and in their best clothes. They looked excited and bewildered, as if they had only that morning heard the news, and they disappeared quietly within seconds of Samuel's appearance. Hauled along by the older ones, the smaller children turned to look back at him. Then he was alone with Alice. He looked around for Mary but she had disappeared too. He had not seen her go. His hands were shaking. Alice's eyes were cast down. Then she glanced upward and for a second he thought he saw the smallest gleam of amusement, but he must have been wrong, because she said gently, "It's all right, Samuel. I'm not afraid if you're not."

This pleased him enormously. He took her hands and held them. What he liked most was that she showed no gratitude, though it would have been natural and even suitable.

Alice's life had depended on Samuel for so long that she had passed the point where gratitude can be experienced. One is only intermittently grateful for a warm hearth, a good bed, a full stomach, in normal times. Though she was consciously aware of having these things, Samuel as their source seemed somehow unassailable, like the sea or the blue mountains across the bay, which would never be substantially changed. Until the day when her mother had told her of his proposal, it had never occurred to her that he might marry some foreign lady and be alienated from Cappagh forever. Since she had made her decision in his favor, its rightness had impressed itself on her.

She said, "My mother says that your father would welcome me."

"Yes. Everyone will welcome you."

"Who else is there?"

He tried to explain some of the feudal complexities of the establishment, some of which she knew already from Morgan and from her mother.

"We're a seedy lot," he said, "but if you don't mind going to the Husseys in Aran for a while, Mrs. Hussey will give you some idea of how to tidy us up."

Delighted with the delicate falsehood of this, Alice said, "You don't look seedy to me, Samuel, but I'll be glad to go. I'll have time to think, in Aran."

Remembering Morgan, Samuel said, "How soon could you go?"

"Any time."

"Tomorrow?"

"Today, if you like. There's nothing to wait for, unless you have to send word to Aran."

"No. They're always ready."

He looked at her in amazement and rapture. What a prize she was! Scarcely anyone, of her class or his, had any capacity to look forward. The poor were in despair and the landlords seemed to live from week to week, almost as if they did not believe in their own system any longer. Yet this marvelous girl was eager to begin a new adventure, the thought of which might well have frightened her into silence for a week. "I'm not afraid if you're not," she had said. He was not afraid, though his decision was born of such bitterness that he might well have been.

So that day, with Mary's connivance, they sailed for Aran from Galway on the *Saint Enda*, stopping at a shop in the town to order three dresses and some other things that would follow in a week. With the general poverty ruining business everywhere, the shop was ready to promise delivery next day if it had been demanded. Alice cared nothing for the shopgirl's knowing eye at the sight of a poor girl being supplied with underwear by such a personable and well-known man as Samuel. In the privacy of the fitting room the girl meanly suggested stays and convinced Alice that they were necessary. She tried to pump Alice for information but Alice would give none. That was up to Samuel whenever he wanted to do it. He had not introduced her as his fiancée but simply as Miss Mac-Donagh. The formality of this title was a shock to Alice and gave her a moment of panic.

At the docks, Mike Troy came shambling out of his cottage. Being a widower he was quite independent. He simply pulled his door to and climbed down into the hooker when he heard that she was to go to Aran. Without comment he helped Alice down the iron ladder set in the wall. One of the bystanders took the gig and promised to put it up at the County Club stables.

It was the half tide and there was still an hour in which the boat could safely clear the bay. The afternoon sun was brilliant and the water shone blue-gray, with the faintest ripple when the breeze flicked over it. The mainsail filled at once and they curved away from the quay wall. Within a minute they had made a great confident arc and were heading out to sea. Samuel and Mike knew every inch of the Corrib estuary and laughed at Alice's momentary anxiety as they crossed the rushing, galloping river's mouth. Then they were free. After Mutton Island, the steady breeze seemed all in their favor and they began to tack sweetly toward distant Aran, the almost mythical shadow on the horizon where Alice had never been.

With the course set and Mike at the helm, Samuel sat forward with Alice and wrapped his coat around her. He kept his arm around her shoulders and she liked this. Samuel's friendliness had always been a joy to her. Mike Troy was a traveled man who had been around the world. There was no need to consider him as an intruder. He looked calmly content, taking out his clay pipe, lighting it for half a dozen pulls and putting it away again every half hour or so. Little puffs of white cloud seemed stationary in the blue sky. The long-familiar hills of Clare took on a strange aspect for Alice as she saw them close to for the first time in her life. Their greenness amazed her, and then their white rockiness as the boat moved farther out into the bay.

"God help us, it's as bad as Connemara," she said to Samuel as she gazed at the endless rocks and then the perpendicular Cliffs of Moher. "I thought we had the worst place of all."

"Some parts are better than others," Samuel said. "Inland it's green and good. You'll see that someday."

Five hours' sailing took them to the quay at Kilronan. The long evening light was still there, sharply pointing the blackish stone of the quay and the reef at the opposite side, half covered with orange-colored seaweed, which formed a tiny bay. Alice was pleased with the solid look of the houses and especially with the gentle faces of the men who came down to watch the hooker arrive. They were shy, slow-spoken people with soft murmuring voices. They all knew the boat and Samuel. They avoided Alice's eyes in a way that she found strange until she surmised that it was because of Samuel. The boat moved slowly in to her moorings with her mainsail down. Mike Troy knew many of the islanders. He sent a coil of rope whirling through the air and was hauled in expertly to the side of the quay.

A man who knew some English came forward and said carefully to Samuel, "You are welcome to Kilronan, Mr. Flaherty. You will be going to Gortnagapall?"

"Thank you, yes. Have you a trap?"

"A sidecar only."

Samuel glanced at Alice, who said instantly, "The sidecar will be fine. I love a spin on a sidecar."

The man's face lit up with pleasure. He said, "I will bring her at once."

Samuel handed Alice ashore, where she was received like a queen, with a little cleared space between her and the islanders. It was an eerie feeling. No one spoke. Presently the sidecar came rumbling along and Alice climbed quickly onto one side of it. Samuel got up beside her and they moved away over the softly grinding gravel. Alice found that she had been holding her breath. She let it out slowly and quietly so that Samuel should not know.

11

Word had already reached the Husseys by the time they arrived. A Kilmurvey boy who happened to be in Kilronan had galloped by the short way over the rocks and down from the cliff to fall into the Husseys' kitchen and pant, "Samuel Flaherty and a country girl have just got off the *Saint Enda* in Kilronan. They're coming on Patcheen Barbara's sidecar."

"A girl?"

Ellen's Irish was awkward. She was not sure that she had perfectly understood.

"A lovely dark girl with shining eyes and skin like a swan, as the song says."

"Who is she?"

"Miss Alice, he called her. A funny name. Oh, she's a beauty! Wait till you see her."

Ellen Hussey darted from the kitchen into the hall with a duster and a mop. The stone floors were clean and the oak furniture shone with wax. There was nothing to do. She went outside and brought in a bunch of heather, torn out at speed by the roots, and placed it, without water because of her hurry, in the round silver bowl on the parlor table. The sidecar was visible now, coming down the hill. She wished that Patcheen would stop flourishing his whip so that the horse would not go so fast. The beds were made. Fires could be lit. She rushed back to the kitchen to send the boy for half a lamb from John Conneeley Pat, or a young chicken. It was to be young, mind, she hooted after him, not an old-timer like they'd eat themselves. The boy ran off and Ellen went to stand quietly by the door. As Samuel had said, the Husseys were always ready.

The house stood in the middle of a hilly green field crossed by a graveled avenue that led directly to the front door. There was no attempt at a garden. A white-graveled semicircle in front of the door gave the place a clean, healthy look. It was a two-story house, with a widely overhanging roof, built by some farsighted O'Flaherty of a hundred years ago. The rooms, like the house, were square and plain, with stone floors downstairs and wide pine boards above.

Alice loved it all. She had never known that one could live like this. Ellen took her to a room over the drawing room with a white-covered oak bed and marble-topped furniture. The ewer and basin and the soap dish had a blue-and-gold pattern. It all smelled more of beeswax than of turf smoke.

Since the day, seventeen years ago, when Samuel had brought two young men who were friends of his to stay in Aran for four days, the Husseys had kept four bedrooms always ready. Ellen had never forgotten the shame and horror of having to keep the young men waiting while she moved her own family's property out of the bedrooms and prepared clean beds. Samuel had been quite unaware of the disturbance he had caused. He had taken his friends scrambling up over the rocks to Dún Aengus and they had come back to an excellent dinner. Ellen was a good cook. Since that day, Tom and Ellen and the children had slept in various linen rooms and store rooms and servants' rooms, never daring to make the main part of the house their own. Samuel had never brought friends there again, though he came himself for a day or two every year.

When Ellen came downstairs alone, he called her into the drawing room. He knew she must be at least seventy but she looked ten years younger because of being so straight and thin. He could not remember the time when she had lived at Moycullen. She was a Dublin woman who had worked in Cheltenham and been trained as a lady's maid. There his mother had employed her, finding her accent and ways pleasantly quaint. It had been considered a further sign of Sylvia's oddity to have employed an Irish personal servant. Even those who married Irish landlords usually had more wit than that.

Since leaving Moycullen for Aran, Ellen had hardly seen a real lady. Samuel wondered how much she remembered of her former trade. She kept the house beautifully, as he could see—far better than Moycullen House was kept nowadays, and this was the knowledge that Alice needed. He explained that he was going to marry Miss Alice in the autumn and that she was to be instructed from beginning to end in how to be a lady.

Ellen's expression did not change. She said, "I'll do that for you, Mr. Samuel. She's a lovely lady, if you don't mind my saying so. She'll need dresses."

"They're coming out from Galway in a week or so. They have to be made. You can order more."

"You thought of that. Her hair—and her hands—"

"All those things," Samuel said impatiently, suddenly hating the idea of Alice being groomed like a horse. Then he experienced a sense of almost detached amusement and curiosity as he speculated on the changes that would be made in her. Improvements they would certainly be.

"Her accent—she must be able for the county ladies."

"I'll ask her to imitate me," said Ellen, "if it's necessary. From what I hear, the new county is not like the old."

"Don't frighten her, don't worry her."

"No, Mr. Samuel."

"She's very young. Only nineteen."

"Yes, Mr. Samuel."

"The place looks lovely, Ellen." He walked across the room and touched the heather in the bowl. "Most big houses are kept like pigsties now, so far as I can see. Of course you didn't have the famine here. That hit us all, rich and poor. Our house gets worse and worse. We need Miss Alice."

So already, long before the change had come about, he had made her over in his mind to be the woman he needed. Alice cooperated with alarmed intelligence. The very first evening, in the dining room, she saw how Samuel's manner to her had changed. It was terrifying. The simple companionship of Cappagh was gone and a horrid, respectful manner had replaced it. He seemed miles away, the Samuel who had come to the wedding, for whom she had translated the tinker woman's song, the straightforward, honest Samuel to whom she had given her promise in the certainty that he would be understandable. A sort of introversion or bitterness had replaced his former directness. Perhaps he was suffering, regretting his decision concerning her. She felt cheated. All her senses became sharpened so that she showed her best table manners as taught by her mother and won the admiration of Ellen Hussey. The half lamb had arrived, and Ellen cooked and served it herself, handing the plates as if she had been a parlormaid instead of a lady's maid. Alice guessed correctly that part of Samuel's stiffness could be explained by Ellen's presence.

In the bedroom later she was careful not to weep with disappointment, lest it might show in her eyes next morning. The room seemed vast to her. Ellen, still expert, helped her into bed, in a long-sleeved cotton nightgown that smelled of age. It had embroidered cuffs and collar. She sat up like a doll —one of those dolls with a painted, vulnerable china head that Samuel sometimes brought her when she was small— afraid to move until Ellen had gone out of the room leaving her with the lamp on the bedside table. Alice had never worn a nightgown before and it fascinated her. She lifted her hands and admired the drooping scalloped cuffs.

Then she began to giggle but that did not last long. So many things were new and unreal, it was hard to be amused even by the great mahogany commode with pink roses on its pottery.

Though she had the lamp lit beside her, the sky was full of daylight. She and Samuel had walked a little after dinner, around the outside of the house, and had met Tom Hussey and Stephen, the only child remaining at home, who was Alice's age. She gave him the easy greeting that she would have given to one of her brothers. She noticed how silent he was and how he watched her walk off with Samuel. Then back in the drawing room Samuel told her all about the estate and the mill, details she had never known before, and about the timber business. That part of it had faded to nothing because no one had a penny to build or repair anything, and for public buildings the materials were nearly all imported from England now. Even quarried stone was brought in from Wales and Portland.

Alice had never before understood how Samuel occupied his time. She teased him, saying, "So you work. You're not a real gentleman at all."

"Thank God," said Samuel, "that is true. I'm in trade, which means I'm an outsider, but having my mother's money invested in England makes me an insider again. Being a Catholic makes me an outsider but having had an English mother makes me an insider again."

"Marrying me is going to make you an outsider for certain sure," said Alice, catching on to the game.

"We can fox them a bit there," said Samuel, "if we care enough. Don't say 'for certain sure.' Just say, 'for certain.' No need to be nervous because of them—they don't matter at all —but it will be interesting to see if you can handle them."

Again he looked at her in that detached way that made Alice shiver with fear. She knew that her old Samuel was still there but she doubted if she would have been so quick with her promise if she had seen this side of him before.

She said, "Who are 'they'?"

"The Burkes, our next-door neighbors, half a mile away by the road, nearer across the woods. Their eldest daughter Amy is a couple of years younger than you." Alice warmed at the thought of a little company but Samuel went on. "They're awfully grand—at least, Lydia Burke is. Jerome Burke and I don't see eye to eye about lots of things. Then there are the Martins, of course. They're up at Ballinahinch Castle. There are Smiths and Bateses and Fowlers and Shaws and Bakers and Blakes. You'll meet them all. There will be parties. You'll be able for them."

But Alice felt that she would not. Yet she did not dare to ask Samuel if it would be possible to avoid all these people and go their own way. He seemed to take it for granted that this could not be done. She could not imagine how the parties would be. She guessed that they would be quite different from the weddings and American wakes in Connemara, when the animals were put out of the house and came around curiously in the evening to find out why, braying or baaing at the open door. She would be very quiet at those parties, of course. She longed for her mother now, lying in the huge white bed which felt cold although it was warm summer. She had never before slept alone. Always there had been one or even two of her sisters, a big one and the small one. Soon she would have Samuel. The strangeness of this thought made her head swim. He was in one of the rooms nearby now, doubtless thinking of her if he was a right kind of a man at all.

She remembered poor Morgan with genuine sympathy. She turned out the lamp but the afterglow still filled the room with a pink light. The noise of the sea was familiar and soothing. It had been an astonishing day. She slept suddenly and completely.

In the morning, Tom Hussey got out his sidecar and drove Samuel back to Kilronan, where the boat was. Alice wept when he left her, but not until he had gone too far to see. Ellen stood and watched her, not knowing what to do for her. Then she said, "It won't be long till he's back. He keeps his word, like his mother."

"Were you fond of her?" Alice asked curiously.

"She was so afraid of everything in Ireland," Ellen said. "She came thinking it was just a part of England. She did up the house beautifully, brought men from Dublin to do papering and painting, and brought furniture and all. But she had no enjoyment with it for thinking of the poor people that had nothing. Mr. Samuel is like that. He never turns anyone away from his door, I've heard. I was fond of her for that. Mr. Flaherty was different."

Alice gathered that she had not been fond of old George, yet her own mother had loved him. Alice did not look forward to living with old George but as against that, there were members of her own family that she would be glad to leave behind.

"Tell me about the house," she said.

"You have never seen it?"

"Never."

Concealing her astonishment, Ellen described the house, beginning with the gate lodge. She had to name every person who had worked there in her time and describe them closely, and say whether she had liked them or not.

"Did you like him? Did you like her?" Alice asked insistently, measuring each one by Ellen's standards. She had not forgotten any of it and Alice soon found out that she had kept herself informed about the fate of the people on the estate that she had known as children. She knew who had gone to America and who had prospered or died there, and she knew who had died of hunger or famine fever at home. She also knew about the new arrivals, whom she had never seen.

"Your nearest neighbor, Jerome Burke, is a bitter pill, God forgive me for saying it," she said. "Mr. Samuel shamed him, feeding the poor people that were starving. Mr. Burke let them die if they could and he put them out on the roadside if they couldn't."

"Our nearest neighbor?"

"That's what I hear," said Ellen. "He has no fear, which is foolish because he has no protection except the Army, and it would take time to get them out from Galway if the Ribbonmen got after him." Then suddenly she cut off the conversation, as if she had remembered that the Flahertys were landlords of the old school too.

In those first days, Alice developed in love and gratitude to Ellen. Somehow she managed without insult to teach Alice how to arrange her hair, how to take a bath, how to trim her nails, how to wear the voluminous dresses and the shoes and stockings that came out from Galway much sooner than they had been expected. Alice found it all rather ridiculous, humiliating and painful, but she recognized more and more its necessity. Besides, she had made her promise to Samuel and breaking it was unthinkable. Sometimes, when she remembered her mother's history, she found her own situation intolerable. She was trapped, lost, drowned in the plans of other people who cared nothing at all for her. But this could not be true of Samuel. She could not help feeling pride in the fact that he had wanted her, even though she could not understand his reasons. He could please himself, of course, a privilege enjoyed by no one else in Alice's experience. Perhaps that, after all, was the whole secret.

"Hair is very important," said Ellen. "It can give dignity and style if it's well done."

She sat Alice before the glass in her own room and dressed her hair in a bun and then in ringlets and at last in a sort of pompadour that left her long neck bare. Alice lifted her chin in fury to get a better look and Ellen said calmly, "That's it. We'll keep that one. The neck is magnificent."

Alice was bewildered at this expressiveness and Ellen did not tell her that it was a quotation from an old lady she had served in Cheltenham, an approving comment on her daughter-in-law.

Ellen brushed and twisted and pinned until Alice was nearly frantic, and at last she had worked out a system as exact as an engineer would use in building a bridge.

"This piece goes across, that piece is turned in over it, now the ends are tucked in, and at last a touch of soap to keep it all in place."

She touched the sides with a wet piece of soap and there it was, as neat as a painted doll's head, the style that Alice wore for the rest of her life.

She demanded, "What do I do in the wind?"

"A lady doesn't walk in the wind without a hat or a veil."

"Glory be to God!"

"And you must learn to call on God privately," said Ellen. "The gentry never mention Him in company. It's considered coarse. Now we'll do your nails. Your hands are good, a good shape, but the nails are roughened."

Sweet Ellen! Alice glanced at Ellen's hands and saw the nails broken and bruised from work. By comparison, because of her youth, Alice's own were already the hands of a lady. She listened dutifully while Ellen told her how to keep them white and soft by the use of creams and juices but mostly by avoiding rough work. She might keep a garden, but only if she wore gloves always. Meekly Alice made no comment but inside her was born then the determination to give this lady business a sparse attention and no more. She could spend her whole life concentrating on it if she were not careful. It was a temptation from the devil, though neither Samuel nor Ellen looked like agents of the devil.

When the tension became unbearable she began to weep and the lessons were called off for the day, but they were resumed inexorably the next morning. She must learn to embroider. That was easy. Already she was able to make lace. Mary had taught her. A lady could embroider—or make lace—in the drawing room, which was sometimes a great help in putting up with unpleasing company. Even her husband's most boring friends could not be abandoned. In the family she could sew underlinen and hem handkerchiefs and sheets. Deeper and deeper Ellen delved into her Cheltenham past. A lady should not talk too knowledgeably about war, as the gentlemen didn't care for this. But of course that had been before Waterloo, she said uncertainly, and perhaps it had changed. A lady must not do any housework at all or her maids will despise her. The only thing she might do was dust the pianoforte. Indeed, this was her duty, Ellen remembered. Alice sat in despair, not bothering to mention that she had never seen a pianoforte, though she knew from her mother what it was. She was glad enough to have some experience of sheets and underlinen, unlike most of her neighbors.

In the evening, Ellen was quite different. Then Alice's whole body softened and relaxed, and for a little while, with her hair in a soft bun, she was herself again. This was the time of the day when she remembered Morgan and wondered how he felt when he found that she had gone off with Samuel. Weakened from all the assaults she had endured, she wanted to think about him long and slowly but this would not do. Since she was promised to Samuel it would be a sin. Besides, there was no time for it. Tom and Stephen Hussey were there, at the kitchen fire, and often a neighbor or two, and they wanted to hear all the news from the mainland. Stories of the "bad times" had reached them in plenty and they needed to have them verified or denied.

"In Cappagh and out to the west, all out along Cois Fharraige, whole families died in their houses," Alice said, "but last year there was more that went away. They're not waiting to die now. They know better."

"Glory be to God," said all the soft voices, "it was a terrible disaster!"

"We were lucky here in Aran. The blast never came on the potatoes and we had hardly any fever."

"And Mr. Flaherty is a good man. They say the landlords are walking devils in Mayo, with people that always paid their rent being turned out of their houses every day of the week."

"And Lord Palmerston in Sligo sending them all to Canada to freeze in the snow."

"The passage money is less to Quebec than to New York and that's why he makes them go there, though it's a longer journey."

Patcheen Barbara, who had driven over from Kilronan, said not at all cynically, "It's a good thing that God loves the poor."

He had a daughter in Boston and another in New York, and having the strain of poetry in them, they were great letter writers. His son was in Portland, Maine, but he was away on a whaler for months at a time so his letters were less frequent. Patcheen read these letters to the company whenever he came, since they nearly always contained news of some other neighbors.

One evening he read aloud, " 'The *Peacock* came safe to New York this week though she had to weather a storm on the way. There was no fever on board. She took three months to come. All the passengers were allowed to land. We went down to see them and knew some from Aran.' "

The names were given and of course they were well known to all the company.

Patcheen read on. " 'The Aran people looked well enough though tired to death, but the Mayo people, God look down on us, were starved and broken. Their bodies were barely covered and they had to get clothes from the people of New York before they would be let come ashore. They said it was their landlord that sent them. The Irish that have made their way are going mad when they see how things are at home. They are saying they will cross the Atlantic Ocean again in ships and make a free Ireland soon, where there will be food and drink for all, the way there used to be in the old times before the Saxons' coming. I am sending five dollars for oatmeal and more later. I am well and have enough of everything. The woman I work for is good and I pray for her because she is a Protestant and I would not like her to go to hell. Some girls have bad mistresses but thank God I am lucky. Mary wrote from Boston that there is terrible news from Canada. The people going there are dying and the winter cold is terrible, so we are lucky, thank God.' "

"Thank God!" said everyone softly.

Alice told them about the *Pheasant,* which was on its way to Boston with Michael and Roger and Martin Connolly on board. If fever broke out, the ship would be sent north to Nova Scotia or maybe to Montreal. It could not be prevented from landing there, in British territory. Terrible stories had come from Montreal, in Black '47, of the people being housed in huts for fear of the fever, and not being allowed to go and look for work, of the coffins full and empty all piled up in the central square among the huts and the priests and doctors dying among the people. Perhaps things were better now, they said to comfort her. And if the *Peacock* could be free of fever, maybe the *Pheasant* would be the same. The contrast between Alice's present position and that of so many of her neighbors hurt and upset her. When Patcheen had gone and she and the Husseys were saying the Rosary before going to bed, she wept with pity and sorrow. In the dark kitchen, no one noticed except Stephen.

12

It was Nora who told Morgan that Alice had gone away with Samuel in the gig. He was up in the highest field on his land, weeding his potato beds. In this part of the country, the potatoes were planted in broad, flat beds, with a foot-deep trench at either side to take off the water. Cabbages could be planted halfway down the sides, making further use of the dressing of seaweed that had been carried up with such labor from the shore.

Morgan enjoyed the work. It was satisfying to see the juicy green cabbages sticking out below the potato stalks. The seaweed that he had buried in the beds in the spring had retained some of the smell of the sea. Its tang mixed pleasantly with the sweet scent of the potato flowers. It was a fine breezy day though the sea was not rough. The larks sang high over his head, clearly heard long after they had disappeared from sight. The earth fell away cleanly from the shining edge of the loy, and it fell easily too from the roots of the weeds and clumps of grass when he shook them before throwing them into a little heap. If they dried out, he would burn them later at the top of the field.

Nora came walking slowly toward him. She was a small girl, who would have looked like a child if she had not been dressed in the clothes of a woman. This innocent, childish look worried Morgan at times. It seemed that she knew nothing at all of the world and its ways. He knew she was lonely since so many of the girls had gone away and she had so much work to do in the house. He would ask Alice to come more often. Alice would be good for Nora. For the thousandth time since Dan's wedding, Morgan dreamed himself into touch with Alice, until he could almost feel his hands on her body as he had done on that terrible night. The loy fell from him and he stooped to pick it up. He had straightened his back by the time Nora reached him.

He saw at once that something was wrong but with Nora this could be a broken mug or a lost penny. Now she seemed to have been crying and her pretty little forehead was all wrinkled. Her soft brown hair was ruffled. He put his hand on her shoulder as one would with a hurt child and said gently, "Nora dear, what's wrong?" Then as she looked at him with eyes of genuine fright, he said, "Come on, tell me. It can't be that bad."

In a whisper she said, "Samuel Flaherty came and took away Alice, Peggy Michael said. Mary told her she's gone to the Husseys in Aran and that Alice is going to marry Samuel."

Suddenly she gave a shriek of horror and pain as she saw his expression change. Wailing with grief, she turned and ran away, down the field, plunging across the potato beds and through the gap that led to the grassy field beyond. Leaning on the loy, he saw her red petticoat flick around the corner of the house and he knew that she had gone inside.

Morgan had to sit down, dragging himself on shaking legs to the headland. His hands felt weak too, so that they would not lift and cover his face, or even brush away the shameful tears that poured from his eyes. He moaned and the tears stopped. Anger seized him, a frightening sensation that stiffened his limbs and stopped his breathing. A pounding began in his head. Samuel. Alice. Samuel and Alice. Samuel took away Alice. Samuel came and took away Alice. They would be married. They would lie together. Alice and Samuel. Weakness overcame Morgan again so that he had to lie on the grass. His neck went rigid. A beetle walked past his eye. Alice was near, near, near. He could touch her if he wanted.

He put out a hand. There was nothing but grass, a stone. The larks sang. This must be what madness was. Mad people were called God's people but they could just as well be called the devil's people. God, God, God help. God help Morgan Connolly. Please God, send help to Morgan Connolly. No, that was wrong. O God, I need you. Where are you? Madness is on me, for a girl, my girl, my Alice. Mine. Mine. Send her back. Raise a storm. Drown the boat. But not Alice. O God, spare Alice. Not for Samuel. Alice belongs to Morgan. Why had he waited? He should have gone at once after Alice when he found that she was promised to Samuel. He had not really believed it. Or he had been afraid. Afraid of Alice, perhaps. Wasted, wasted days.

Then his whole body went slack. His brain began to work craftily. Leave God out of it. God helps those who help themselves. There were things that he could do. Alice was not a miss that could be ordered by her parents to do this or that. He could see Mary's hand in this. It would be like old times to her. She would welcome the move to Aran. It was as good as seeing Alice married to Samuel already. It put a stop to all argument and it gave Alice no chance of weakening. But there were ways in which she could be made to weaken and ways too for putting a stop to that marriage.

He stood up and looked at his precious potatoes as if they had no importance at all. He walked down through the fields and around by the gable of the house to the door. Nora was crouched on the hob with her hands clutched together on her breast. Her face was pitiful. Morgan scarcely saw her.

"I'm going over Moycullen way," he said. "I'll be gone for a while." For a moment he saw her clearly and he added, "If you're afraid, you can go down to Peggy Michael's at night."

She said softly, "Don't do anything bad, Morgan."

They looked directly at each other and then Morgan turned away. Bad was good and good was bad. What did it matter now? When the time came, he would know what to do.

He took the bridle from the peg behind the door and went out without another word. Catching the horse took an age. When he had him safe, Morgan let the headstall slip out of his hands and the horse leaped away and had to be cornered at the end of the field. Morgan got the bridle on him and led him to the lean-to shed for the saddle. The aged girths seemed made of steel and would not close. At last he was in the saddle, revenging himself by kicking the brute and then in terror patting his neck to quiet him. To plunge away from Cappagh in obvious temper would be foolish. He took the horse quietly out of Cappagh, keeping to the grassy verge of the road at a meek trot, though he longed to gallop. He was sure, however, that Mary would know he had gone, and where he had gone. He wished her pain and fear.

At Moycullen, Father Kenny received him anxiously.

"Of course you can stay. Are you on the run?"

"No. I'm on other business. That bastard Flaherty has taken away Alice."

"Which Flaherty?"

Then Morgan had to apologize for using such language to the priest, who said impatiently, "Which Flaherty? Old George?"

"No. Samuel says he's going to marry her. He's taken her away from Cappagh to the Aran island. I came to find out from you if—"

"Well?"

Father Kenny glanced toward the sitting room door, which was shut.

"Maybe you know what's in my mind. Could Alice be old George's daughter?"

This was the easy solution. He gazed at Father Kenny in hope and saw only pity. He knew what the answer would be.

"No. It would be neat but it's impossible. Mary never came here after she left for Cappagh to be married. If she had come, or if George had gone to Cappagh, don't you know well the whole townland would have known about it? George can't move a toe without the knowledge of every man, woman and child in Moycullen. Anything he does can mean life or death to them, so you may be sure they keep a close eye on him."

Morgan said, "I thought that Alice, with her fine ways—that her father might have been a gentleman—"

"No. When I came first, the peole talked a lot about him to me until they were sure I knew all about him. He hasn't been to Galway for fifteen years. Before that, he went twice a week and spent two hours at the mill and had lunch at the County Club and then went home. They knew everything he did. He seems to have put Mary out of his mind when she married. I was told there was talk of the daughter of a gamekeeper in Cong about twenty years ago but it fizzled out. I think the girl went to America. It's not my parish. I heard she was willing but old George cooled off. Times were different. If he had paid even one visit to Cappagh, or if Mary came to Moycullen, the news would have traveled faster and farther than a bird can fly. I have other ways of knowing too."

This surely meant that the subject had come up when old

George went to Confession, which he had begun to do at Christmas and Easter soon after Father Kenny came to the parish. It could not be mentioned, since the seal of Confession was on it. Morgan dropped his eyes so that the priest could not see the devil in them. Devil or God, it had a hold of him now and he knew what nonsense it was to talk of resisting temptation. His certainty gave him sound sleep, under the roof of the priest who had always been his friend, who had trusted him and helped him.

He left in the morning early to ride to Galway. Father Kenny asked him to stay longer, looking at him sharply.

"You should stay with me for a while. You wouldn't bother me. You don't look fit to go off by yourself." He put his hand on Morgan's arm. "This will pass. There are other girls. I know how it is, believe me. Let me help you."

Morgan looked down at the friendly hand and saw no hope in it. There were no other girls.

He mumbled his reply. "Yes, I know you'd like to help me but it's no use. I've got to go. I'll come back some time or other."

"Come back soon."

Morgan jerked the horse into a trot and waved to Father Kenny, who stood at his gate to watch him go. Another moment and he would have asked a direct question that could not easily have been avoided.

Morgan was on his way to Aran. He had been there only once before and he knew that getting onto the island unobserved was out of the question. His boat would be seen miles away. He had to get to Alice. When she saw him, she would understand everything. She was good. She was no murderer. Afterward she would be his. That was how it always was. He had known it on the night of Dan's wedding but then she had jeered at him for his ignorance. She had been wrong. If he had stretched her and taken her then, now she would be his. That would have stopped Samuel. Better still, it would have stopped Alice. She had called him a Connemara man. She was a Connemara girl, for all her airs.

Morgan rode straight to the Claddagh, not quite knowing yet what he wanted. He sprang from his horse as if he had mounted only a few minutes ago. There was a great new force in him that he could feel out to his fingertips. He was in luck. Craftily disguising his urgency, he led the horse by the ring of the bridle, walked to the edge of the quay and looked down into the boats that were there. Turf smoke from the brazier came from the hold of one so that he knew there was someone down there.

He called out. "Hoy!"

The answer came back. *"Hóra!"* A head popped out to look at him.

Morgan said, "You're going out?"

"Yes," the man said. He was broad, grizzled, weather-beaten, a real Claddagh man.

Morgan did not know him. He asked, "Are you going to Aran?"

"We're going where the fish go."

"How many days will you be out?"

"While the weather and the fishing last. Two days, maybe three. We could lie in at Aran tonight. Do you want to go there?"

There was little curiosity in the question. The Claddagh men were not usually curious. They had traveled the world in great ships and they had too much in their heads for small things to trouble them. This was why Morgan had come here.

He said, "Yes, I want to go to Aran. How soon are you going?"

"In half an hour, if the man we're waiting on comes. Tell me, can you sail a boat?"

"Indeed I can. I have my own boat out in Connemara."

He saw the man look at his hands to assess their toughness and value. Then he said, "You can come with us. We needn't wait for that man. How long do you need to be on the island?"

"One night only."

The words stopped his breath so that the man looked at him more closely.

Morgan said, "I must go to one house there. Then I would come back to the boat."

It had been clever of Samuel to send her to such a lonely place. He had money. Morgan had only God and the strength of his love.

"My wife will take the horse," said the man, and he pointed out a cottage facing the quay.

Morgan led the horse to the cottage and gave him into the hands of a short, cheerful-looking woman who came out of the dark kitchen to speak to him. Her face was smoked to the color of old oak.

"You're going with Michael, then," she said, looking him up and down. "A fine lad you are, God bless you."

Back at the boat, another man had come up out of the hold.

They gave him bread and sour milk, which he ate while they prepared to cast off. Their nets were old. While they sailed out along the bay, he took a needle and mended them here and there. The work kept his hands at ease and the occasional attention he had to give it was a relief. The breeze was steady and from the southwest so that they tacked easily toward Ballyvaughan. There they fished for a while, expertly. The catch was mostly mackerel and rockfish. Farther out they hoped for better, they said. The long day wore away. They boiled potatoes on the brazier and talked of their voyages in the China Seas. Both of them had been on three-masters around the Horn. They compared captains and ships as if they had never met before, though Morgan knew that they always fished together.

The long, long evening seemed as if it would never end. It was still broad daylight when they came in to the quay at Kilronan. They were well known there, so the waiting group was a small one. A little interest was shown in Morgan but not much. The two Claddagh men climbed ashore and made for Kilronan. Morgan left them at the crossing and turned away toward Killaney. There were several poor houses visible there and he knew it would be presumed that he was visiting one of these. Soon the huge fortresslike police barracks cut off the view of the road from Kilronan. A single policeman was weeding the cabbage patch by the side of the barracks. He did not look up when Morgan passed.

A hundred yards farther on, he saw a track that led down to the shore. He followed it and came to a rocky beach. Deep fissures cut into the land, making the beach almost impassable. He made his way along it for a while, negotiating the rocks with care, and then he saw that he would have to climb up to the cliff above if he were to make any headway. In winter this place would be quite horrible, with the Atlantic wind blowing into it directly. Even now, in summer, the wind had to be reckoned with. He crawled up the flowing rock face and lay gasping for a few minutes on the short, blown grass. It was full of blue harebells just coming into bloom. They were the color of her eyes.

He sprang to his feet so violently that he came down on his hands and knees again. Then he was running in a crouched position along the cliff top. It was almost dark but the great sweep of the afterglow lit the heavy sky. There was no need to remember the way—it would be daylight when he would be coming back.

13

Morgan recognized the Husseys' house at once, the only two-story house on the island except the barracks and the parson's house in Kilronan. Its white gravel shone in the half-darkness. The only light to the front was in a room upstairs. From his place high on the hill he could see a fan of light faintly color the grass at the back of the house, as if a door stood open there. While he watched, it disappeared. He looked up at the lighted window and then stole very softly and very slowly on the gravel so as to make no sound. The window was open at the top. With his head bent backward he studied it. He could just see the ceiling of the room. A curlew whistled, quite close, a good sign. Standing under the window he called her name twice.

"Alice! Alice!"

Suddenly there she was at the window, her dark hair down around her shoulders, as it always used to be when she was a child. She lifted the window from the bottom slowly, soundlessly. She leaned out, with her hands on the sill, and whispered, "Is that you, Morgan?"

"Let me in, Alice."

When she disappeared he stood on the step, waiting, listening, guardedly looking right and left. He heard a bolt being softly drawn and there she stood, clad only in her long white nightdress. She leaned outward and took his arm and drew him in. The hall was in darkness except for the faint light that came down the well of the stairs. On her bare feet she went without a sound toward the stairs and he followed. At the landing above she was waiting for him and went before him into the lighted bedroom.

It was only a little oil lamp and its light was dim. Morgan closed the door and at once gripped her in his arms, feeling the wonder of her slim waist, shoulders, breasts and buttocks through the thin cloth of the nightdress, madly kissing her face, her neck, her hair, her shoulders. They spoke in whispers.

"Oh, Alice," he groaned, "why did you leave me?"

"Morgan, let me go, for God's sake. You shouldn't have come."

"You shouldn't have left me. You should have told me you were going. You're mine. You were always mine."

She tried to pull away from him but he held her.

"My mother and father decided it. I've never had who or what I want. What I want doesn't come into it."

"You want me. That's the truth, isn't it? Isn't it?"

"Oh, Morgan, it's a sin for you to be here."

"It would have been a sin to keep me out."

He gripped her still closer, his hands moving down her sides, all over her body, his mouth feeding on her mouth, until slowly, slowly he felt her go limp and knew that he had conquered her, and tearing her nightdress down about her breast and waist, he laid her on the white-covered bed. After that she resisted no longer and spoke only once.

"When I heard the curlew," she whispered, "I began to think of you and there you were at my door."

Their lovemaking was as silent and intense as the still night and the silent sea.

When it was over and they lay exhausted side by side, Morgan was filled with such pure happiness as he had not known could exist in this world. The lamp was burning low. In the last of its light he gazed rapturously at her white body and saw her smile at him sardonically.

"We're a nice pair," she said. "And I always held my head so high."

He drew her closer to him and stroked her shoulder. He heard a slight noise.

"What's that? Where are the Husseys?"

"At the back of the house. There's no one in this part except ourselves."

"Well, this is the end of them. You won't be needing them from this night on."

Abruptly the light went out. In the darkness he heard her say slowly and sadly, "Morgan, all that you've done is to make my life much harder from this night on. I belong to Samuel because I'm promised to him. If I deceive him now I'll never see God."

"But you have deceived him. We have both deceived him."

"We have deceived him but I still must keep my promise to him."

"How can you think like that and lie naked here with me, in his bed?"

"I can think it because when you leave me now you'll have to leave me for ever and ever. That's my misfortune and my punishment."

He thrust his face into the warm hollow of her neck, felt the steady, strong beating of her heart and said with supreme confidence, "I will never leave you now. You'll never leave me. Tomorrow we'll ge back on the hooker with the Claddagh men and we'll be married. After that there will be no more talk of sins or of Samuel. I'll fix it all with your father."

"Samuel fixed it all with my mother, and if you were to talk to my father, what could you say? That you came here secretly and that I let you into my bed and we took each other? He would kill you."

"If that is the only way to get you, I would do it."

He could feel her tears on his forehead.

"Since I was four years old, Morgan, I've loved you. Do you remember the summer when there were fifteen weddings in Cappagh and we went to them all, and maddened everyone by running around under their feet and taking up space on the dancing floor with our games? You were a huge fellow, seven years old. That was when I fell in love with you."

"Why didn't I know?"

"Boys never know anything." She laughed and began stroking his hair and the length of his cheek until he was nearly driven to madness. "They are too busy with other things. A girl can see a hundred things that a boy will miss. When you went to Moycullen I nearly died of loneliness. I even asked my mother if I could go, too, and be in the same school with you."

At the thought that for the whole of her life she had belonged to him, he was so flooded with happiness that his body began to burn and he wanted to make love to her again.

"So you see, Morgan, this is an old story for me. And that was what I thought of when the curlew cried and that was why I let you in, though in my heart I knew I was doing wrong. You got the better of me, though I had sworn you would not."

"You let me in because you love me. You've just proved it."

"Love is the talk of the gentry. People like us can't always have the love we want."

At this he pressed her shoulders and her knees away from his and took her again.

They woke to find the sun reflected from the waves beating on the white ceiling. In fright she sprang up.

"It is morning! We will be caught and I will be destroyed."

"When does Mrs. Hussey come in the mornings?"

"About eight o'colck."

"It's no more than six now," Morgan said, examining the sunlight. "I'll stay here while you dress yourself and then before anyone is up we'll steal away quietly, back along the cliff.

The men will be waiting. I'll make them take us straight to Galway. My horse is there. We'll ride together to Cappagh."

"This is mad talk. You know I can't do that."

Morgan felt a little explosion of anger in his head.

"You don't love me at all."

She shook with weeping. He had not known that anything could reduce any woman in this way.

"I'm doing terrible things to you, Alice. It would be better if we were both dead."

She rose from the bed, and beautiful in her nakedness, she stood on the floor and spoke to him calmly.

"But we have to live."

Then she dressed herself slowly, while Morgan kept his eyes fixed on her in love, terror and despair. Before her mirror she ran her hands under her wonderful dark hair and spread it evenly on her shoulders. When she turned slowly around she said, "You must go away now, Morgan. I've done you an injury. A piece of you will always be with me from this day on, and all your life you will be missing that piece, and it will be the same for me. After this neither you nor I will ever be the same person again."

As she said this she was looking out of the window and she did not turn to look at him. He began to pull on his clothes and noticed how worn his dark-blue jersey looked, faded to gray in places. It was shown up by the fresh cleanliness of Samuel's furnishings and bedding.

When he joined her at the window there were sea gulls on the grass, picking for worms or insects. When she raised the window they took off in full sail, smoothly, in well-judged arcs.

"I'll take you downstairs now," she said, "and you must be gone before anyone is stirring."

"I'll come back tonight. You'll have all day to think it out and you'll see I'm right. Oh, Alice, I love you so much!"

He saw delight in her face before she turned quickly away from him.

She made him wait while she looked down the stair well and listened. Then she beckoned to him and led the way down the stairs, opened the door softly and held it while he went out onto the step. When he turned for one last look, the door was already shut. He ran across the gravel, up the grassy hill, and went quickly to the top of the cliff and began to make his way back by the shore to Killaney.

14

When Alice came into the kitchen at eight o'clock, the look that Ellen gave her was frightening. What if Morgan had been seen coming or going? Ellen was such a good, innocent person that she would never think Alice could be so bad.

But perhaps Ellen was not so simple. Long ago, when she was very small, Alice had imagined her mother would be shocked even by a bad word. She had had to change her ideas when she had heard for the first time about Mary's young days. A jealous girl, Nellie Cooney, had mocked her with it.

"You needn't put on airs to me, Alice MacDonagh. Wasn't your mother the kept woman of Flaherty in Moycullen? You should be down on your knees praying for her instead of putting up to be better than your neighbors."

Alice had slapped her hard enough to knock her down and sent her home howling but Nellie would have been well satisfied with the result of her words. Now Alice trusted few people, except Morgan, since she knew that her family was the talk of the parish. At the memory of Morgan she smiled and Ellen immediately looked relieved.

"You've been crying," she said. "It's natural. This is a hard time for a girl. I remember it well with my own two daughters."

"Were they married here in Aran?"

Alice knew they were both in America now.

"Maria was married here, to Macdara Conneeley from Inishere. They lived there a few years then they went out to his brother in Portland. Sally went to be married in New York. They said it was a grand wedding, just like at home." Ellen sighed and then said briskly, "This morning you'll have your breakfast in the dining room. I have it all laid ready for you."

"When did you do that?" Alice asked, quickly working out that Morgan had been gone at least an hour.

"Just now, when I came in from the yard," Ellen said. "It's no trouble, only a few minutes' work, and I want you to learn how to eat breakfast."

Alice shouted with laughter.

"I thought I was eating breakfast all my life."

"A lady never comes to breakfast in her dressing gown," Ellen said. "Some do it but it's a slovenly habit and gentlemen don't like it. Even when they compliment the lady, they always think less of her. Some ladies go riding before breakfast, or take a walk. Some cut the flowers and leave them ready to arrange later but it's quite proper to go directly to the dining room."

The oak dining table was spread with a white cloth that must have cost Ellen hours of starching and ironing. She placed Alice at the head of the table.

"At breakfast there is no need to wait for the other members of the family to come down," she said. "Sometimes the gentlemen are cross in the morning but it's not necessary to make conversation at this meal."

The man who would sit with her would be Samuel and not Morgan. Hearing her little moan of pain Ellen said, "Don't be frightened. Breakfast is easy. There will be fruit and porridge and bacon and eggs and kidneys, liver perhaps. Some gentlemen like a chop at breakfast. Then there is tea and toast and marmalade, coffee for them that like it."

"Lord God, Ellen! Do people eat all that first thing in the morning?"

"Don't say 'Lord God!' I was just going to tell you about that. There is no need to eat all the things at breakfast. You can take what you like. Ladies usually take very little because they must eat so much later in the day. The lady's business at breakfast is to see that her husband eats well but not too much. If he likes to talk, she must stay with him, but if he reads the papers she may go when she has finished. But I don't think there will be morning papers in Moycullen," Ellen said. "There were none in my time. All these things I'm telling you are the right way. You may find that they don't know them in Moycullen. My old mistress did things right but perhaps they have changed since then."

"Samuel said they have changed."

"Yes, but he told me he wants you to put them right. The best thing is for you to learn the right things and then see how many of them you'll be able to use."

"What makes them right?"

"The customs of the best people, I suppose. There's a right and a wrong way for doing everything. Now, sit up straight. It looks better, though at breakfast both the ladies and the gentlemen always lounge a little. If you sit too straight you may look uneasy. Turn a little sideways." She arranged Alice in a casual position, even trying her with one elbow on the table but that was quickly rejected. "The fruit and the marmalade will be on the table. All the dishes of hot food will be on the sideboard, so you can pick out as much or as little as you like."

"But isn't there terrible waste?"

"It will be eaten up in the kitchen later."

Ellen did not have a quarter of the things she described but she did have several boiled eggs and a dish of bacon and three tiny kidneys from infant Aran lambs. She made Alice rise and walk slowly to the sideboard and take a plate and transfer some of these things unhurriedly to it and return to her place and eat them.

"If there is a footman or a parlormaid, you may be served by them. That will make it easier. Don't be afraid. You're learning everything very quickly."

So it went on until at last she was released and left in the drawing room with her embroidery. Two minutes of that was enough. She hurled it to the floor in a temper. Then she picked it up and smoothed it out and laid it on the table. It was a tea cloth in *broderie anglaise,* very suitable to a lady, all white, no color whatever. For Ellen's sake, Alice stroked it flat and then went out of the house by the front door.

She walked across the grass and up to the top of the cliff, following in Morgan's footsteps, imagining that a track showed faintly in the grass. Standing back from the window of her room she had watched him go, knowing that he could not see her and fearing that he would delay. He had not even turned his head at the top of the cliff. There was agony in watching his shoulders disappear, and then his dark head, leaving the blank, empty sky. She had wept again, shocking herself at the violence of her grief. So this was what love did to you! She would go mad, like Morgan, if she were not careful.

When she walked quickly to the top of the hill, the places where Morgan's feet had touched were surely warm under her feet. She looked down toward the sea and gave a squeal of fright at the horror of Morgan climbing up over those black, shiny rocks, worn so smooth by the sea that every one was a deathtrap. What if he had fallen from one of them on the way back? But this was madness too. She had often seen Morgan climb the face of a cliff far steeper than this one when he went after gulls' eggs. He was able to carry the eggs down again in a loop of his jersey without breaking one of them. This cliff would be easy to him. He would come back the same way to-night and she would be on the watch for him this time. There would be no need for him to call. She would open the door at once and let him in and lead him up the stairs. He would come into her room as he had done last night.

What then? Sorrow and sin and death were the fruits of

love, the song said. What if sin were delightful? How could this be? She knew it was filthy, vile, wallowing in slime, turning away the face of God, reducing man to the level of the beasts and making him only fit company for the devil. The priest gave it out every Sunday in one shape or another and she feared he was right. How well he described the course of sin! First came the devil's offer of joy that could not be resisted. Afterward came God's turn, when the sinner was condemned to hell, even in this world. But she knew now that there was a hell, too, in throwing away the joy of sin. Even now, her sin was not much if she intended to marry Morgan and leave Samuel.

She got back to the drawing room before Ellen came in from the yard where she had been feeding the pigs. The sour smell of them was all around her though she always washed her hands on her way through the kitchen. Aware of this, she stood by the door to speak to Alice.

"You look lovely there, so calm and happy and at ease. It's well to have your luck and to be able to enjoy it."

If the state of her mind did not show today, then perhaps it would never show at all. There was hope that she would be able to deceive everyone. It was going to be hell on earth and that was exactly what her kind of sin brought with it. While she answered Ellen she felt panic at the burning in her body, which was already waiting for Morgan.

By good fortune Ellen said, "You're at that embroidery long enough. I have to go to Bungowla today and perhaps you could take a holiday and come with me. It's a long walk but it will be good for your health. Mr. Samuel would like me to see to your health, too."

She made Alice wear shoes and walk like a lady for as much of the way as there was a road. When this became a grassy track, she allowed her to leave the shoes by the side of it, where they could be recovered on the way home. Without them, Alice skipped along like a child. Surprisingly, shockingly, something in her had been freed. She knew that Ellen was watching her with the pleasure one feels in watching a child at play, or a young lamb.

Alice found that Bungowla belonged to Samuel, all the tiny cottages and potato fields and little walled pastures where the strong, small cattle grazed. Ellen's business was to visit every one of the houses in turn and make sure that no one was in want. The people received her with respect, as if she were the landlord of their holdings, but there was none of the hatred that the Cappagh people had for their landlord's agent. They got out a stool and dusted it for Ellen, and one for Alice, too, and gave them little wooden mugs of milk to drink. There were stools and beds in all the houses, unlike Connemara. She admired the delicate way that Ellen discovered what was happening in each family, who had gone to America, who was planning to stay at home and who was getting married. The people were more confident than the Connemara people. Their potato fields looked healthy and their children were fat and energetic.

Ellen told no one that Alice and Samuel were to be married. In one house, where they joined the family for their dinner of potatoes and sour milk, she asked for a knife and fork for Alice though everyone else was using his fingers.

In the afternoon, when they were on their way home, Alice asked, "Why did you make me different, Ellen, asking for a knife and fork? I could have done without them."

"I did it for their sake as much as yours," Ellen said. "When they hear that you're married to Mr. Samuel, they'll be glad to know they treated you right when you came to their house. Otherwise they would be ashamed."

"Why didn't you tell them?"

"It's not their business," Ellen said. "A lady must keep her distance."

On this evening of all others, Tom Hussey and Stephen decided to profit by the fine weather after supper. They had a little hayfield that had been cut two days ago and was dry enough now to be put into small cocks. This meant that the Rosary was delayed and it was eleven o'clock before Ellen made the thin porridge that everyone had before going to bed. The long walk to Bungowla would ensure that Ellen would sleep well and the men were tired from the haymaking. Alice could have gone to bed early but then she would not have known when it was safe for Morgan to come.

At last Ellen lit her lamp for her and came with her to her room as usual. She was teaching Alice the ritual of going to bed with the help of a maid, how to stand still and wait while her hooks were undone, how to sit at the dressing table while her hair was brushed, how to put first one foot forward and then the other to have her shoes and stockings taken off.

At this stage Alice said, "Please let me finish myself tonight, Ellen. I hate to see you on your knees before me."

"It's my place."

"You can do it tomorrow night again. Please, Ellen."

Ellen agreed and went away soon afterward. Alice was breathing quickly in fright because she had not warned Morgan that Ellen would spend half an hour with her in the bedroom at night. Ellen did not notice. It would have been a disaster if he had come under the window while she was there. The light would draw him like a moth to a candle.

Alice sat on the edge of the bed and then leaped up to dart to the window. In the dusk she could see nothing but she stood there motionless until her feet were sore. He was not coming. All her excitement had been for nothing because he had more sense than she had. He had gone home. He knew it would be a sin to come back tonight. There was some excuse for last night but for tonight there would be none. He would not come.

Then she saw his head appear over the top of the cliff. He paused there, looking around, as a fox does when it is uneasy. His shoulders appeared and then he was lost for a while in the darkness of the grass, and showed against the white gravel a moment later. She fled silently down the stairs, listening for a sound from the back of the house, and opened the heavy door, and there he was standing on the step. Without a second's hesitation she stretched out her arms to him and felt herself gripped closely in his.

15

This time it was Morgan who led the way upstairs. He saw at once that she was his and he need only take her away with him.

When he had left her, early in the morning, he had known it. He was wild and lightheaded with hunger but this was nothing new for him. Alice should have offered him some food but perhaps she was afraid to go to the kitchen. He slipped and slid along the rocks like a seal, never in a moment's danger. The tide was out and the long black rocks were covered with brilliantly colored orange bladder wrack. He broke off a frond and crushed the little bladders one by one, watching the sea water squirt out. It was always warm. He remembered with a shiver a ferocious beating he had had from Master Fahy for introducing a bagful of this weed into the school in Moycullen, where it had been the cause of a riot among the inland children.

The Claddagh men were already in their boat when he reached Kilronan. They had gone out to fish before the dawn and had come back specially for him. They gave him fresh bread that they had got from an island woman. As he ate it his head cleared.

"My business is not finished," he said. "I need another day. Maybe you'll be coming back this way. If not, someone from the island will be going to Galway."

"We'll come for you," they said after consulting with each other. "Can you be earlier than you were today? The fish will begin to rot if we stay out too long."

"I'll come soon after the dawn," Morgan said.

This would suit him because he would have to help Alice over the rocks. They could leave her room at the first light and on the way he would show her the cave he had seen where the seals surely went for shelter from the storms and where they probably had their pups. If the light was strong enough he would show her the starfish and anemones glittering like fat jewels in their rock pools. Alice always loved things of that sort. Morgan would rather find a stranded rockfish or a crab that could be eaten.

Alice was his now, as he had known she would be. He felt it at once in the way she clung to him and on the stairs in the way that she allowed herself to be drawn along by him. To please her he went quietly, though it hardly mattered now if the Husseys heard. Every sign showed that she wanted him and had been waiting for him. She could have been dressed, for instance, if she had really meant all that talk of sin. She need not have been in the same white nightdress, or she could have had Mrs. Hussey with her. Instead she said, "I thought that Ellen would never leave me tonight. I was afraid she would still be here when you came. She always helps me to go to bed like a lady."

She shut the door gently and turned back to him.

"I can see you have made up your mind," he said.

"Yes."

She did not look at him directly, which was natural enough. He took her by the shoulders and led her to bed. At first she resisted and then she seemed to abandon herself to him, even more than she had done last night. He felt powerful with her, afraid of nothing. He sighed happily and stroked her hair with both hands, holding her face firmly so that she could not turn away from him.

"So now you know for certain what the right thing is," he said. "We'll have no more talk of sins."

He kissed her hungrily, as if he could never have enough of her, and saw her close her eyes.

"Alice, look at me," he said. "We'll go away if you like. We don't need to stay in Cappagh. We won't need anyone but the two of ourselves. We can go to America, or to England, or even to some other part of Ireland if we like. America would be the best. People make fortunes in America that could hardly add two and two at home."

"That's not what I'm thinking of."

"What, then? Leave all the thinking to me."

"I can't." He could feel her body shaking. Again she said, "I can't. Today I nearly went mad. I wished I were hunchbacked and skinny and wizened and yellow. Then I'd be let alone. A woman is like a bone between dogs when the men want her."

"I'm not like that!"

"It's you that are, and who is to blame you? It's the nature of all men."

More gently he asked, "Are you afraid of your mother, or of Samuel?"

"I have no need to be afraid of either of them. They'll be very well pleased with me."

He gripped her tightly.

"Why will they be pleased with you?"

"Because I'll do as I'm told. I must be married to Samuel. He's a good man and I gave him my promise. I can't deceive him. I told you this last night but you didn't believe me."

By the time she had finished he could scarcely hear her. She was twisting and turning her head on the pillow like an animal in a trap. He let her go.

"You mean to leave me and go to Samuel?"

"What else can I do? Don't talk to me in that hard way."

"You'd like me to talk softly to you and make love to you and then to go off quietly and be thankful for what I got?"

"Oh, Morgan, how can you say such things to me? I didn't ask you to come. Last night I told you to go away."

"Tonight you let me in. You were waiting for me."

"I couldn't stop you."

"That's not true. You love me. I saw at once that you wanted me as much as I wanted you. Why didn't you shout that there was a man outside on the gravel? The Husseys would have come running."

"What are you saying?" she asked in misery. "How can you talk like this now?"

He would not pity her.

"How can you turn me out now?"

"I must do right."

"Right is to marry me. I'm not asking you to be my tally-woman." For a moment he thought she would strike him and he said, "I shouldn't have said that. I know Samuel won't harm you. He's decent, God help him, but he's too old. In ten years he'll be worn out and you'll be his housekeeper."

"For God's sake, Morgan, don't say things like that."

"It's the truth and you know it. I've had you before Samuel and now you belong to me as surely as if we went to the church together. We heard it often enough, that the people being married are more important than the priest. It's a sin to marry a man you don't love."

"You twist everything around. I know what's right for me."

"And so do I."

They glared at each other like dogs circling before a fight. The open look that he had always known on Alice was gone and instead she looked tormented, but it seemed mad to let her go out of pity. He tried a new persuasive tone.

"Alice, have you thought how it will be when Samuel holds you in his arms as I did?"

"How can you say that to me, Morgan?" she moaned.

"It's better to say it now, while there's time to think of it. Will it be the same to be taken every night by Samuel?" He had to pity her then and he said more softly, "You can come away with me and forget about Samuel. He'll get over it because he knows you were always my girl."

"Do you think that would make it easier for him?"

Anger flared in him.

"You're trying to force yourself to do something that will kill you."

"What can I do? I can't work it out. I wish I had time—"

"You've had all day. It's long enough. Why did you let me in last night and tonight?"

She sat up and pushed him away from her with a rough movement. He longed to take her naked body in his arms but he did not dare to do it now.

She said, "Morgan, you must go away. I said it to you yesterday, that we can't have what we want. My heart is torn in two, if that gives you any satisfaction. I know one thing about pain, that I'll get used to it."

"I never will."

"Go quickly, Morgan, quickly!"

"Are you going to put me out into the darkness?"

So she had to let him stay. She had made sure that the lamp was filled tonight so that it would last. They lay side by side, like children lost on a mountainside, waiting for the dawn to break. Morgan was quiet, to give her the idea that he had despaired, but he knew still that she belonged to him as surely as his skin did. He thought she dozed a little but he was not sure. All night long he could hear the beating of the sea on the rocks.

The first light in the sky was hateful to him. Greenish streaks, tinted with pink and gray, stretched across the windowpane. Then the lamp seemed to go dim. Small birds twittered and then came the squawk of a sea gull. Soon the air was shaken with their long-drawn-out cries, which grew fainter as they went out over the sea to fish. Morgan saw that Alice was awake too. She lay slackly, her hair tangled and spread on the pillow. She drew her hand out of his slowly and gazed at him like a sick person whose mind has begun to ramble. When she spoke it was in a tired, dispirited voice.

"It's time for you to go, Morgan. I'm afraid I've done you harm."

She made no move while he dressed but lay there looking at him. He went to the window and stood for a minute but when he turned around, still she had not moved.

"Aren't you coming to the door with me?" he asked, more gently than he had intended.

She stretched her arms wide and let them fall.

"Yes, I'll come to the door," she said.

She pulled on her nightdress and this time she took a dressing gown from a hook by the door and put it on too and went before him down the stairs, opened the front door and stood aside, waiting for him to pass through. They clung to each other in desperation, held off and clung again without a word. Then she eased away from him and leaned against the open door while Morgan stepped outside. When he looked back from the hillside, there she was at the window.

He could hurry, since he was alone. At Killaney the houses were shut up tight. A donkey was busy knocking down the wall of his field so as to get out, pushing one stone after another with his nose until they rolled to the ground. The sun was well above the horizon and the sea reflected a clear sky like a copper plate.

When he got to Kilronan the hooker was out at the end of the quay. The men had seen him coming and were ready to sail, but they cooked some mackerel on the brazier in the foul hold and gave him time to eat. They had had a good night and were well loaded with various kinds of fish that they were sorting. The mackerel were the most plentiful, and they had plaice and sole, too, and several fat cod.

"You got your business done," Michael said.

"Yes."

"We were told you spent the day in Kilronan."

"Yes. The person I had to see was not at home until the nighttime."

Of course they would have heard this much. By various hints he had given the impression that he had come to Aran to get recruits for the secret political organization that everyone knew of, and this had stopped questions before they became too close. The Aran people were cautious and would be slow to join the organization until they could find out how dangerous it was.

There was a good westerly breeze to blow them home. A school of porpoises, a sign of good luck, followed them most of the way back to Galway.

16

When Morgan got back to Cappagh, he went home for a night's sleep and to tell Nora that he was safe. At first she was nervous about him but soon she seemed to think he had recovered from the shock of Alice's leaving him. About noon the next day, he went up to MacDonaghs' to speak to Mary.

He knew he was the last person that Mary would want to see but she had no protection from him. He timed his visit well. A small shoal of mackerel was in and everyone who could walk was down on the strand. A mackerel was a feast, a debauch, a gift straight from God.

Morgan had seen Thomas MacDonagh go out in the currach with Joeen and he guessed that the girls would be waiting for their return with the catch. He should have been out himself, but with Alice gone, he could not settle to any work. Today he had actually loaned his boat to Mike Folan, a reckless act that had made Nora cry with vexation. Not only would they have no mackerel unless someone gave them a present but Mike was notorious for his heavy-handed use of other people's property. His look of surprise when someone had broken a shovel or gashed a currach only added to the offense. "A man of God," some people called him, meaning that he was not quite right in the head, but Nora said that he put it all on so as to get the name of being a fool and the people would have to feed him.

The two smallest MacDonagh children were playing comfortably in the dust of the front yard when Morgan came around from the side of the house. He had made sure not to come by the lane from the main road so that Mary should not have time to escape. When he saw her unwelcoming expression he knew that he had done right. She looked so like Alice that he felt weakened.

"How are you, Morgan?" she said innocently. "We haven't seen you this while back."

But her nervousness showed by a tremble in the last words. He knew that the astonishment of everyone at the news that Samuel was actually going to marry Alice was mixed with a suggestion that Mary had made up that part of the story. The whole townland had seen Alice go off with Samuel and Mary had quickly informed Peggy Michael and Sally that the match was made. In no time at all, the news was in every house in the district and most people said that the tallywoman was only doing what one would expect—like mother, like daughter, they said. That Alice had always thought too much of herself, with her tongue so bold against the landlords, a dangerous tongue. And look how the landlord had been able to buy her now. She was not going to marry Samuel, no more than the cat. Bitterly Morgan heard it all from Nora, and he remembered his brother's warning: "The bad drop is in her, exactly like her mother. You'll find that out." On the way to see Mary this morning Morgan was even congratulated on his escape from marrying Alice by Molly Hernon, who had a daughter of the right age herself.

"You'd have to be always watching that one," Molly said, "like a rambling hen. You'd never have peace of mind. You're well out of her."

Morgan said mildly, "I had no bargain made with Alice. She can marry anyone she likes."

"Marry!" Molly snorted rudely, but Morgan gave her such a strange look that she ended the conversation in a hurry and scuttled into her house.

With burning eyes fixed on Mary, Morgan said, "I came to ask for Alice."

"She's well, Morgan. She's in Aran."

"The world knows that. I came to ask for her for my wife."

"She's promised to Samuel Flaherty."

"He'll never marry her."

"He will! He will!" Mary was showing her agitation in spite of herself. She clutched her hands together, then got them between her knees and began to rock up and down on the hob.

110

"Samuel will marry her soon. He swore to me that he would. Why should he tell lies? I guessed the people were saying this, though no one said it to me. I saw it in Kate's face that she heard it but she didn't dare to tell me. Samuel is a gentleman."

"That's why he won't marry Alice. 'Three things you can never trust: a horse's hoof, the smile of an Englishman and a gentleman's word unless it's in writing.' Mary," he said, as sweetly as a serpent, "if Samuel doesn't marry Alice after all, can I have her?"

"How do I know? I suppose you can. God help us, why are you tormenting me?"

Morgan went away without answering that question. Mary would hardly have heard him and in any case she knew the reason quite well.

Then he went on to his second plan, which was shameful, wicked, unforgivable but quite logical. Affecting an ignorant syntax and handwriting, he wrote a letter to Samuel and posted it in Galway:

> Yr Honor,
> Yr Alice is a bad woman. In Aran she do be spending time with an islandman Stephen Hussey and making a mock of you. How she do be is a scandal and all knows it.
>
> A Friend

Samuel reacted quickly to the letter but not in the way that Morgan had hoped. By noon, an hour after it had reached him, he was on his way to Galway, on horseback so that he could canter faster along the grassy verge of the road. It was as if the venom from the little letter had stung him physically. He knew that his intention to marry Alice must have caused a sensation but he had foolishly imagined that the misfortunes that everyone had suffered in the last six years would have taught some lesson in charity. Obviously jealousy had been a more natural result. It now seemed stupid to have abandoned Alice to the mercy of her own kind, without even the protection of her mother. He trusted Ellen, however. He clung to the memory of Ellen as he had last seen her. She would not let anything happen to Alice. Alice was safe with Ellen. Not for a moment did he believe that Ellen's son would molest her. But a vicious memory tormented him, of a Connemara girl who had been read off the altar for keeping company with a Protestant policeman, and who had been thrust out of her father's house to fend for herself, living alone in a cabin on the mountainside. Anything could happen in a community where such righteous cruelty was possible.

There was some satisfaction in galloping the mare to Galway but Samuel could have exploded with frustration during the long slow trip to Aran. Mike Troy and his imperturbable pipe infuriated him. So did the slow, shining swell and the clean, light breeze. To sit still was labor. He was appalled at the vulnerability of women. "Yr Alice is a bad woman." Would anyone have thought of writing "Yr Samuel is a bad man"? Or if they did, would she be supposed to care? He would never leave her open to this kind of injury again. She must be taught to be strong and aggressive. These things were in her and must be brought out. He doubted if she would ever be respected with the easy respect given to scoundrelly landlords of long pedigree but at least she could earn the respect that must be given to personal strength. He remembered her at the wedding, moving easily through the mixed crowd, chatting to the parish priest, whom everyone else obviously found a problem, and above all translating the tinker woman's song line by line for him.

The boat had been recognized in the clear evening half an hour before it reached the quay at Kilronan. The sun was still high since it was only seven o'clock. Patcheen Barbara was waiting with the sidecar and so, of course, was the usual group of soft-voiced islanders. Samuel was ravenously hungry, having forgotten to provide for the journey. Mike Troy had perhaps lived on his pipe for he seemed not at all put out. While he drove off with Patcheen, Samuel could see him calmly tidying up before leaving the boat for his usual lodgings. Only now it occurred to Samuel to appreciate the promptness with which Mike always walked out of his house and down to the boat without warning, as if he had nothing else in the world to do but serve it.

Aching with tension and hunger, he turned to Patcheen and asked, "Is Miss Alice well?"

"She is well, indeed. I have seen her often."

"She goes out to visit?"

"No, never that, but I go to Husseys' in my sidecar in the evening time. I do like the company of good talking people."

"And Miss Alice is there?"

"Why would she not? She is a lovely lady, as good as ourselves, I can say." He glanced at Samuel. "She will be glad to see you. The island is lonely if you are not bred to it and she told us she is from a big family, God bless them."

It had not struck Samuel that she might be lonely. In any case, none of it mattered now. After the tedium of the sail from Galway, the drive to Gortnagapall seemed short and easy. This time no one had run with the news and Ellen was not standing waiting at the door. The sinking sun shone on the glass of the windows, blinding them with a coppery gold sheen. Patcheen trotted the horse up to the front door. Samuel sprang to the ground and darted inside, as lively as a boy of twenty. Ever afterwards he remembered the picture that Alice made, sitting by the end window, in one of her new dresses and with her hair brushed upward to show her long, elegant neck. She was working at a piece of embroidery, holding it high to catch the fading light, prodding her needle with quick, impatient fingers.

After a rush of pure admiration, he was dismayed at the change that Ellen had made in her. Alice doing embroidery! This must be wrong. He walked quickly across the floor to her. She let out a lengthy curse in Irish and sucked her finger. Then she began to laugh.

"Where did you come from, Samuel?"

"On the boat with Mike, of course." He leaned over her with a hand on each of her shoulders. "What are you doing?"

"A lady does embroidery in the drawing room every evening," said Alice grimly, "but that can't be, because the world would be full of embroidery and the ladies would all be in the asylum." She stood up and twirled around so that her skirt flew out in a circle. "How do you like my dress? It's like something you'd wear to a ball if you were in the way of going to one."

"I'll take you to a ball."

"You'll never!"

"Indeed I will." He felt life bubble up in him, such as he had not experienced in ten years. The project that he had started in bitterness was turning into something so delightful that it was changing him through all his being. The sourness that he had thought would be with him forever seemed to have evaporated. He held Alice out from him and looked into her clear, shining eyes.

She did not look away but gazed back at him with a gradual softening, until at last she said, "Glad I am to see you, Samuel. How long can you stay with me?"

"Do you like the island people?"

"They're frightened," she said, "though they have less to fear than we have. But they're good people. I do like them. Ellen is a lovely woman. She's like a sister to me."

"Would you like to have her in Moycullen?"

"But she lives here, in Aran."

"That could be arranged. She could be your own maid."

"Must I have a maid? I wouldn't like that."

"It's hard for a lady to dress without one. But you needn't have one at first if you don't want. We can ask Ellen. When I go back to Moycullen, you'll come with me. I'm not leaving you here any longer. There's nothing more for you to learn."

"Thank God for that," said Alice, but she added, "I'll do whatever you want, Samuel. You know that."

He did not tell her about the ugly little letter that was in his breast pocket. In his room later on, he burned it with a lucifer but its words had been scored on his brain so that he was never able to rid himself of them.

The next morning he took Alice to Galway on the boat, accompanied by Ellen, who had agreed to come and supervise the wedding. It would be enough for her, Samuel decided. In the strong light of the morning, she looked an old woman.

PART
TWO

17

Samuel and Alice were married in Moycullen church. It should have been in Barna because that was Alice's parish but Samuel decided on Moycullen after long thought. There were arguments on both sides. It was necessary that many people should see them actually married. This was for Alice's protection, otherwise there was a likelihood that her neighbors in Cappagh would refuse to believe that she was married at all. To convince them, Barna would have been better but it was more important that the Moycullen people should see that Samuel was not taking after his father.

After her return from Aran, she stayed at Samuel's house, carefully chaperoned by Ellen Hussey. There she learned that Morgan had gone away and she remembered painfully the days when she had lain in bed without moving, in Aran, until poor Ellen was distracted. But she had recovered, as she had known she would, before Samuel came for her.

Before the wedding, once only, she visited Cappagh. Just loud enough to be heard, Kate said as Alice came into the kitchen, "Here comes the lady."

Alice flashed back at her, "You're the same as you always were." Then she regretted it and said, "I'll never be a lady, however I may look, and I'll never do you harm, Kate."

Kate retreated quickly from her mother's threatening looks. Samuel was still outside, talking to Thomas, and when they came in Kate busied herself with the mugs of punch made from the whiskey that Samuel had brought. She could not take in the new relationship between herself and Samuel or imagine that it could possibly be the same as that which existed between her and Dan's Agnes. She wished she had kept her mouth shut at first sight of Alice in her lady's gown. The shock had been great. A pity it had not struck her dumb, as it had the rest of the family.

She soon saw that Alice held nothing against her. As the next sister, Kate was to come to the wedding with her father, since obviously the whole family could not be there and Mary had decided not to go. Her decision was a second shock but no one had the nerve to discuss her reasons with her, especially in the presence of Samuel.

"I'll be here praying for you," she said, and saw by Alice's expression that she approved.

Alice had no patience with the ritual of the wedding. The less fuss, the better, she said, and Samuel agreed. Nevertheless there were certain rules and customs that had to be followed. Alice had to wear a white dress and veil, held in place by a wreath of artificial orange blossoms that had been worn by Samuel's mother. Ellen knew exactly where to find it, and she cleaned and renovated it expertly.

"Walk slowly," she said to Alice. "A bride should never appear to be in a hurry. Keep your eyes down but not your chin. Everyone will be watching you but don't think about that. You'll have enough to do to think about your skirt and not fall over it."

Idiotically Alice remembered and said, "Samuel will be there."

"He will, indeed," Ellen said. "He'll be in the church before you. He does everything right. That's how he likes it."

And that, Ellen knew, was why he was marrying Alice instead of borrowing her for a few years as his father had done with Mary. Though Alice had never mentioned Morgan, Ellen could see that she was not in love with Samuel. A certain uneasiness in her expression when she spoke of him made this clear. At last Ellen summoned up courage to say, as she fitted the wreath and veil on the morning of the wedding, "You won't take it hard if I say my mind, Miss Alice? I have daughters of my own and I feel for you as if you were one of them."

Touched in the midst of a sensation of general fright, Alice said, "I won't take it hard, Ellen." Seeing the old woman flushed with anxiety, she took her hand and held it.

Ellen said, "You're not like young ladies that know nothing about men and get the shock of their life when they find themselves in bed with one."

Alice chuckled.

"Are they like that? No, I won't get a shock."

"The men don't like it if you do. It's a kind of insult to them. My old mistress in Cheltenham said that she was told to pretend to be shocked and timid, and to slip out of the bed at the other side when her husband made a move toward her, so that he would respect her. But the poor man's feelings were hurt and that's how it would be with most men."

"I won't pretend anything," Alice said.

"Yes, you should pretend to love him," said Ellen in a rush. Then she stopped and could not go on until Alice said,

"Why? Why should I? It was all fixed with my mother. I agreed but I had to agree. Samuel knows that."

"Maybe I shouldn't have said anything. It's not my place."

"For the love of God, Ellen, how can there be talk of place between you and me? What is there between us? Say what you want to say and no more nonsense about it."

"All right. I married my Tom because old Mr. Flaherty wanted me and him out of the house. I didn't know him, hardly, and he didn't know me. The times were hard. He wanted the house and land in Aran and I wanted a safe roof over my head. That's the way most people get married. I didn't care a straw for him at first but after a few weeks it was different. We'd lie there in the bed in Aran, a strange place for both of us, with the sound of the sea all around us, and he'd tell me all the things he thought about. I found out he used to make poems and ballads. He knew the names of all the birds and their different songs from listening to them while he waited with the horses outside some gentleman's door while the mistress was visiting. I began to watch for him coming home from the fields and I got to know his step a long way off. He'd ask me about myself and I'd tell him things I never told anyone else. I was thirty-five years of age before I married and all set to be an old maid. If I had been younger I would have refused, and I'd have gone to find another job and missed him altogether. Wait a little and you'll be like that with Mr. Samuel." Suddenly she was agitated again, perhaps as the mention of his name recalled him to her mind. "Didn't your mother say these things to you? I only said them because your mother is not here and I thought—"

"I'm glad you did, Ellen. My mother said nothing." Alice had had no inclination to question her mother about such intimate business. "My mother had life hard. I'm glad you spoke, Ellen."

They got on with their preparations in silence. It had been a strange conversation but Alice found that it had had the effect of lessening her fear of Samuel. It may have helped her to love him, as she certainly began to do from the day of her wedding onward. It began when he stepped out of the front seat of the church and accompanied her to the altar rails for the ceremony. He glanced at her nervously and smiled with a slightly ironic look which conveyed that they must go through with this exhibition together and give each other support.

Nevertheless, she saw that like herself he was awed by the ceremony. Father Kenny in his vestments looked different and powerful, so that there was no reason to doubt his capacity to call down the blessing of the God of Isaac and Abraham and Jacob on them, or the efficacy of his prayer that they would see their children and their children's children even to the third and fourth generation. The notion of Samuel with children of his own delighted Alice so that she longed to turn to look at him to see how he was taking it. She feared for her veil, however, and besides it would not have been decent.

On her left, Kate in a new dress looked strange but not awkward. James Fahy, who accompanied Samuel, was twitching and fidgeting in a maddening way, as nervous as a horse on a hot day. He was such an innocent poor lad, Alice felt sorry for him and was already planning ways to make him feel at home in the big house. Though he was only three years younger than she, she felt old enough in the ways of the world to be his mother.

At the wedding luncheon, Alice was angered by the blatant inspection of her by the local ladies, all of whom looked pretty scruffy except Mrs. Burke. Jerome Burke was beautifully dressed, too, as well as Samuel was, but he had the mean mouth of a rat for all his fine accent and neat talk. The Burkes were not Catholics and neither they nor the other guests had been to the church. Most of the time, Alice was able to follow Ellen's advice and keep her eyes modestly down but now and then she sent a blue flash through some impertinent lady who commented too loud on her appearance. That the comments were favorable made them no less impertinent, Alice thought. God had sent a fine golden September day and the marquee looked clean and hospitable with its white-covered tables. The Dublin caterers scurried through the mob of guests and ushered them to suitable places more by instinct than by any special knowledge of their ranks. Old George Flaherty looked almost happy but he hardly said a word throughout the morning.

When everyone had had some champagne, Ellen took Alice away and helped her into a brown traveling dress and cape. Not a song was sung, and if there were any tinkers, they were in the kitchen. The house servants were having a party of their own down there but Alice was not allowed to go to visit them. Master Fahy had gone to attend a sick man early in the morning. Whether this was truth or fiction Alice did not know. She missed his odd figure and old-fashioned speech. She had taken a great fancy to him. One great comfort was that by the time Samuel and Alice returned, the crowd of rowdy, red-faced drinkers would be gone, marquee and all, and the house would be as she had seen it on the first day when she had driven there from the Claddagh with Samuel.

In the carriage at last, she turned to him and said, "Thanks be to God we're out of that. It wasn't like a real wedding at all."

"Were you disappointed?"

"No. But I don't like those people much. I can't help it. I thought we were downhearted in Cappagh since the great hunger, but those people had enough food before them to fill a parish for a month and they looked miserable with it all."

"Most of them are in debt for double what they can pay," Samuel said. "They have no rents coming in but they still live like lords. A few are trying to avoid the crash by getting in sheep instead of tenants. I didn't want any of them there— it was my father that did."

"Your father!"

"Yes, for your sake. He put his reasons so well I had to agree. No wedding feast would be a slight to you, he said. He may have been right. He understands that bunch of thieves better than I ever will. Can we forget them now, please?"

The horses' hooves ground on the sandy road while she lay against his shoulder companionably. His arm around her was a comfort.

She asked after a moment, "Where did the priest go? He didn't come to the house."

"He won't sit down to a feast while the people are starving. He says it's not right."

"The poor man. Sure, even starving people can enjoy a wedding."

Then she was suddenly shy and silent, remembering that the wedding was her own and that Samuel of all people had acquired rights in her person because of it. From now on, it would be a sin to refuse him what it would have been a sin to give him before. The oddity of this would take getting used to. She blushed strongly as she remembered the bawdy jokes that had sped every young couple she knew on their way from the wedding house. Of course these jokes had been made about herself and Samuel. The excitement of getting into the carriage, remembering Ellen's lessons in how to do it with dignity, had closed her ears to the sounds around her but a pictorial vision remained of smirking faces and lewd grins.

Samuel watching her closely saw the change in her mood and asked anxiously, "What's the matter? Father Kenny meant no harm—"

"It's not that. I'm just trying to get used to the idea of being married."

"So am I."

But it was easy, after all. The train journey to Dublin was an amazing experience and took the rest of the day. Tea came in a basket, handed through the window at a station in a flat, windy part of the country without a rock or a stone in sight. Where the railway ran by the canal, Alice exclaimed at its beauty and admired the heavy barges laden high with sacks, drawn by huge, slow horses. Ripples of shiny water tickled the legs of the swans that stood on the rushy margins. Ungainly, tall herons flapped away with trailing feet at the sound of the noisy train. Samuel watched Alice's delight and felt the new life that she had implanted in him grow where an arid desert had been for years.

It was almost dark when they came into the station at Dublin. Samuel took one of the cabs that stood waiting and directed the driver to the hotel in Sackville Street where they were to spend the night. Alice was silent with exhaustion while they clattered downhill over the coblestones and while they were shown their room and the luggage was brought up. A maid waited to undo the leather case that contained her night things. Samuel had a similar one. The trunks remained strapped up, ready for tomorrow's journey to London.

Samuel took his nightshirt and went into the dressing room. When she was unhooked, Alice sent the maid away and finished herself. When Samuel came back, she was in bed, simply waiting for him. He stood looking down at her. She saw his eyes and mouth soften to the expression of a happy boy. Then he said, "Thank God for you, Alice. I thought there were no more good things in the world."

After that she did not remember Morgan at all because Samuel absorbed her completely. She found that she loved him perfectly, so that even the obvious fact that he had had this experience before did not upset her. Poor Samuel! It was a pity he had had to go roving after love. There would be no more need for that. She smiled in the darkness complacently, in the moments before going to sleep, at the memory of his pleasure in her. All Ellen's advice would never make a real lady of her, it seemed. Yet Ellen would have been pleased with her tonight.

Alice was overwhelmed by London at first and then to Samuel's amusement she began to pick out landmarks that had connections with Ireland: the Tower, where so many Irish prisoners had suffered; Hampton Court, where Queen Eliza-

121

beth of evil memory had lived and where her victorious generals had come to report the devastation of Ireland; Buckingham Palace, where the present Queen lived, who said she cared for the people of Ireland but who had allowed them to die in their thousands of hunger and fever.

"She should make it her business to find out what is happening," Alice said when Samuel suggested that the Queen did not know the conditions in Ireland. "Ignorance is no excuse." Later she said, "Her husband is a good man. Perhaps they'll come to Ireland again and see how things really are. When she came two years ago, they let her see only the best."

It was a short honeymoon, barely two weeks, because Samuel feared for his tenants under the care of old George. He explained to Alice, "My father is inclined to emigrate them, thinking he's doing well for them. He doesn't mean them any harm, and he doesn't believe the stories about what the people suffer on the ships and after landing, too. I told him with chapter and verse about some of it—the captain using a false measure for drinking water, and the people lying in their bunks with the sick and dying for three months, and the food crawling with vermin. All he would say, over and over, was, 'They were worse off at home.'"

"There's truth in that," Alice said. "There's not much to be said for dying of hunger in the corner of your own house. Clean water or green grass won't feed you when you're starving. Tell me about Jerome Burke. I didn't like an inch of him, or his wife either."

"Why?"

"Something about their mouths; and the way she lifts her eyebrows. She's a Dublin lady, of course. Perhaps they're different," Alice added quickly, fearing she had given offense.

Samuel was amused. "She is from Galway," he said, "and I don't like her much either but for more definite reasons. She could restrain Jerome but instead she eggs him on. It is she who wants a clean sweep of all those hovels by the gate so that her friends will admire the avenue as they drive in. She has a heart like a rock."

"But she looks so nice and clean," Alice exclaimed, shocked at this judgment of the elegant lady, though it agreed with her own.

"I've never said such things to anyone before now," Samuel said. "Perhaps I'm too cruel. Perhaps it's not true. She was brought up that way."

"What would the cat's son do but to kill a mouse?" Alice said in Irish, affecting a tolerance she did not feel.

The loss of her freedom was painful. She wanted to condemn Mrs. Burke roundly for her wickedness to the helpless people who depended on her. Fortunately Alice had always cultivated a quiet tongue where necessary. But there was surely great cowardice in keeping a shut mouth when gross injustice cried out for vengeance. Her problem had not existed before she had Samuel to think of. He had always come to the house as a courteous visitor, a very different proposition from the man who now shared almost every moment of the day and night with her and who had an insight into her mind that was often inconvenient. Alice noticed that this insight seemed to have a purpose behind it. Samuel seemed to be probing for information that he intended to use. At first she disliked the sensation of being watched but soon she noticed that he never referred back to an earlier remark of hers except to encourage her.

"Look facts in the face," he said. "Self-deception is self-destruction. The Irish landlords have destroyed themselves by trying to keep up a standard of living that no one can afford. I could buy out any landlord for miles around but I would have to think twice before setting up a house in Dublin or London or Bath as they do. You have told me you always see when people are fooling themselves. Use that knowledge."

"When did I tell you that?"

"When people were emigrating to America and saying they would come back rich, you could see in their eyes that they didn't believe it."

"They had to fool themselves or they couldn't have faced it at all."

"Trust your own judgment," Samuel said. "No need to say what you know until the time is ripe, but when the time comes, say it loud and clear. You're my wife. You can't be ignored. Aside from your position now, you have knowledge that many people have not got."

"God help us! Sure, I know nothing!"

"Talk like a lady," said Samuel calmly.

"Heavens!" said Alice meekly, "I'm afraid I'm rather ignorant in some things."

"Good girl," Samuel said. "You know Irish and you know how to talk to your own people. Use that knowledge whenever you get the chance. It won't happen for a while but your time will come. When it comes, recognize it and remember what I said."

"But you'll be here too, Samuel!" Alice said in a panic.

"Who knows where he'll be in these times? You must learn

everything you can, now. Watch and learn, and remember everything you hear."

These words depressed her and gave her an unpleasant sensation of being abandoned in a strange world. Yet Samuel was there, and Samuel's child was growing steadily inside her. He was clearly overjoyed at the prospect of it and anxious for Alice's welfare, yet his whole attitude was that of a man who has a small expectation of life.

18

On a morning soon after Christmas, Alice prevailed on Master Fahy to spend the day in the house instead of retreating to the coach house as he usually did after breakfast. There was a savage wind that turned the lake olive-green, reflecting a dirty, snow-filled sky. No one could come to school in this weather and Fahy had announced a further week's holiday even for the children of the local gentry, though they always came in carriages. Christmas had been a miserable business, with a token goose for dinner and her own people miles away in Cappagh. Every day Alice fed a silent little crowd in the yard on oatmeal porridge and bread, which was all they would accept. There was little satisfaction in it, knowing as she did that so many thousands were going hungry.

Samuel had gone to Galway, taking James with him. The university term had just opened and they would meet at the County Club for luncheon and drive home again in the evening. They had taken the gig and were well wrapped up against the cold. James had looked rather relaxed today, glad not to have to drive himself.

To justify his enjoyment of the huge turf fire, Master Fahy was searching the shelves for a volume of Shakespeare to read to Alice. Watching his tall figure move slowly along in front of the shelves, she said, "Master Fahy, why does Samuel talk as if he were a dying man?"

Fahy paused but he did not turn at once. After a moment he said, "Does he talk like that?"

"Yes. He's always telling me what to do when he's gone." Alice felt suddenly weak, as if the child were already born and distracting her by pulling at her skirt. "He tells me how to provide for the child and how to manage the mill and how to know a thief and a rogue, as if he expects me to have to deal with all these things soon.'

Her voice broke in spite of her. Fahy took a little red-bound volume deliberately from the shelf and went to sit, with his back to the light, by the fire. Then he said carefully, "The times are bad. You know that. Any man could be afraid for his wife and child."

"This is not just fear of the fever. There's something else in it, I'm sure, though he won't admit it."

"Perhaps it's the warnings his father got,' Master Fahy said gently. "No one would touch Samuel. They all know he's a decent man. But his father has made a few enemies, whether he meant to or no."

"Warnings from the Whiteboys?"

"Yes."

"Are they very active around here? Over in Cappagh there's no fight in anyone except the ones that had the wit to go away—" She realized that she was siding with the Whiteboys and stopped.

Fahy said, "Cappagh is poorer than Moycullen. Courage often comes out of the cooking pot."

"My mother said something about the Whiteboys. How many warnings has he had?"

"I know he has had two. They always give three but I don't think he has had the third one yet."

"What have they against him?"

"Selling the Clonbur land, of course, but it's not only that. They know there's a plan to tumble all the houses down by the lake and have the land for grazing. All Creevagh village is to be knocked."

"But that would be Samuel's business."

"Mr. Flaherty has agreed to it without consulting Samuel. Most of the Creevagh houses belong to Jerome Burke."

Alice felt a sharp twinge of fear.

"Has he had warnings too?"

"Very likely."

"How do the Whiteboys know?"

"They have their ways of finding out," Fahy said. "It's Burke's wish to knock the houses. Mr. Flaherty doesn't want it but he has ideas of loyalty to his class." The sardonic note in his voice made clear his opinion of this. Then he looked at her with pity and said, "Ladies shouldn't have to think of these things. In your condition you should have a quiet mind. Now we'll read *The Merchant of Venice* and be calm."

But when he read of the argosies with portly sail, she saw emigrant ships, and when Shylock was being persecuted in court, she heard Portia's voice as the mean, shrill voice of a magistrate sending a prisoner to transportation. Keeping still was an effort but Master Fahy would not tolerate the smallest lack of attention during his class, even from Alice. His sharp eye fixed on her was enough to make her sit motionless again and presently she found his intoned words had a soothing effect after all.

They had many such sessions for it was a hard winter. Though she valued the readings, Alice was glad when the school reassembled after three weeks and she was free again. Sometimes in the mornings she saw the youngest Burke children, a boy and a girl, creeping up the stairs to the schoolroom, with unusually silent children from the shops and from the farms in the neighborhood. She knew that fear of their teacher was one reason for their depressed look but it seemed as if they were also affected by the knowledge that they were inevitably committed, with their elders, to an ugly situation. Fahy's portentous look had an extra, perhaps gratuitous significance.

Because of the life within her, Alice felt that there was something monstrous in the threat of death hanging over the house. When she could stand it no longer, she went to talk to old George one soft, sunny morning in late February, when Samuel had left for Galway. As she crossed the hall, she was aware of the slightly hostile presence of Andy Hanlon in his pantry. As usual, he had the door standing open so that he could see everyone come and go. His little pile of silver and his polishing cloth were his excuse for being there. He smiled obsequiously, since she was his employer now, but the coldness of his eyes affected her unpleasantly.

George was cleaning his eternal guns. He welcomed her immediately, saying, "Come in, Mary, and talk to me. I'm glad to see you know your way here."

It was a moment before she realized that the name was only a slip. Old George was not rambling in his mind at all. He knew quite well that she was Samuel's wife and that she was soon to have his first grandchild.

He placed a chair for her with its back to the window but at an angle to avoid the draft. Then he asked solicitously, "How are you? Feeling well, I hope."

"Very well," Alice said and watched him pick up a flintlock

gun and clean it with an oily rag. The instrument of death disgusted her. She wondered how he could bring himself to handle it so casually.

After a minute's silence he said, "Are you enjoying life in Moycullen? Spring will soon be here and you can go for some drives."

"Yes," Alice said. "I'd like to go down to the lake. There is a road to it, isn't there?"

"Yes, through Creevagh." Old George's voice was cool at the mention of the fatal village, which Alice had seen only once, in the late autumn. "You can drive for several miles along by the side of the lake. Then the road comes to an end but there is a place to turn the carriage."

"Are there more villages, after Creevagh?"

Still she did not dare to ask directly after it.

"No. Soon Creevagh will be gone, too, and then it will be a beautiful drive."

She felt a quivering sensation go right through her; then she relaxed deliberately, since this could not be good for the baby. She said, "How can Creevagh be gone? Don't lots of people live there?"

"It's to be knocked. Jerome Burke owns most of the houses and he's sick and tired of getting no rent."

"Who is his agent?"

She had wanted to know this for a long time. Most of the agents lived in houses on their employers' land. In some cases they lived in the big house itself, if its owner was permanently absent. Then they behaved like landlords, quite forgetting that they were not the actual owners of the property, and they managed to bully the tenants into a hate-inspired respect. Samuel had no agent. They were all scoundrels, he said, and he could do the work better himself.

"Burke's agent is Fennell in Galway," George said. "He drives out when he needs to. Dangerous enough when the house is empty except for a couple of servants. Not one of them would lift a finger to save him if he were attacked."

"Has that happened?"

"Twice, but not in this area. He's agent for Butler of Ballinahown, too. They potted at him there but they missed, of course."

"Perhaps they won't always miss."

"Indeed." Old George sounded quite detached. "My father's agent was stabbed to death in this very room. It was the rent room. Foolish to use a room with only one door. After that they used to put a table in the hall and they set up Andy's pantry with a guard in it. How is your mother?"

"I hear she's well," Alice said shakily.

"She won't come to Moycullen," old George said. "It's a pity but I don't blame her. Why don't you invite your sister for a while? That nice little girl that was at the wedding." He licked his lips in an utterly unconscious gesture of appreciation. "She'd be company for you. Bring a bit of life around the place."

But Alice did not want Kate around the place and soon she was going to have life enough of her own. Its little flutter amazed her. This was already a person, who would make an appearance at the end of June if all went well, and have descendants for ever and ever as long as the world lasted. The notion of the continuity of reproduction delighted Alice and she felt a need to know all about how it worked. The midwife, a widow named Mrs. Neilan, in stately black, who had visited her at Samuel's request, thought this was indecent.

"My dear Mrs. Flaherty," she said, "you don't have to think of such things. I'll take care of everything, from start to finish."

Restraining her giggles, Alice tried to imagine Mrs. Neilan coping with Samuel at the starting part. She continued the conversation solemnly and listened to advice about her diet and the amount of exercise she should take, with wry thought for her mother's arrangements in this respect. Digging and eating potatoes and harvesting turf made fine mothers and children, so long as the fever didn't get them. For Samuel's sake she had behaved like a lady, however, and Mrs. Neilan had gone off looking as if she had achieved something.

Alice had promised to keep calm. Deep, slow breathing helped her now. Old George hung up his gun and took down another.

"This is my favorite for hares," he said, "though it tears them up rather. Makes them harder to cook. Great sport in hares—they dart about so much, makes you feel you've done something worthwhile when you get one. Kate does a good jugged hare."

Warmed by his kindly attitude toward her, Alice got the courage to say, "Would it be any use trying to persuade Jerome Burke to leave Creevagh village standing? Times have changed. The people won't put up with being thrown out of their houses nowadays, the way they did five years ago."

"You think not? I doubt if you're right. The people seem to me weak and discouraged. They have no spirit left, if they ever had it. In any case, a whole policy is involved and we can't do much to change it. The landlords are all agreed that the people must go. There is no living there for them."

Never before had he said so much on the subject. Still Alice's courage failed her, so that she could not ask as she longed to do: "Where will the people go? Are they animals to be slaughtered? Are you not afraid of driving them to murder, arson, terrorism? Are you not afraid of God?"

George went on, in a cool, detached tone. "The people will have to stand for being put out. It's sad in a way but better for them in the end. Naturally you feel sympathy for them because you know them." He flashed a pale-blue glance at her suddenly and then said in a half mutter that she could scarcely distinguish, "It's not easy to solve these problems without giving pain to someone. I remember worse times than the present."

He closed up then, at the memory of those bad times, Alice presumed. She did not want to hear details even if he had been willing to give them, but she guessed he was thinking of the burnings and hangings of 1798, after the Rising had been suppressed. She knew from Mary that it was the shock of hearing that men of his own class were brutally executed at Wexford and their heads spiked on the town gates as a warning in that year of liberty that had made a permanent political eunuch of old George.

She sat with him a little longer and then said in her lady's language, "I think I'll walk a little. It's such a nice morning."

He held the door for her, in the courteous way that always charmed her, and did not close it until she had reached the front door.

Alice had learned from Samuel and from Ellen that a lady may take a walk of an entirely useless kind. Her walks, however, always ended in the great cobbled yard, or in the walled garden, or in the paddock where the horses grazed. Paddy Egan was friendly and always welcomed her. His horses looked polished and clean from his grooming and from the regular feeds of oats that they consumed—food that would equally well have kept a man alive.

Her pregnancy dispensed her from the obligation to ride now but Samuel had a quiet pony waiting for her whenever she would be ready for it. She walked along the line of stables, rubbing her own pony's nose to their mutual pleasure. Then, remembering one of Ellen's lessons, she complimented Paddy on the shining condition of the traps and the carriage. She left him in the coach house, meticulously mending a worn trace.

Her nose wrinkled happily at the smell of saddle soap and clean leather, mixed with the slightly musty scent of last year's hay trailing wispily from the loft above. Comfortable hens pecked among the cobbles for grains of oats. A squawking from the hen house announced the achievement of an egg and the little black hen came racing out to tell the world about it in earsplitting shrieks. Gold sunlight trapped in this sheltered place gave an illusion of warmth and well-being. Alice felt a rush of pure happiness flow through her. Samuel's love and protection were a strong wall to keep out danger. Since her infancy she had not experienced this sense of security and peace. The same scent of hay and saddle soap clung to Samuel's day clothes. She folded her arms on her breast, to savor the memory of his arms around her and of his incredible, delightful kisses. Glowing with joy she walked in a kind of dream into the kitchen by the back door and found Kate with her head down on her outspread arms and her body shaking with sobs.

Instantly Alice darted forward.

"Kate—Kate, love! What is it? What happened?"

She lifted Kate's shoulders and held them firmly. Her sister's name was incongruous on this Kate but Alice was accustomed to it now. She shook her slightly as if to awaken her and said, "Is someone dead? Did someone talk roughly to you? What happened, Kate? Tell me, tell me!"

Kate leaned on Alice for a moment in friendship and then sat upright. She cleared the tears from her eyes with her fists. She was a stumpy black-haired woman who should by now have been the mother of a family but that her friend, as she called him, had gone to America years ago and died there within a week of landing, perhaps of fever, perhaps of hardship. Alice knew this much of her history from Samuel and that she had lately been promoted from kitchenmaid to cook when the English cook left in fear. In moments of loneliness for the bustle of home, Kate had been there to remind Alice that normality still existed. Without any specific knowledge she had sensed the cottage background very like her own, the family warmth that had produced Kate, with her humorous, kindly eye and sympathetic friendship.

"My brother Fintan was here," Kate said in a dead voice. "They're for the road."

"What do you mean?"

"Out, like tinkers' horses. Out on the road. The whole lot is going."

"Where? Where?"

"Creevagh."

"Are you from Creevagh? I didn't know." Fear seized Alice with a shaking hand. "Who is at home?"

"Ann, my sister, and her husband Pat Crehan, and Fintan and my mother. She should have died like my father but she didn't. They paid the rent always. Mr. Samuel gave me meal for them. They were never beggars before but that's what they'll be now."

The bitterness of her tone shocked Alice. Kate's voice dropped almost to a whisper.

"They'll be worse than beggars. They'll be murderers."

"What do you mean?"

"Fintan told me. They're warning Mr. Burke for the last time. Two warnings he has had but he pays no heed, or won't, from what I hear. Maggie Duffy that does the kitchen and the hens over there—she hears everything and she told me that Mr. Burke was laughing. Laughing! I told her it's how he has no understanding and she says that is so. He'll get the soldiers out from Galway tomorrow, he says. They'll make a day's show of it."

"We'll find a place for your mother here," Alice said in desperation. "They can all come here. We'll make room for them."

"Fintan says they're going to fight," Kate said in awe, while tears filled her eyes again. "Sure, how can they fight? In our house there's only an old woman and a young one and a houseful of children and two men. The Creevagh people were never fighters, I said to him. If they fight, they'll fight alone. He knows it, God help him. He knows it as well as I do myself." She looked at Alice as if she were seeing her for the first time. "I shouldn't talk of it," she said.

Outraged, Alice said, "To me? Because I'm a landlord's wife?"

" 'Tis what you are, Miss Alice," said Kate, using the title by which Alice had been known when first she came to Moycullen, and which had stayed with her ever since. "God help us, these are terrible times. What's going to become of us all?"

"Is Fintan long gone?"

"Ten minutes. Less, maybe."

"Is he gone to Burke's now, in the broad daylight?"

"No. They'll go by night, of course."

"Why did he tell you? Did he want you to help? To do something?"

"No. He had to tell me. It's my business to know a thing like that. But I shouldn't talk of it, though I know you're our friend," she added hurriedly. "If Mr. Samuel were here, he'd speak to Mr. Burke, maybe. His father owns three houses there in Creevagh and they're going too. I don't think Mr. Samuel or anyone can stop them now. It's too late."

Her head went down on the table again. Alice watched her for a few seconds while anger of a terrifying strength swept right through her body. She put out her hand and touched Kate's shoulder lightly. Then she turned and left the kitchen at a half-run. Kate sprang up.

"Don't run, ma'am! Don't run! Take care of yourself! Oh, God in heaven, help us all!"

Alice slowed to a walk and crossed the yard to the great double doors of the coach house.

19

Alice had been to Burke's twice already, once to an afternoon tea where there were neighbors only and once at night to a ball where the guests came from all over the county. With Samuel at her elbow she was able for all comers, even for the ladies. With the men she had less trouble. They were as unhappy as she was, with their teacups and their little cakes crumbling, except for Mr. Conway and he was not a real man at all. He had soft cheeks, and a satirical eye like a woman's, and he folded his legs and his feet as neatly as a bird. He gave Alice the expressionless glance of a bird, too, but late in the afternoon she noticed how his sniggering stopped when she came near, proving perhaps that it had been directed at her. He was a Galway lawyer who did great business with the landlords and was said to be buying several of them out in these hard times.

The formality of the two visits had discouraged Alice from dropping in on the Burkes, as she would have done with her neighbors in Cappagh. Mrs. Burke had said, gazing at Alice with her large, insincere eyes, not meaning a word of it, "Do come, at any time. We'll always be glad to see you. We're so glad to have you as a neighbor—we all thought Samuel was a confirmed bachelor."

Hurt deeply at this unpleasant aspect of the game, Alice said meekly, "Thank you. I'd like that."

She had never done it. She was coming now, however, and she felt that her hand was strengthened by the lack of contact thus far. There was no secret to be kept. Jerome Burke had had two warnings. By now he must know what this meant. She wished Samuel were at home, but since he was not, she must do this work herself.

She went into the coach house and called out, "Paddy! I want you to take me to Burke's at once. The tub trap will do."

He went quite still for a moment, so that she knew he was well aware of what was happening.

"To Burke's?" he said softly.

"Yes, and quickly."

They assessed each other. She could almost see him deciding that she might go to Burke's, that she would wish to do no harm even if this were in her power.

She said sharply, "I've been talking to Kate. Something must be done at once. I'm going to try, though I don't believe it will do any good. Hurry with the trap."

He did hurry and within ten minutes they were trotting down the avenue. There was no sign of Billy Thornton, so Paddy had to get out and open the gates himself. Alice shook her shoulders with impatience. She walked the pony through the gateway. He twitched his ears, as if he felt her urgency, and when Paddy climbed into the trap again he set off at a trot before the door could be closed.

Paddy said, "You heard about Creevagh."

"Yes. I didn't know it's tomorrow. Kate says there will be a fight."

"The mouse fighting the cat," said Paddy scornfully. "How can they fight? They have no practice in it."

Again the hand of fear gripped at Alice but Paddy's words had aroused some demon in her that had to be held down by force. Burke's lodgekeeper saw them coming and opened the gate, staring at Alice in her house dress and light shawl. Only now she began to feel the cold, damp wind begin to chill her arms. Paddy trotted the pony to the door of the house and helped Alice to the ground. Already she walked heavily and she had to pick her steps to keep her balance.

As she was admitted by the English parlormaid, Lydia Burke came into the hall. Through the open drawing-room door, Alice saw Jerome sprawled in an armchair. She said, brushing past the staring maid, "Thank God you're both here."

With a lifted eyebrow at such *farouche* behavior, Lydia led her into the drawing room, saying, "Jerome, it's our little neighbor. Do sit down, Mrs. Flaherty."

The adjective could only denote disparagement, since Alice was by inches the taller.

For all her urbanity, Lydia's eyes looked anxious and sharp. She spoke with her usual drawl, however.

"Is Samuel all right? Is something the matter?"

"Nothing is the matter with us. There's plenty the matter with you."

"Really?"

The curving intonation of Jerome's voice infuriated her. It was true, then, that he was laughing. She was shocked at the foolishness of his attitude. Until now she had thought that mere callousness was the cause of the landlord's behavior toward their tenants. She had not expected contempt as well.

Carefully lightening her voice she said, "I have just heard that there will be trouble if you tumble the Creevagh houses. Times have changed. When the landlords threw down the houses in '47 and after, the people walked away like sheep that would be turned out of a field." Catching sight of Lydia's satirical smile at this homely comparison, Alice rounded on her in anger. "Laugh now. You won't laugh later. A roof thrown down from a big house is just as bad as from a small one. Do you want your house burned over your head?"

Jerome Burke leaned forward in his chair and snarled at her. "What are you saying? Have you heard that they're going to burn us out?"

A child called from the hall, "Mama! Mama!"

Lydia hurried out of the room, throwing a terrified look at Alice as if she had threatened her personally.

Jerome said softly, "I'll thank you not to frighten my wife, Mrs. Flaherty. You may have come with a friendly intention but if you were not Samuel's wife I'd show you to the door. It's no use those fools asking me to leave Creevagh standing. I can't afford it. No one pays rent. Am I to keep them all out of my charity? Yes, I've had their warnings and I've sent them word that they can go to the devil. Law and order will be on my side." He leaned back and spoke more calmly but the long look he sent from Alice's head to her feet was insulting. "You've done well for yourself. Now take my advice and stay at home as a woman should and attend to your housekeeping. That will give you plenty to do. Times are changing, as you say. Neither of us can do anything about it."

"Am I to forget everything I've seen, then?" Alice said, relieved rather than upset at this plain speaking. "Am I to forget the black boats full of starving people, sailing, sailing in all day from Connemara to Galway? Have you ever seen people huddled in a corner of their own kitchen with the fear and savagery of hunger on their faces, a man grudging a bite to his wife and a woman to her child? Have you ever seen how quiet they get when the starvation is on them? They don't speak at all in the last days. They just look at you. Nothing can save them then, soup nor meal nor prayers. Have you ever seen that?"

His look frightened her. She could tell that he had seen those things, all right. She was silent, and watched him. He glared at her. She stood up awkwardly and went toward the door. There she paused and said, "Your house and your family and your own life are in danger. I came to tell you that, while you have time to stop the evictions. You won't. Your kind never will. You haven't looked out of the window for a hundred years."

Then she was overcome with nausea and had to rush out of the room, out of the house, and haul herself somehow into the trap.

Paddy said quietly as he walked the pony down the avenue, "You did no good. Did he strike you?"

"Oh, God! No, he did not."

It had never occurred to her that he might. The idea of it disturbed her as nothing else had done. When she reached home she found that she was aching in every muscle. Prudence told her to go to bed and stay there, but as she lay in the huge room, frustration and anger at this inconvenient baby made it impossible for her to rest. She longed for Samuel's return. Late in the afternoon she dozed nightmarishly. Then Kate brought a lamp and some tea and made her sit up. Dusk filled the corners of the room and increased the dead weight of loneliness that had settled on her.

When Samuel appeared at last, looking anxious and uncertain, she said to him, "Well, I had courage, as you told me to do, and now I'm paying for it."

"Is the child all right?"

"So far, yes. I'm feeling a little better. I think I've been asleep too long. What time is it?"

"Seven o'clock. James had a lecture at four. I should have been here. Paddy told me you went to Burke's place."

"He told you that? Did he tell you why I went?"

"To try to stop the evictions in Creevagh tomorrow."

"Yes. It was no use talking to them. They're beyond sense. Jerome is a pig. Maggie told Kate he whips the little boy nearly every day. How can he have care for the poor when he treats his own like that?"

The thought of the child being beaten by that smooth-handed monster brought tears to Alice at last. Samuel sat with her a long time. He said, "It was good that you went. Even when it's useless, you must make a protest. Never let things lie in silence. This is the only hope. See everything and say everything. Now rest. Afterward you must always rest."

She leaned on him, to feel peace and strength flow from him into her.

When she seemed more at ease, Samuel went downstairs. The lamp was lit, standing on its bracket, but there was no sign of Andy. Blue dusk filled the fanlight over the front door. The dining room was empty and the fire had died down. His father was not in the dining room. An hour ago, when Paddy had taken the gig and told him that Alice was in bed, he had not noticed whether the usual people were about as he hurried through the hall. James had disappeared, probably to his room to study. Samuel stood uncertainly for a moment and then made for the kitchen. It was empty but the coal fire in the range had been stoked. Surely this meant that Kate was not far off.

In the corner of the kitchen, a steep, scrubbed stairway led to the hot little room where she slept.

He stood at the foot of the stairs and called out, "Kate! Kate!"

She was there, all right. She came out onto the stairs, red and flustered.

"Where is my father? Where is Andy?"

"Gone to Burke's, sir. I was trying to see from the window."

"To Burke's! My father!"

"Yes, sir. There's trouble over there. Andy is gone too. It was he brought the news."

"What kind of trouble?"

It was a largely used word and could denote anything from murder to a confinement.

"Mr. Burke sent for the soldiers to come out from Galway tonight, sir. They haven't come yet. It's about Creevagh."

"Yes, yes, I've heard about the Creevagh business. God damn him for a fool. He'll get away with it now."

"Don't curse him, sir!" Kate sounded shocked. "A fool is what he is but don't curse him."

Of course she made no mention of the Whiteboys' warnings. She would be as likely to speak to him in Irish.

Samuel asked, "Where is Master Fahy?"

"Gone to Burke's too, maybe. I didn't see him this while back."

"I'd better go there and see what's happening. Stay here, Kate, and look after Miss Alice."

"Yes, sir."

Running across the paddock, climbing the mossy wall and plunging through the underbrush of Burke's wood, Samuel felt a purely spontaneous exhilaration in being at the scene of action. He knew every stone, every hill and hollow of this ground from his childhood. It was cold now, and the bare branches patterning the dark sky were stark and unfriendly. A little hard wind had come up and was stirring them slowly, so that they moaned. He stopped at the edge of the wood to listen. It was deathly still—too still to be natural. Birds or rabbits should have been moving. There were lights here and there in the square, solid shape of Burke's house, giving a false look of tranquillity.

He crossed the dewy lawn, irritated as he felt the damp soak into the leather of his fine boots. For this kind of thing, town boots were useless. He paused by the house wall, listening now for the soldiers on their way out from Galway. On such a night, they would be heard almost a mile away, trotting hooves and rattling brass and clattering harness. There was no sound.

He walked along in the deep shadow by the side of the house and had almost reached the corner when he became aware of a change in the quality of the silence. It was hardly a rustle, rather a breath of change that made itself sufficiently apparent for him to pause in the darkness by the wall. Hesitation was so unusual to Samuel that he prolonged it. A vague memory of Kate's words disturbed him: she had been trying to see from the window of her room. But in the dim light and through the wood, what could she have seen? A fire only.

Moonlight filled the gravel sweep before the front door. Samuel abandoned the idea of entering the house that way. Looking back across the lawn he realized that he had moved entirely in the shadows, though unintentionally. He began to walk toward the back of the house. Above him a lighted window went suddenly dark. He paused against the trunk of a tree at the corner of the house and turned in the direction of the yard. The tall wooden gates showed clear in the moonlight, standing open.

Burke's yard was three times the size of Samuel's own. The coach houses and the horses' stables were near the house, and at the outer end, to the side, there was a haggard for hay, sheltered from the weather by the walls of the other buildings. Just inside the gate, opposite the haggard, was the long milking shed for the cows. The yard was neatly cobbled and sloped gently away from the house to carry off rain water and manure. Samuel had always admired the arrangements there, so spacious and secure. It was extremely odd that the gates should be open at night.

Men were moving in there. In a daze he saw one carrying a long-handled implement whose tip was wound around with heavy cloth. They were no more than ten feet away from him. They murmured gently among themselves. Two of them saw him but made no move toward him, so that it seemed they thought he was one of themselves. He stayed quite still, in fear of his life now and yet cool enough not to run. A light was struck and was applied caressingly to the oil-soaked cloth which flared up immediately. Swift as a fox, the man carrying the torch ran with it to the hayrick. Again and again he thrust it into the base of the rick, moving along first one side and then the other. Fire crawled up the surface of the hay, sparked and died and flared again as the wind lifted it and spread it wide. In their stables the horses began to neigh.

Now lights appeared at the back of the house. The fire was roaring, a dull, ugly sound, droning steadily. A man darted across the yard and worked at the bung of a huge water barrel that stood there until he got it free. The man carried a long-barreled gun loosely balanced under his arm. The others began to gather by the gate. There were five or six of them. Samuel recognized Kate's brother Fintan because of his great height and his shaggy, wild hair. They seemed uncertain what to do. Samuel began to creep away from them, but before he had gone a yard, he heard the cavalry coming. There was no mistaking that regular trotting, accompanied by a metallic rattle. He turned back to the men by the gate and called out in a voice thinned by anxiety, "Run! Run for your lives! The redcoats are here!"

At this unfortunate moment, the back door of the house burst open and several men came running into the yard. In the glare of the fire from the burning rick, Samuel saw Jerome Burke and his steward and the yardman, who kept rather to the back of the group.

Old George was the last out. He was silhouetted in the doorway where he stopped, evidently shocked at the sight of the burning rick. The man at the water barrel began to lope across the yard. Someone from the house fired a shot. The fleeing man turned and fired toward the house before running with a crouching gait out of the yard. Either he or another called out in a queer, high-pitched note like a night bird, "That's for Clonbur and Creevagh, Flaherty!"

The rest of the men had disappeared. Samuel saw his father pitch forward down the single step onto the cobbles.

While he and Jerome lifted old George and carried him into the kitchen, they could hear the arrival of the cavalry and the shouts of the officers as they set the men to contain the fire. The yardman was leading Burke's prancing horses away from the terrifying smell and smoke of the burning hay. Then Samuel kicked the door shut and they heard no more.

They laid old George on the kitchen table. The bullet had entered his throat. He looked at Samuel with the surprised eyes of an injured animal. Blood stained the flags on the floor, and their hands and clothes. Neither of them could speak, though Samuel knew he should be praying aloud for his father. Instead, he took his hand and held it until it went limp, which was only a matter of moments in any case.

20

Later it seemed to Alice that the weeks after old George's death passed in a dream. There was no doctor nearer than Galway and Master Fahy ordered her to stay in bed. At first she was glad of this. She would not have been allowed to attend old George's funeral, since it was considered wrong for a pregnant woman to have anything to do with death. Mrs. Neilan, the midwife, told her this. Alice concluded rightly that Mrs. Neilan's patients were all rich people who could choose their company.

A frightening aspect of the dream was that Alice began to think again of Morgan. Even when she lay with Samuel, often she imagined Morgan's hands on her body and Morgan's kisses on her lips. It was wrong and unfair. Samuel needed to have her all to himself. He encouraged her to stay in their bedroom, to sit in a chaise longue and do some of that embroidery Ellen had trained her in. He came into the room with an air of escaping from horrors below. Alice loved him more than ever but not with all her heart. A fine slice of that belonged to Morgan Connolly, it seemed. In fact, now that she had tasted the joys of love, she was appalled at how easily she had given Morgan up. He had belonged to the life she knew. He had felt her thoughts in a way that Samuel for all his intelligence could never do. He had the vigor of youth as well as its unpredictability. She also recognized his deadly poverty and knew what she had escaped. This hurt her and led her into hours of speculation about her reasons for loving Samuel, and whether in fact it was respect and not love that she felt for him. There was nothing strange in that, as she knew well from the many marriages of convenience that she had seen, but she had not intended to be caught out in that way. She had to fight her tongue not to speak constantly of Morgan.

At last she realized that the torment would never stop until she left her room and resumed ordinary life. She came cautiously downstairs one morning and was reassured to find that things had hardly changed at all in her absence. Andy was in the hall and Kate was clattering in the kitchen. Paddy was in the yard. She could hear Master Fahy droning upstairs in the schoolroom.

The great difference was that old George's gun room was empty and clean, as it had never been in his lifetime. A breath of air had got in and swept away the smell of tobacco, and it had removed the aura of its former occupant at the same time. She guessed that this room would never be used again, except perhaps as a storeroom. They had no game at meals since he was gone.

When the child was born in June, for the first time she realized how much she missed old George. Odd as it was, his former relationship with her mother had created a bond of understanding, even of love, between them. He had welcomed her to the house as a daughter or a granddaughter long expected, rather than a stranger. It was largely because of him that she had slipped so easily into such a different way of life. His manner, rough enough on occasion, helped her to adapt her own to the new requirements. Often she saw him tone down a gesture or a statement to make it fit for polite society. The example of this was an important part of her own re-education. He would have been pleased to have a grandchild, even though it was a girl.

Alice was surprisingly ignorant of the processes of birth. Her mother had always sent the whole family out, in her charge, when a new baby was arriving. For the last one, only four years ago, Alice had tried to stay but Mary had been so outraged at the idea that she had had to leave with the rest. She had seen her mother's distress, which was more than usual, and had wanted to comfort her. The effect had been to send Mary into hysterics, which had sent the midwife and all her old segoshioners into a fit of prayers, which soon turned into abuse of Alice for suggesting such an unnatural thing.

Alice knew, however, that her mother was always very quiet

during a birth and she managed to live up to this standard even during the most inept fumblings of Mrs. Neilan. She showed her irritation only once, when she asked her abruptly to remove the array of ludicrous little garments airing before the turf fire. The fire was necessary for the mysterious kettle of hot water that appeared to be part of the ritual of birth. The clothes could be fetched if they were needed, Alice pointed out.

"God forgive you! Don't bring bad luck on the child!" Mrs. Neilan said gruesomely, turning up her eyes.

Alice asked for Samuel but when he came he looked so helpless that she sent him away again. Then she wept because she had to be alone, and she wanted her mother, and she had to swallow this new, terrible pain lest Mrs. Neilan should get possession of her. She became absorbed in her own survival, so that even the infant for whom she had developed an almost personal affection no longer concerned her much.

Seeing the stark poverty all around her, Alice was shocked to find that her first child was dressed in twenty-four garments. Petticoats and vests of cotton and silk and wool, a binder and a pilch, bonnet and socks and shawls, all added up to the ridiculous number. It was one area in which Alice did not put up a fight, and because of it the infant Anna belonged more to the nurse than to herself. It was a pity that the nurse had worked at Burke's because she brought her strong ideas of discipline with her. Alice knew that the sense of release she had felt at the birth, and her fears for the plight of her neighbors, must have been communicated to the child. She did not put it that way.

"Anna knew I was glad to be rid of her," she tried to explain to Samuel when the child was clamoring for her attention or loitering on the edge of an adult group. "God knows we had little enough at home but our mother was aways there. Somehow she was able to look out for her neighbors as well."

"Children would eat you, if they could," Samuel said. "You give them life, they give you death."

"Surely you don't believe that!"

Alice was distressed, until she was told that it was a quotation. In no time, Master Fahy had her reading Balzac, and the complicated horrors of French family life made her see her own with a calmer eye.

Having a small child in the house had a strange effect on James Fahy. Gradually he had been losing a little of his air of uneasy gentility. He was pleased that Anna liked him. Alice watched with amusement and compassion as their relationship developed, especially when Anna could sit up and look around her. Then at the approach of Christmas, James made a doll out of pieces of wood picked up here and there, jointed with nails that were carefully filed down so that no sharp edge remained. He worked on this for days, whittling its head into a round shape and painting on hair and features. He sat for hours at the kitchen table with Kate, stitching a long skirt and bodice and shawl and an apron in which they dressed the doll.

Kate was very silent now, and Samuel was glad to see her so naturally occupied. Her brother Fintan was on the run since the night of old George's death but Kate had not said whether she knew where he was. On that terrible night, Samuel had gone straight to the kitchen after his father had been laid in the dining room. This time he climbed the stairs to Kate's room and saw obvious signs that Fintan had stayed there, perhaps for a few nights, perhaps for a day. There was a stained tea mug and a dinner plate, and a shirt on the back of the single chair, drying. Kate shrank by the little window, watching the red glare of the fire in the distance.

Samuel said softly, "They've murdered my father, Kate. We've brought him home. Before anyone comes, I want to tell you that it was not Fintan who fired the shot. Now I need your help. I can't find Andy. He ought to be here. Why didn't you stay with Miss Alice?"

"God help you, sir. She sent me to bed. She said she was feeling better."

"Good. Then we needn't tell her until the morning."

But he had not been strong enough to keep silent. When old George had been given a more seemly appearance and Jerome Burke's men had gone home, Master Fahy came into the dining room and said abruptly, "Go to bed, Samuel. I'll stay here for the night."

"Where have you been?"

"Out and about. I've heard all about it. Go and sleep, while you can." Seeing Samuel make for his study he said, "No, not there. In your own bed. Up with you, quickly."

It was the tone he used in the schoolroom. Samuel could not have disobeyed him. The joy and relief of finding Alice in his bed held him fascinated, with the lamp in his hand, almost tasting the perfection of her relaxed beauty. Had any woman such translucent skin, such a long, curved throat, such strong black hair, such large and luminous eyes? She was looking at him, half asleep, and now she stretched out her long, white arms to him, with an endearment in her own language, which she used only in most intimate moments. He put the lamp down carefully and lay against her breast, and immediately was telling her what he had seen and done, what he had felt for that dry oddity who had been his father, and how Jerome Burke, who had suffered only the loss of an old musty rick of hay, was reduced to a twittering jelly, quite useless and impractical. Then he slept in his clothes and woke in the thin daylight to find that she was holding him still.

The memory of that night sustained him through the horrors of the following days, so that he deliberately prolonged it by making Alice stay in their room. The child was his excuse but in fact this had become unnecessary. Alice had excellent health and soon recovered completely.

The business of managing the household became somehow easier after old George's death. When Alice found that she was pregnant again she set up a daily routine that gradually centered around the miserable, apologetic group of starving people to be fed at mealtime. Caldrons of porridge and soup were prepared, and Alice made the people come into the yard instead of feeding them at the gates as some did. She knew they found it humiliating to be kept outside, and she wanted to give them some feeling of being brought into the precincts of her house, though their numbers made this impossible. She bought their starved cattle to make soup for them, paying exorbitant prices so as to help with passages to America.

There was endless emigration from the little holdings that had been scraped out of the wet mountainside after the Cromwellian war of two hundred years ago. Advice and passage money and introductions had to be given to the young people who were leaving. Alice cleared out attics and storerooms, searching for old clothes to give away. She went to many, many wakes and funerals, knowing that this caused her to be despised by the other landlords and their wives. She knew well what they were saying: that she was reverting to type, keeping company with her own kind, dragging Samuel down with her. She cared nothing for this. Samuel was the richest of them all and he had taught her to keep her chin high as she had done, on Ellen's advice, on her wedding day.

Alice learned to drive the tub trap herself so that she could go occasionally to Cappagh. Michael and Roger were doing well in America, working for a builder in Boston and sending home money through the Irish Emigrant Industrial Savings Bank. Often when Alice came with her presents, she found that there was already enough meal and flour for the family's needs. Her sister Kate watched her with a smirk while Mary said as much. Alice said quickly, "Then give it to someone else. There's plenty in want."

But she knew that Kate's obvious resentment of her new prosperity was felt to some extent by the other members of the family. After old George's death, she could see that Mary found her visits a painful reminder of the man whom she had always regarded as her second maker. At first this hurt Alice, but when the infant Thomas was about to be born, her visits to Cappagh became difficult because of the distance and the roughness of the road. Then she felt a sense of relief and turned her attention to Moycullen and her own household. Four years after she had left Cappagh to be married, she had pushed it unwillingly into a recess of her mind as a phase of her life that was over and done with.

She was taken by surprise, therefore, when Mike Sherwin trotted his yellow cob into the yard one October day in 1855 and brought her news of Morgan. Mike was shabbier every year and he fell on his food at the Flaherty's kitchen table in a way that suggested that his last days had been hungry ones. When he had finished, he followed Alice into the dining room, which was still the family living room because it was placed so conveniently downstairs. The hearth was swept clean and the fire glowed, and a huge creel of good black turf stood ready to replenish it. His last visit had been in the spring. As usual his news was mostly bad but he began by complimenting Alice.

"When I'm coming near Moycullen, ma'am, my heart is rising every moment at the thought of yourself and your husband and your good house. They're few and far between now, the big houses where you get an old Irish welcome with the newest of food and the oldest of drink. Most of the houses are closed up or else they're gone into the hands of gombeen men that would hardly give a bite of food to their own mother."

Alice asked the usual question. "Where did you come from?"

"I was in Limerick. It's not the worst. Limerick and Tipperary. The land is good but it's all in the wrong hands. Five shillings a week is big wages in those places and what is a man to do when he knows he can earn nearly as much in one day in Washington or Boston? The hours are long—four in the morning till eight at night, cold and heat—but there's a dollar at the end of every day and that's four English shillings. Out in the west, in San Francisco, he can earn three times as much. A man that can work is rich in no time. Good lodgings, too, for ten shillings a week, two and a half dollars."

"Where did you hear all this?"

Alice was amused at Mike's precision.

"It's in Father O'Hanlon's *Guidebook for Emigrants*. I've been reading it to the people by every fire and dip in Limerick. They get out the book when they see me coming, or anyone else that can read. You can see the light coming into their eyes and they listening. Not a word in it, of course, about the fights between the Irish and the Swedes and Norwegians that's building the railroad."

"And where did you hear that?"

"A traveling man hears everything," Mike said. "A woman in Limerick gave me a letter to read from her son in Kentucky and it seems they have something like the Whiteboys out there, all against the Irish. They're called the Know-Nothings. They murdered a few Irishmen there only a couple of years ago. I'm telling you, ma'am, there's another thing besides health that you need in America and that's wits. God forgive me, ma'am, I didn't ask you yet about the children. Tell me, now, how are they at all?"

"Very well, Mike, thank God."

And then, quite casually, Mike said, "There's a friend of yours in Tipperary town will be glad to hear that—Morgan Connolly."

Alice made some answer but she was almost overcome by the wave of excitement that passed through her at the mention of Morgan's name. It seemed impossible that she should be so affected after so many years. She was filled with anger at herself, and an illogical vexation with Morgan for being the cause of her disturbance.

Mike had noticed nothing. He was going on, saying, "Morgan has been in a lot of places in the last few years—London, Paris—places you can't go with just a horse and buggy. He's not long back. He'll be coming over this way to see yourself and Mr. Flaherty and Father Kenny."

Alice asked softly, "When? Did he say when he's coming?"

Her casual tone was successfully assumed, apparently, for Mike answered, "He didn't say for sure."

Mike stayed for several days and Alice was able to question him again about Morgan. He was in good health and spirits. He had learned a lot of things on his travels, Mike said, and the note of admiration in his voice was quite clear. Morgan knew of old George's death.

"The whole country heard of that, of course," said Mike. "Some call it murder, some have another name for it. With things fairly quiet, there isn't much else to talk about."

"Would you say things are quiet?"

"Too quiet. We're back to the beginning again. You'd think Thomas Davis had never lived. There's no spirit in anyone. They're gone off to the Crimea like sheep to the slaughter-house, every man paid for like an animal."

"Don't they sing? Don't they know the words of the songs any more? We don't hear much singing here," said Alice, "unless someone is dead or going to America. Sometimes they sing 'The West's Awake' but mostly it's the old songs about people leaving home and country forever."

"There nothing stirring in Tipperary that I could see, though it was a good county once."

Then Mike cut the conversation short, as was always done with Alice at a certain point. She was accustomed to this now and no longer resented it.

The arrival of Morgan became an obsession with Alice. She wanted to see him enter the village of Moycullen and walk up the path to Father Kenny's door. She made excuses to take the trap over to the village every afternoon, though the weather was getting cold. She had picked Mike's brains clean of information about the exact day when he planned to come but she had to conclude that Mike did not know. She dared not ask Father Kenny. He was inconveniently intelligent and might easily spot the truth. The thought of this possibility covered her with shame for her condition, so that she stayed at home for a day. She had a fire lit in the drawing room and had the children brought down from the nursery under the roof to play there. She got out her piece of fine crocheted lace, which was a solid link with Cappagh, and tried pitifully to work out what was happening to her brain and body. It seemed a crazy thing that she could love two men at the same time, as she did Samuel and Morgan. By all the rules, Samuel was love and Morgan was lust, but surely poor Morgan could not be dismissed with such a short, rude word. She preached a sermon to herself on fidelity and constancy and the sacredness of marriage, while the sad image of Morgan stayed out somewhere on the perimeter of her mind. It was well there was not a third, a fourth, a fifth man for whom she felt these emotions. She had room for them all. She was a trollop, probably. She longed for Samuel but he had said he would be late. She tried to feel the strength of his hand, to see his penetrating eyes, and so to steady herself.

At five o'clock exactly, Kate opened the door and said excitedly, "Miss Alice—ma'am—here's Morgan Connolly himself!"

And there he was. Alice stood up, trailing her lace, surprised into upright stillness. Morgan walked across the room and kissed her solidly on the mouth. He had promised himself that.

21

Alice kept her head. Long years of practice were useful. She held Morgan off, but gently, keeping her hands on his shoulders while she looked him up and down. He had always been thin and straight but now he was also neat and trimmed and well dressed, with clean white shirt and a cravat and well-polished boots.

Her admiration burst forth in a cry, in Irish, "Morgan, you're beautiful! Long may you live to wear your finery!"

"A century and a year to repent," said Morgan, in Irish too.

And then Alice said, "Sit down and tell me where you have been." In English she said to Anna, "Come over and shake hands with Morgan."

Anna did so, and Morgan kissed her hand solemnly, as if she were a full-grown young lady. At three years old she was perfectly made and moved as effortlessly and elegantly as a cat. Her hair was fair, with darker strands that matched her dark eyebrows and lashes. Her eyes were gray, like Samuel's. For the drawing room, the nurse had put her into a strangely adult dress with a wide neck and bare shoulders. Alice had added a little knitted shawl as soon as the nurse had gone, knowing that the child was cold, so she was dressed like a miniature lady. She moved forward with her hand extended in a gesture inherited from her English grandmother and stood before Morgan with her little black pumps turned out at the toes and a section of tightly drawn white stockings showing above her ankles.

She said, "How do you do, Morgan."

She turned back to her game with Thomas, of rolling colored wooden balls to each other along the carpet. Thomas sat firmly, too lazy to walk, and waved genially to Morgan.

Alice said, "Leave them to their play. I heard from Mike Sherwin that you'd be coming."

"Were you glad?"

"Of course I was glad. I was longing every day to see you."

"You have a fine life. You sit in the drawing room all day making lace."

"Faith and I do not!" Alice flashed at him. "It's a very rare thing for me to do." She stopped and blushed and bowed her head, remembering why she was here today.

Morgan appeared to misinterpret her confusion. He said, "Alice, I was only joking. I've heard all over the country how you work and help the poor people, and what fine children you have, and how you keep your house so well."

Now she blushed again because these compliments were much too sweet to her. Then she sat up abruptly and said, "Where have you been? Mike Sherwin said you were in London and Paris."

"Yes, and hardly a day passed that I didn't think of you, Alice."

She looked uneasily at the children but they were quite preoccupied with their game. Years of calm were going to be no use to her. She could feel her agitation rising like nausea, unpleasantly. She had thought this would never happen again. Life with Samuel had no surprises. Of course she loved him, but not madly, suddenly, as it seemed she loved Morgan.

She said in a low voice, "I've thought of you too, Morgan."

"You have?"

He looked so pleased that she was sorry she had said it.

"How could I not?" she said a little sharply.

She had meant to keep a polite distance between them, so that he would see that she had put their days in Aran behind her once and for all. She had meant to show him that she valued his friendship, but now from the beginning it was all going wrong. Time should have destroyed the marvelous bond that had grown between them then, and if she had been disappointed at her first sight of him, all the better. Instead, he had cheated again by growing into the fine, well set up, personable man who was miraculously sitting before her now, where secretly she had often imagined him. Perhaps this was her crime, for which God would punish her. But she could not control the picture that kept leaping into her vision at the most unlikely times. Sometimes a door would open and before the real person could come in, there would be the presence of Morgan quite unasked for. Sometimes she would look up from her eternal sewing, either downstairs in the dining room or here where they were sitting now, and there he would be, sitting in the chair that properly belonged to Samuel, the master's chair. For a long time she thought it was her own wickedness that conjured up these images, and the priest in Galway to whom she confessed her sins was inclined to agree with her that they were manifestations of the devil, but Alice did not really believe this. He told her not to entertain them but they never stayed long enough for that. Reality always returned, all too soon. She was too practical for daydreaming. Indeed, as time went on she longed to be able to do it but the outlines of the Morgan she had known had begun to blur. When she tried accurately to recall him, the man she remembered was surely far different from the one she managed to envisage. She did not tell this to the priest. It was too complicated to be explained in hoarse whispers, too near the waiting rows of people in the benches outside the confessional.

With Morgan actually sitting there in front of her, it would have been madness to have wasted time in thinking about sin. She felt so happy that there was no possibility of concealing it. Each time she lowered her eyes, she had to raise them again and look at him. The flash of love was as unmistakable as a flash of lightning. She knew it, as she knew so much about Morgan, by the sharp look of understanding that he sent back to her. That this should be combined with such warmhearted softness as showed in his eyes seemed to her irresistible. But it had to be resisted at all costs.

"Morgan," she burst out suddenly, "I hope you haven't come back to torment me."

At once he looked hurt and immediately afterward extremely satisfied. She blushed with shame for having given herself away again. She was like a cornered hen, running this way and that, uselessly. After all these years, surely she could have done better, but Morgan always had this effect on her, of sending her in a direction that she had been determined to avoid. She wished he did not have this power. Surely she was exaggerating his fluency in reading her mind. If she were to look blank, mildly interested, as she often looked at the landlords and their agents that she had to meet socially, surely it would have the same effect of concealing what she was thinking.

But instantly Morgan said, "Alice, keep that face for your grand occasions. Let's be friends as we always were."

This was to ask the impossible and she gazed at him helplessly. Then with an effort she said, "Mike Sherwin told me you were in Tipperary."

"Yes. I went from there to Cappagh to see Nora. She's thinking of going to America. She stayed in Cappagh to look after me and then I left her. She'd be as well off in America. All the young people are going. Martin is on his way home for a visit."

"I heard he did well there."

"Yes—in the building business, like all the Irish. There's a new organization starting. He'll have things to tell us."

"Martin never liked me."

"That's a long time ago. He thinks of nothing but Ireland now. He knows from your brothers what you have been doing."

"It's a drop in the ocean. The people are so downhearted now, all they hope for is to get to heaven when they die."

"Do you ever try to stir them up?"

"No. What would be the use? Risings are done with."

"Martin wouldn't agree with you."

Instantly she was terrified for Morgan. Her fear was real, since she knew that once he had received a glimmer of hope, he would have to follow it to its end. This was in prison and death. She had seen others go the same way and knew there was no stopping them once the idea had got hold of them. He would leave her again—she could see it already. She clung to a memory.

"Mike Sherwin said there's nothing stirring in Tipperary."

"Mike has a long tongue. He would be the last to hear what's going on."

When she was younger she would have wept but at least she had learned that much. Anna was glancing at them every moment, sensing the tension between them. To recall her to himself, Thomas threw one of the wooden balls at her. She had an excuse then to run to Alice and bury her face in her skirt, wailing for comfort. Alice stroked her hair helplessly. It was Morgan who restored order by collecting the balls and rolling them to her. The sight of the huge, beautiful man folded up so small, crawling on the carpet, was a diversion that the children could not resist. Neither could Alice. She joined in the game for a while and then Morgan began to tell them a story about Finn MacCool and the dog with eight legs. When Samuel came back at six o'clock they were sitting on the hearthrug, listening to him solemnly, though Thomas could not understand a word.

Samuel greeted Morgan warmly, clasping him in his arms and then holding him off to admire him as Alice had done.

"Morgan, you look magnificent! Where have you been?"

"Paris, London," Morgan said, smiling. "I've seen a salon like Madame d'Arblay's."

"It's good to have you back. Can you stay with us here?"

A good man, unsuspicious, clean of heart—that was Samuel. Alice had a feeling almost of irritation with him for his innocence. Then she repented and wished that her stored-up energy could be used decently. Morgan was staying with Father Kenny, he said, and he could hardly be in a'safer place. Now he would remain for dinner. Like wasp stings she recalled his clandestine visits to the Husseys' house in Aran and wondered at herself for being able to look so cool. She dared not speak but it did not matter since Samuel took it for granted that she was leaving Morgan to him while she went to tell Kate that he would dine with them.

At the dinner table she was free to watch him because Master Fahy took him over. Fahy was as straight as ever but he had shrunk a little in height. Alice had given him a new velvet jacket that he was wearing in honor of Morgan. His white hair was still plentiful and looked rather well, tied back with a narrow black ribbon. She had given him this, too, very tentatively offering it with the jacket, and he had not been offended. It certainly looked better than the bootlace. She felt pleased that her household looked well for Morgan, who had known it before she did herself. She knew he would recognize the improvements she had made, the clean cloth on the table, the matching china and dishes, the polished silver and glass, Andy serving quietly at each chair, on the left-hand side. This was probably the most astonishing achievement. She had discovered that Andy knew quite well how to do it and was afraid to refuse her as he had done Kate. She also enjoyed watching how calmly Morgan took this service, as if he had been born to it.

When he had had some soup, Fahy said, "So you've been to France at last. A great experience. One I've always longed for. Now I wish you were home for good." And he lifted his chin and intoned:

> " 'Heureux qui comme Ulisse a fait un beau voyage,
> Ou comme cetui-là qui conquit la toison,
> Et puis est retourné, plein d'usage et raison,
> Vivre entre ses parents le reste de son âge.' "

Still with his chin high he sent a gaze like a lighthouse beam all around the table and asked in thundering tones, "Now who knows the author of that?"

His accent in French was abominable. Morgan obviously could not forbear from smiling as he answered, "Du Bellay, Master, one of the Pléiade, friend of Ronsard."

"Very good, very good," Master Fahy said while Andy ran with the wine bottle to reward Morgan.

Alice enjoyed the respectful way he poured it, with his ferret's eye gauging when to stop, and not a drop on the cloth. Samuel looked happy this evening, watching Andy, proud of his household, too, and pleased to have Morgan in it again. He fitted perfectly into the role of landlord, patron of all and automatically the most knowledgeable man in any company. He showed no sign whatever of becoming seedy or bucolic in appearance, as she knew well from their occasional trips to Dublin. There he was as neat and trim as any city man, perhaps because he used a Dublin tailor, but also because he moved swiftly and precisely, as if he knew what he was about. He never looked lost, as she had often seen country people do in Dublin, wandering glassy-eyed, like cattle waiting for a lazy herdsman to prod them on. He took her to the best shops and eating places.

They were talking about Paris. Master Fahy was saying, "All my life I longed to go there but now it's too late. My vision of it is so fixed, I would be sure to be disappointed. Have you seen the Emperor?"

"Often. The Tuileries palace is quite near the Sorbonne."

"What an opportunity. Martin is very good to you. Did he not ask you to go to America and make money? That's what most people seem to want," Samuel said. "It's very understandable. What you're doing is much better. The only pity is that you must leave so soon."

Alice felt weak and hot. She had to wait silently, hoping that she was not noticed, until the information she wanted came of itself.

It was not long. Master Fahy said, "James's term in London began three weeks ago. It's always much later in Paris. You see, I know a good deal about such things."

"James in London? Then I'll see him on my way through. What took him there?"

"A scholarship," Fahy said proudly. "It's a special one. I didn't want him to go but he was bent on it. He may change his mind and settle in Dublin later."

"So you must go almost at once?" Samuel asked.

"The day after tomorrow." Morgan looked along the length of the table toward Alice. She made no attempt to avoid his eyes. "I wish I had more time," he said. And then he turned deliberately to Samuel and said, "Do you ever think of coming to Paris? If you do, I'll be happy to see you there."

"Why not?" Samuel said enthusiastically. "We haven't had a proper holiday for years—not since we were married, in fact. Alice! Would you like to go to Paris?"

"More than anything in the world!"

She knew that she should not have spoken so strongly but no one seemed surprised. After all, any reasonable young woman would enjoy a trip to Paris.

Samuel said, "Then that's settled. I'll go to work on it at once."

22

Knowing that he would see Alice soon in Paris, Morgan went off to London two days later with little feeling of loss. In fact he felt strengthened and revitalized by meeting her, as if he had sucked her blood. It had been good to see her household and to know how she spent her days. His jealousy of Samuel was less since he had played with Samuel's children, but his last view of Alice at her own door was painful. Father Kenny took him to Galway, borrowing Samuel's trap and a quiet pony for the purpose. They drove around to the front of the house from the yard and there she was, with Samuel. She was holding his hand tightly and standing close against him. He was in riding boots, ready to go to Cong to see about felling some trees. It was a warm, clear day. Yellow leaves still clung to the lower boughs of the trees beyond the lawn but the tops were bare. Against the pale sky, tapering from pale gray to blue, the upper branches seemed to fly and fade into nothingness. The sun touched Alice's gold-and-black dress, whose flowing skirt partly covered one of Samuel's boots. Morgan chose to remember her alone, not waving to them, not smiling, but gazing with her steady, uncompromising look after them as they drove away.

On his one evening in London, he went to visit James Fahy in the rooms he shared with another Irish student named Charles Murphy. They had a fine carpeted living room all their own and a bedroom each. Morgan was astonished at the change in James. He asked politely after his father and made no comment when he heard that he was well. He mixed a drink for his guest with an air of assurance and showed only one sign of dissatisfaction with his small size. This was when he stood on the stone curb of the fireplace, balanced like a bird on a branch, while he discoursed to Morgan on the joys of being in London and on his plans for the future. He held a glass of milk and water in his hand. Morgan sat back in a leather-covered armchair, filled with real amusement.

"London is the capital of Ireland without any doubt," said James. "One feels free, free of provincialism and stupidity and oppression and ignorance. It's the center of a great Empire. Hard work and good manners go a long way here. One is accepted. I have a friend, Walter Lawrence, in rooms downstairs, who has invited me several times to his family's country house in Gloucestershire. He agrees with me that if one conquers London, one conquers the whole world."

"And suffers the loss of one's own soul," said Morgan with deliberately wicked intention to provoke.

"No. Why should it be so? Even for you, wouldn't it be better to go straight to the heart rather than to be continually snapping at the heels of the Empire?"

"Are you suggesting that we should launch an attack on the center of London?"

"A moral attack, not a military one. I'm not in touch with the nationalists here so I don't know just what is happening but I suspect it's the usual inept plotting."

"Plotting but not inept this time."

"I'm no fighter in your sense. Perhaps I take after my father in that. If you succeed, you're going to need fighters of another kind, politicians, and parliamentarians."

"We'll have them."

"Good. At the moment Ireland is a backwater. Nothing ever happens there. You could drift your whole life away and never have lived at all. We're like cows in a field, munching our day's grass here and there and swishing off the flies from time to time to keep things interesting."

"Some people have pretty big flies to swish off—famine, emigration, disease, eviction."

"I'm speaking of the educated classes," said James blandly. "The poor are another problem. I haven't been in Dublin except when I was passing through but I don't think I should care to settle there. I like to be really near the sources of preferment so that I can make my own impression instead of having it made for me by friends, however willing."

Only a few years had made this change. His parentage could account for it, the man of learning, whose capitals were Athens and Rome, and the daughter of a landlord, small but absolute in his power. James's accent had become anglicized, an easy imposition on his already clear articulation. He would never look ridiculous in spite of his small size. Morgan was impressed with his alertness and was rather glad to be accepted by him as a member of the same class. This was what made James speak his mind so honestly.

He asked, "What are you studying in Paris, Morgan? Medicine? I've heard there are lots of medical students there from Ireland."

"No. I'm not studying medicine but I know several who are. I'm studying to be a teacher. There are classes at the Sorbonne. Martin pays for all. When we were in the attic in Moycullen, I never thought I'd reach Paris."

"How did Mr. Wilson's French serve you?"

Mr. Wilson was the traveling teacher of French who had spent a month at Moycullen twice a year, pounding the thirty-two tenses in French grammar into the heads and tails of Master Fahy's pupils.

"Surprisingly well," Morgan said. "I'm told I have a good grasp of the grammar. The accent comes in time."

"Do you know, I never really believed in the existence of that language at all," said James. "It was like learning longer and longer formulas that had to be absorbed but were never going to be put to use. Any day now, they may come in useful, of course. Do you like Paris?"

"Very much." And he could not forbear from mentioning that Alice and Samuel were coming for a holiday.

"I'm delighted. Alice was very good to me when I was an ignorant, self-absorbed boy cluttering up her house. Samuel was always good to everyone."

Morgan admired this detached criticism of himself that James had achieved. He seemed almost to be speaking of another person. London really had done him good.

On an impulse Morgan said, "Why don't you come to Paris sometime?"

"At the moment I go to the hospital every day for clinics. That ties me down. I'd like to go to Paris, indeed. The political situation there is most interesting."

"What about the medical schools?"

"Less so, to me," James said. "Watching the mess in Ireland gives us all an interest in politics, I suppose. I doubt if I'll ever be able to keep out of them."

Morgan's visit had a deep effect on James. He stayed perched on the curb for a long time afterward. He had always known that Morgan was intelligent but he had not thought it possible that he could have made himself over to the extent that he had done. Perhaps it was a special faculty of Irish people. It was well to be reminded of Ireland from time to time. The scholarship that had taken him to London would run out this year and then he would have to work. He could not take any more patronage from Samuel and deeply ingrained in James was the conviction that working for fees represented degradation. Besides, he had found that he did not enjoy the practice of medicine. The dirt and darkness of the hospitals distressed him, as did the diseased bodies on which he had to operate. He had never become accustomed to the sight of blood since the day when he had been sick while his father was digging the bullets out of Martin's leg.

James had observed in Walter Lawrence's family that one made little contact with upper-class people in the medical profession unless one became a fashionable doctor. Even then, while the doctor was admitted as an equal, the fact that he was paid a fee resulted in a slight loss of dignity or independence for him. He had thought of going to India, where many a young man had proved that you could forge ahead, but one could easily get lost there too.

With perception heightened by Morgan's visit, James decided to take the bold step of giving up medicine altogether. He tried out his notion on Charles Murphy that very evening but Charles was muddleheaded from a party and could contribute nothing. Being abstemious, James slept well.

In the morning he rose at seven. The winter darkness did not dismay him. He took a cold bath, folding his little body neatly into the tin hip bath for a few excruciating minutes. While he rubbed himself briskly dry, whole sentences of the letter he planned to write formed themselves in his mind. In writing he had inherited some of his father's old-fashioned turns of phrase. Since he was unaware of their source, he was able to make use of them now. Before eight o'clock he was sitting at his desk with clean paper in front of him.

The letter was long, more than four pages of his small, neat, perfectly formed handwriting. It was necessary, he explained, to write a long letter in order to make clear why his application could not go through the normal channels, but had to be addressed directly to Lord Granville himself. The Lord President of the Council would understand and sympathize with the special difficulties of an Irishman in a country that while not being foreign was still strange to him. He could see by his curriculum vitae and recommendations that what James was offering was no small service, in fact his life's work, to a country that held the admiration of the civilized world and in which James would be proud to play a small part at first. He looked long at the "at first" and then decided to leave it in.

James wanted Lord Granville to get him a job, however

156

small, in the Civil Service, but he enclosed this request in delightful wrappings. The Lord President must have felt as one does with a Christmas parcel, that half of the pleasure is in the glowing, flowery cover. Whatever the reason, the complacency of James with his letter was justified. Twenty-four hours later, while Morgan was on the packet boat for Boulogne, a letter was brought to James by special messenger, asking him to call at Downing Street at two o'clock.

Now he experienced a sense of shock, as one might when after an elaborate ceremony the summoned devil actually appears. He stood holding the letter for quite five minutes, as still as a lizard on a wall. He had a good suit. Murphy had already gone out. His hair was recently trimmed. His boots were new. Walter's mother had given him a cravat in excellent taste. English people preferred small to large men. His father was safe in Moycullen.

He straightened his shoulders and slowly expanded his little chest. His letter had made the proper impression, then. The world was before him, as he had arranged. It was barely ten o'clock. With four hours in hand, he spent the time before luncheon in tidying away his medical books.

When Charles Murphy came back from the hospital in the evening he said, "You sent no excuse. The professor was sounding off about people who neglect their classes. You'll catch it tomorrow."

"Tomorrow?" said James, with a satisfied smile that added years to his age. "I won't be there tomorrow either. Next week I start work in the Privy Council Office."

"What!"

"Why not? Medicine turns my stomach. I've finished with it forever. I told you about it the other night but you took no notice."

"You can't be finished with medicine."

"Why not?"

"You're a doctor, within months of your finals. It's your profession—you've spent years at it. Your family—"

"I have no family," James said coolly. "Very few people are as independent as I am. I hate medicine. I hate doctors. I hate professors. Why should I endure them for the rest of my life? I'm moving into a new world. I've got my foot in and my patron is the Lord President of the Council. You'll see, I'll suffer nothing by my courage. I'd much prefer a small post in a Government office, with prospects of improvement."

"What prospects?"

"They're infinite."

Charles Murphy looked at him in awe. Charles was a tall, gangling young man who would fill out in later life to the shape of a successful doctor. His father's shop in Croom was busy all day that he might qualify himself to earn a thousand pounds a year. His sisters and his mother drove harder and harder bargains, all for him. He knew it, and that it shackled him. James was free, it was true. For the first time in his life, Charles considered how freedom could be used. He seized little James by the shoulders, for after all he was fond of him, and whirled him around the room.

"By God, James, you're a new man. Now all you need is a rich wife."

23

Samuel did go to work, and within a month of Morgan's departure he and Alice were installed in a hotel near the Sorbonne. It was a small hotel but they had two good rooms, a sitting room and a bedroom, and Samuel said he wanted to be as near as possible to Morgan so that they could see him every day.

Alice knew very little of Samuel's youth. He did not speak of it much and with her lack of experience it had been impossible to fill in details that would have made a clear picture. Now she found that he had been to Paris as a young man and knew it rather well. It had been some kind of grand tour, and Jerome Burke, of all people, had been with him.

"It's almost our only point of contact now," Samuel said. "It's probably why we've never fallen out. Once you've shared an experience like that with someone, he has a right to your friendship afterward. Times when I've wanted to pitch Jerome to the devil, I've remembered sitting with him in a restaurant here, or walking in the Bois de Boulogne, or boating on the Seine, or a wonderful trip we made to Blois. I saw a side of him then that has almost disappeared. That's why I dislike Lydia so much. She put a limit on him, for her own purposes. Such silly purposes, too—social success and parties and cutting a dash, even when there was such revolting poverty all around her."

"Why did he give in to her?" Alice asked. "He's no man."

"I don't think he gave in easily but he has a sense of duty to her and she plays on that. Did you ever notice how she pretends to be helpless? That always works with Jerome. His mother had the same trick. It's useful. You never do it."

He gave her one of those long looks that always alarmed her with their suggestion of coming demands on her strength.

She said, "I'm not weak."

"No. I doubt if Lydia is either but one never knows with a carefully trained woman. Most men don't understand the tricks. That's why I love you, Alice, because you never stoop to them, even if you know them."

"God help you, Samuel, no one could live up to your notion of me!"

"You do," he said with the same long look.

"Perhaps Lydia really is weak," Alice suggested.

But Samuel said, "I doubt it very much. Jerome was never the master of his own house. She even used the children against him."

Perhaps this was why he showed so little affection for the children. Alice had thought it was a kind of convention, to cover up feelings that he would have thought unmanly.

Samuel said, "Marriage shouldn't make such enormous changes—it should develop what's there already. A cheerful man, as Jerome was, shouldn't become irritable. If he does, one must conclude that he has made a bad marriage. I can't resist preaching to you, Alice, you look so receptive. It makes me feel powerful and wise."

"So you are!"

"Now you're laughing at me."

"It's the commonest revenge women take on men who bully them."

"Do I bully you?"

"Of course."

Though Morgan was waiting in the sitting room while they prepared to go out to dinner together, Samuel took her in his arms and murmured in her ear as he so often did, "Thank God for you, Alice."

She had to smooth her hair again and she sent him out to chat with Morgan until she was ready. Watching her flushed face in the glass she knew why she was so happy this evening. It was for Morgan, who had shown in the one day that they had spent in Paris together that he had moved into a different world. In Moycullen this had seemed to be so but the confirmation of it was clearly there in Paris. He was no longer the passionate boy she had known. Except on the first evening in Moycullen, they had not been alone together and she had no way of knowing what he expected of her now, or even if he expected anything at all. Perhaps the years of torment that she had suffered for him had been unnecessary after all. She felt a leap of anger against him for this but knew it was nonsensical.

When she appeared in the sitting room, Morgan kissed her hand and bowed low, saying, "We've had to adopt French manners. Master Fahy would be pleased."

They dined in a restaurant near the Panthéon where Morgan said the students often went. It was a cheap place with plain food.

"I want you to see how we live here," Morgan said, "though it's hard on Samuel."

Samuel said he was quite happy and seemed to dislike the apology, so that Alice wished Morgan had not made it. She must tell him later not to mention Samuel's wealth since he did not like it. Indeed, she did not like it herself. Since she had come to Paris she had been oppressed by memories of Ireland and the life they lived there. Though France had just come through a revolution, though the city was being rebuilt, though there was poverty all around them wherever they walked or rode, still this was abounding wealth by comparison with the stark starvation in Ireland. Here the poor lived in tenements that would have been palaces to Irish countrymen. No one seemed to fear that the roof would be knocked in over the heads of himself and his family. no children screamed and wailed with hunger. Being poor did not mean you had no right to live. Remembering the fate of the people of Castlebar and Ballinrobe whose houses had been leveled by the Earl of Lucan since she had come to live at Moycullen, Alice was amazed at the stability of this prosperous city. It was easy to see how generations of Irishmen had found hope in France, how the songs and ballads told of help coming over the sea.

She glanced again with sudden uneasiness at Morgan. Was he teasing Samuel? Morgan was sitting upright, looking so clean and bright and clever and so fully in charge of himself that it was hard to believe he would make a remark that might offend. Neither of them was looking at her and she felt helpless between them.

Samuel said, "Tomorrow night, then, we'll dine at the Café de Paris. Since you are in Paris, it would be well to see all sides of it."

"Thank you," said Morgan coolly. "That would be very nice."

Then they seemed to call a truce. She sat quietly, afraid to call attention to herself until they had relaxed, but then they became fidgety, twitching and turning nervously on the benches to watch the people come and go in the restaurant. There was a great deal of noise. The glass of the windows was misted with the November cold outside. In the room it was hot and smelled of all the meals that had been eaten there for years. The floor under their feet was soft with dirt and the painted walls were stained and rubbed by the bodies of the customers and by their sweaty hands. Each time the swing doors opened, a sweet flow of fresh air came in to keep them alive until the next customer came or went. Morgan had chosen a table near the door for this reason. Alice needed that air, though once she had been content to live and sleep cramped in tiny rooms with eleven other people, even drawing strength from their closeness, feeling it as a support. It would have been good to talk to Morgan about these things but now she was afraid that they would never again be alone together, and it was too old a memory to be shared with Samuel.

When they had eaten a strange-tasting stew and had finished the wine, Samuel said lightly, "Do you think we might walk home? Morgan and I could smoke a cigar on the way."

It was only three streets away, not far enough at all for Alice. She said, "Couldn't we walk down to the river? It's not too cold."

It was one of those nights when autumn seems to come back briefly, as a reminder that winter is not yet all-powerful. There was a full moon, lighting up the sleeping barges on the river and making the black mass of the Ile de la Cité glitter in all its dark windows. Where lamps were lit in the houses, the dim yellow color glowed with an extra warmth by contrast with the cold moonlight. There were few carriages because it was too early for people coming from the theaters. Samuel took Alice's arm in his. At his touch, her hand moved instinctively to Morgan's arm and stopped just in time. Samuel did not have his cigar, knowing that one does not smoke with a lady on one's arm, but Morgan did and the smoke came with them in a sweet little cloud that ever afterwards was part of her memory of Paris. It intoxicated her, filling her with a passionate wish that by some magic trick this moment of communion might never end. No detail of this night was to be forgotten, the shining water reflecting the moonlight and the cold air on her face, and above all the closeness of love.

Samuel said, "I'd like to send James here for a while. You said you have some friends at the École de Médecine. Perhaps he could go there."

"Yes, Kevin O'Doherty has just come. He's back from Van Diemen's Land after six years' transportation. He's not allowed to live in Ireland. I was at his wedding in London in August. His wife is Mary Anne Kelly, a neighbor of your own from the far side of the lake, Lisdonagh. And John O'Leary is here too. He's a cousin of Mary Anne's. He knew James in the medical school in Galway."

"Has he been in prison too? I think I heard he was."

"Not so far."

"James doesn't like sedition. Perhaps he had better stay in London."

The walk downhill had been easy but for the return they took a cab. They went first to Morgan's lodgings, which were in a tall house at right angles to the street, with a walled garden. When Morgan opened the wicket gate and went inside, though she knew she would see him tomorrow, Alice felt a sensation of total loss. It was as if the closing of that little gate closed off her blood supply.

24

There was something wild in the air of Paris that made Alice want to break free of all the ties that held her life together. It was mixed up with a growing terror in her that she was losing the small amount of contentment she had had in Moycullen. Being close to Morgan was agony, especially when he took her hand to help her into a cab or when she sat between him and Samuel at the Opéra. The rough cloth of his sleeve against her bare arm was delightful at first and then filled her with such excitement that she could scarcely bear to be still. How could she have been such a fool as to think she could stand this? It was true what Morgan had said, that to be taken by Samuel was a poor thing compared with the wildness and strength of himself. That was love. Any other girl in Cappagh would have known what lay in store for her if she left her true love behind and let a match be made for her.

Poor Samuel was not to blame. He was a fine man, a real man, who had his passions too and had shared them with her. It was because of this that she was feeling now this far greater passion for a far wilder man. And there the final revelation burst upon her, filling her with pride and shame: she had been chosen as his wife by a fine gentleman, dressed like a lady, taken to great houses, loved and admired, and at the end of it all she was still Alice MacDonagh from Cappagh, the daughter of the tallywoman, longing for the love of her own kind. If Samuel had any least inkling of this, if he guessed at the thoughts that raced through her mind during his lovemaking, he had never shown it. On the contrary, when they left a ball or a luncheon or a dinner party at one of the neighboring great houses, he always said she was the best-looking, the most intelligent, the most spirited woman there. That was a great word of his—spirited.

She might have let Morgan and Paris wear out their grip on her if Samuel had not fallen ill. He had food poisoning, the doctor said, and he dosed him with opium. He had not got it in the dirty student restaurant but in the Café de Paris, where they had dined with Morgan the evening before. The lobster had had a bad taste. Alice and Morgan had refused theirs, the experts, after one bite. Samuel spent a day of agony and by evening had only begun to recover. This was the evening that Morgan had promised to take them to the house of John Leonard, an Irishman living in Paris who lectured at the Sorbonne and who Morgan said liked to meet all the Irish who came to the city to study or visit.

"Morgan will take you there, Alice," Samuel said. "There's no need to stay with me. You've never been to Paris before and heaven knows when we'll get here again with the way things are at home. Go out and enjoy yourself."

"I'd rather stay with you in case you need something later."

"Nonsense," Samuel said. "What could I need that the hotel servants can't get for me? Why should you spend a dull evening here when you could be out enjoying yourself? Don't be such a hen. I'll probably sleep, in any case. I'm exhausted by this illness."

He looked it, indeed. His angular face seemed thinner than ever and with a shiver she saw what he would look like when he would be old. Disgusted with herself she pushed this vision from her and said, "Very well, then. I'll go with Morgan."

She saw the exultation in Morgan's face the moment he found that they were to be alone. Still they had to go to John Leonard's house and explain Samuel's absence and sit for the whole evening in the company as if they had nothing to hide.

Alice soon realized that they were plotting revolution in Ireland and had been at it for more than two years.

A heavy-faced man named Michael Duffy, just returned from America, said, "It's not a chance to be lost. England's trouble with Russia is Ireland's opportunity. We all know that. I've been working with John O'Mahony in America and now I'm going on to Ireland to meet James Stephens. He and Mr. Luby are traveling the country. Things are worst in the west but there's a good spirit there. Men fight well when their backs are to the wall. You must have seen a lot of that mush that's being written but it's no harm—no one will believe there are guns in the background. That's what we believe in, in America. We can't sit back getting fat and comfortable while the men at home pay for all. We'll need people like you, Mrs. Flaherty. Will you be afraid?"

Alice saw gentle Mrs. O'Doherty's eyes on her and said, "Of course I'll be afraid but that won't stop me."

"I'm sorry your husband is not here," Duffy said, "though I'm not sure we could talk so freely if he were. He's a good man. We have none of his class in the Brotherhood but we need friends like Mr. Flaherty."

"The Brotherhood? What is that?"

"The Fenian Brotherhood. Hasn't Morgan told you about it?"

"I haven't had a chance," Morgan said. "James Stephens calls it the Irish Republican Brotherhood. The Americans like a more romantic name. Isn't that so, Michael?"

"John O'Mahony christened it that," Duffy said. "I suppose it is a bit romantic. Not much romance about James Stephens. He says we're always dreaming about ancient Greece and Rome. He's not having any of that this time. He's all for army discipline, army methods, well-drilled men who are trained to come out and fight at the call of the trumpet. That takes discipline—most people sneak off home at the hour of danger."

"Have you an oath?"

"Yes, but Stephens says a man who needs to be sworn to loyalty isn't worth having." He chuckled, an unexpectedly warm sound. "It's proved by his plan of enrolling Irishmen in the British Army into the Brotherhood. He's banking a lot on that part of the plan."

The host, John Leonard, said sardonically, "There is trouble with the clergy, of course, and there will be more when they hear about the oath. They'll come in on the winning side later."

"Can you be sure of that?" Alice asked.

"That's Stephens' view, and he's conveniently outside the problem, not being a Catholic. If he's right, then it's only a question of waiting."

Alice said, "So long as God is not down on us, the priests can do as they like. They're frightened for the people and no wonder." Then it occurred to her to ask, "Does Father Ned Kenny know all this? What does he think of it?"

"He's reliable, as usual," Morgan said. "In a way he's like the Army members—he's fighting with a halter around his neck—and of course he makes one less in the ranks of the enemy."

Quietly Alice listened while they discussed the details of the new Brotherhood. James Stephens, whom they seemed to respect but not like, was the chief organizer. He was assisted by a council of four, one for each province of Ireland, who were known as the V's, or Head Centers. Each V organized his own province, searching out men of some education and influence who could be trusted. A great many national school teachers had joined and it seemed strange to Alice that the commercial travelers were also said to be very useful. In the wilds of Connacht they were few and far between. Traveling hucksters were more usual, with a cardboard case full of oleographs of the Holy Family and miserable rags of clothes that seemed always the same. Alice bought pinafores for the children and aprons for the servants and anything else that looked remotely useful. The travelers often ate and slept at Moycullen House, looking hungrily at the food, as if they expected never to see another bite. Samuel had given instructions to Kate that they were always to be given a parcel of food to take along with them when they left. In the less poor parts of the country, a commercial traveler was well dressed and traveled by train or Bianconi car, looking so sure of himself that the authorities did not molest him.

The second grade of Brotherhood organizer was called a Center, or an A. When one of these was selected, the V sounded him on his willingness to risk his life and property for Ireland. If he were satisfactory in this, he was shown the V's credentials and sworn in, with no one present but the two of them. He swore to withdraw all allegiance from the British monarch and be faithful to the Irish republic and keep all the secrets of the Brotherhood and be ready to take up arms at a moment's notice. Then he set out to select his captains, who were called B's. They were sworn in separately in the same way, so that if anyone turned informer he could bring no evidence except his own word. Next the B's swore in C's, who were to be sergeants, and the C's swore in D's who were the privates. The D's were to assemble twice a week with their C for drill with arms.

The plans were so coordinated and clear that Alice had to

believe they would succeed. Michael Duffy was impressive, used to success. Kevin O'Doherty had proved his capacity for endurance with his six years in Van Diemen's Land. He was well educated and so was his wife, who wrote for *The Nation* newspaper. John O'Leary, a thin, rather elegant young man, seemed a little aloof from the others but they listened to his opinions with respect. One and all spoke with contempt of their effort at a rising seven years ago. Its only merit, they said, was to commemorate the fiftieth anniversary of the Rising of 1798.

Michael Duffy said to Alice, "You need to leave Ireland to get the full shock of coming back and seeing how the people are. I'm in the building trade in Boston, like a lot of the Irish. I'm in partnership with Martin Connolly. I have a good house and three square meals a day. They nearly choke me when I think of the starvation at home. To see the beggars following the carriages and the long cars, all whining and howling for a penny or a bite of food, and the hovels the people live in, with holes in the roof and damp oozing from the walls and the floor, and the animals in on top of them, and the rags they have that barely cover them—those things would make a man fight while there's the breath of life in him. John Mitchel is a quiet, scholarly sort of a man but he's never done talking about the devilry of the English landlords, taking cartloads of food out of the country, passing by the people who were dying of starvation on the roads during the famine of '47. That's what made a fighting man of him. People like yourself make things a little easier but it's only a drop in the ocean."

"How do you know what I do?"

"We know all our friends. We know who we can trust."

The look he gave her made her shiver. There seemed to be a threat in it, though it was probably not what he intended.

When she left the house with Morgan at ten o'clock, she found herself exhilarated in a new way that seemed to reach into a part of her that she had not been aware of. She wanted to dive deep into these new plans instead of doggedly and bitterly attempting the impossible task of relieving the distress of her immediate neighbors. It brought back the old problem she had faced years ago, of how to be a landlord's wife without following their traditions of meanness. Some of it had been simple. Never once had she accepted gifts of eggs and chickens and geese and turkeys and potatoes, which indeed were rarely offered nowadays because they were not there to give. Old George had accepted them in his lifetime but he had not asked for them.

In the cab she said to Morgan, "How would they have been if Samuel had been with us?"

"More cautious, as Michael said."

A tension between them silenced her. He sat rigidly, looking straight ahead. In the greenish light of passing street lamps his face looked ghostly. His neatly trimmed beard and side whiskers gave his profile a sharper look that was strange to her.

In sudden comprehension she said softly, "We're not going back to the hotel."

"No."

"Where are we going?"

"To my lodgings."

"Can we?"

The moment for indignant refusal had passed. She saw him raise his eyebrows in triumphant amusement.

He said, "Yes. At this hour there's no one about."

He did not touch her and she was glad of it. Her hands were hot and shaking. She was glad of the darkness and resented the rhythmic flashes of light as the smoothly running cab passed by the lampposts. Time went much too fast. She could open the cab door now and spring out or she could wait until they reached Morgan's lodgings and then firmly walk away. In the presence of the cabman he could not prevent her. That would be to make a scene, however. Much better to go inside with him for a few minutes, or she could ask him now to take her back to her hotel. It was not far. He could easily redirect the cabman.

But he was obviously a member of the Fenian Brotherhood. She would go back to Moycullen and he would take up his work of organization. He would be arrested and she would never see him again. The visit to Paris was nearly ended in any case. Even if he were not arrested, she would not see him for a long time. Ellen had not prepared her for this.

While Morgan paid off the cab, she stood quietly on the pavement. With her head bent, she waited while he opened the wicket gate and stood aside to let her pass into the walled garden, faintly lit by the street lamp outside. The windows of the house were dark. He opened the door with his key and then at last he took her hand to lead her inside. A single candle burned on the table in the hall. She let herself be led up the stairs to his room on the second floor, where he lit two candles in cheap brass candlesticks on the mantel. It was a poorly furnished room with a carpet worn down to the canvas, a uniform brown. Two leather-covered chairs and a rickety round table stood by the window. A massive bed with carved oak ends filled the corner behind the door. The table was littered with books and papers.

Alice stood with her back to the closed door. Halfway across the room, Morgan turned around to face her. His look of determination alarmed her.

She said, "Morgan, I didn't want to quarrel with you in the cab. This won't do. We're not children."

"That's the truest word you ever said. We're not children. We can do as we please."

"What about Samuel?"

"You don't love Samuel. You love me. I know it, if you never told me. I've waited for four years for you, since that last night in Aran. You can't deny me now." He came toward her, not touching her, and she felt herself begin to burn with longing for him. Very softly he asked, "Are you happy with Samuel?"

"Who is happy in Ireland? I live, and that's enough for me."

"It's not enough for you. It's as good as being dead. Alice, you're just as I imagined you all the years I was away. Now you're here with me and you have no good to say to me."

"I shouldn't be here."

But she knew he could overcome her with a look and a few words. Suddenly the miseries of the last four years seemed to come together to overwhelm her and she held out her arms to him. The moment was enough, the utter joy of possessing Morgan and of knowing the power and depth of his love for her.

Samuel was asleep when she got back to the hotel. He looked like a dead man, lying on his back, drugged with the opium which had taken all the natural color from his skin. She crept into bed and lay beside him, illogically, ridiculously happy, wide awake and aware of the extraordinary things that had happened to her. Not a soul had seen her come and go from Morgan's lodgings. It was like a house of dead people. They all went to bed early, Morgan said, exhausted from overwork and bad food and their own tiresome minds. He did not like the impoverished French aristocrats who had gravitated to this miserable house. How many of them were genuine aristocrats and how many were shams was a question. The owner of the house, a fat, blowzy woman with a mechanical urge for making and keeping money, lived at the top of the house. If she had heard Alice leave, she would take no interest.

"She gives the cheapest dinner in Paris," Morgan said. "John O'Leary and the O'Dohertys and several other medical students come here for dinner every day. It's not bad. You can live on it, at least."

Morgan walked with her to the corner and hailed a passing cab and accompanied her to the hotel. They leaned back, shoulder to shoulder, in perfect companionship, their hands locked together. She remembered her fearful grief when he had left her in Aran.

"I was ill for several days," she told him now. "Poor Ellen was frantic. I could give her no idea of the reason."

"And still you went ahead and married Samuel."

"I had promised. Samuel loves me. I can never leave him— I'm his whole life now. He would be disgraced and laughed at but I'm not thinking of that. Going to bed with you is wrong but it's nothing to the wrong it would be to leave Samuel."

"How will you bear it?"

She had spoken quickly, not knowing how he would take her statement, and she was relieved at the reasonable tone of his reply.

"I don't know. I don't know anything. It's another world. I thought you might have turned against me. That was the worst of all."

"I could never do that."

Lying in bed now, Alice relived every moment of the evening, from the moment of Morgan's arrival to the final fulfillment. The squalid room where he lodged took on the appearance of a paradise. The voices of the other people at John Leonard's house faded into nothing. Only Morgan's voice rang, every word precious, every word remembered as if it had a special value. The new force that he had given her spun through her body, so that it seemed, ridiculously, as if it would be a logical thing to devote the rest of her life to renewing and remembering it. This was happiness indeed. Tomorrow she would see him again. For the moment that was enough.

Just before she blew out the candle, Samuel whimpered with pain in his sleep.

PART
THREE

25

James loved his work at the Privy Council Office. He sat at a big desk with three other clerks in a heavenly room with a thick carpet and a huge coal fire that was stoked by men in overalls several times a day. He learned to pretend not to notice these servants, though he quickly knew them all one from another. He kept his back straight as he sat at his desk and made a point of not answering at once when he was spoken to. Still he knew that the others liked him. They teased him about being Irish and even maddeningly imitated his accent sometimes, but it was all very gentlemanly and clean compared with the raucous, smelly students and patients he had left at the hospital.

Walking briskly to work every morning to keep fit, he planned the first things he would say when he reached the office.

"Good morning, Jones. Nice brisk morning. Ah, fine fire they give us—keep themselves comfortable, too, you may be sure."

Sometimes he saw the Secretary of State for Foreign Affairs arrive in a cab, or the President of the Board of Trade. They used the Downing Street entrance, too, and it was a thrilling business to stand aside and let them go up the stairs before him. Once he saw his patron, Lord Granville, the Lord President of the Council, step out of his carriage. James felt suddenly shy and wanted to run but the great man did not turn his head at all. Lord Granville came to look at him one day, however. The office door opened and there he was. He glanced around sharply and asked, "Which of you is Fahy?"

"I, sir," said James, leaping to his feet and walking a step forward.

Lord Granville looked him up and down with an amused expression and said, "Ah. Do you like it here? Better than doctoring?"

"Much better, sir."

He had to lift his chin to look up into Lord Granville's face. It was full of interest and kindness.

He said boldly, "I like seeing how the Empire is run, sir. It's very interesting."

"So it is, my boy. With that attitude, you'll go far. Keep to your work."

"Yes, sir."

The other three clerks were astonished.

Jones said, "You didn't tell us you're a doctor."

"It didn't arise," James said. "I was glad to leave it. I don't care to talk about it."

"Thrown out, were you?"

This was Middleton, of course, who was always joking.

James said cheerfully, "Not at all. I just like it better here."

"Doctors don't have to live on eighty pounds a year," Jones said.

"Living on a scholarship teaches one to manage. Besides, one is always progressing. We won't always have to live on so little."

"Obviously *you* won't, with the Lord President taking an interest."

At home, in the rooms he still shared with Murphy, James was bubbling with excitement in the evening. Murphy was out and he had to tell someone. He went downstairs to talk to Walter Lawrence.

"Perhaps I'm building too much on it," he said, "but he seemed so kind and good."

"It's a good sign," Walter said. "You'll get on, with someone like that to see to you. But you must apply yourself to getting more and more education. That's what will count in the end. Work steadily and you'll make progress."

James trusted Walter. It was good to be able to talk freely, at least to one person.

He said, "I've always worked steadily but it was in the wrong direction. On my first day in the medical school in Galway, we were taken to the hospital and had to stand by watching while the professor tore the tonsils out of a screaming islandman. I should have deserted that day but I went back like a sheep and had a go at some tonsils myself a few days later. No one pressed me to do it but I had made the choice so firmly that I was ashamed to retract. I felt that if I did, I'd never be able to handle my father."

"Even I can't handle my father," said Walter, "though we don't bother each other much. You Irish are odd about that—always wanting to do the right thing, I suppose. You need to be independent. You should qualify yourself in another way. Why don't you read for a degree in law? That's extremely useful and it's sure to be noticed in the right places. I'll get you some useful invitations, too."

Inside a month, James had left Charles Murphy behind and had gone to live in rooms in the Middle Temple. They were very cheap but still he blessed his small appetite, which he had once thought would be a drawback. He had to stay inside almost every night to study but he did not mind that in the least. Just living there was such a pleasure, and when he invited the clerks from the office or other students to come and drink a glass of punch, he felt himself quite able for them. He never spoke to them without planning it carefully in advance since he had noticed that even the cleverest people can say foolish things at times.

James had never forgotten what Charles Murphy had said about getting a rich wife. There was nothing disgraceful in the idea, as he could easily tell by the way that the girls were shown off at balls and receptions. Walter had got him invitations to some of these, as he had promised, and the law students who came from good families did so too. He saw that the mothers approved of him for his nice appearance and his good accent. He found out to his surprise that his work gave him prestige, and he was careful not to mention that he spent his days in copying letters. Perhaps they knew but were not interested, since what mattered was that he rubbed shoulders with great men who were teaching the Russians a lesson in the Crimea. No one seemed to care quite what that lesson was. A general sense of the power of the Empire had raised the tension in a delightful way.

It was Middleton of all people who introduced him to Lavinia Taylor. Usually James avoided Middleton at receptions because he tended to talk shop, and in any case it looked bad for two very young men to stand together as if they needed each other's support—almost as bad as when girls stood together.

This particular reception was part of the Christmas round, though it was well into January of 1856. It was in Hamilton Terrace, at the town house of a duke, and James had been nervous enough without having the strain of finding Middleton waiting for him, looking eagerly toward the door and pouncing as soon as James had finished greeting the duchess. It had been bad enough to hear his name called out by the servant at the door.

"Mr. James Fahy!"

A silly name, with no bite in it, and he would have been more ashamed of it only that some of the other names announced were almost as bad. Middleton was lucky with his, a solid English name.

He took James's arm now and walked him across the great drawing room, saying eagerly in a low voice, "There's a delightful girl here that I want you to meet. She's with her mother, all quite proper. I like them older but she's just right for you, sweet, too, and innocent, just the thing for a modest Irishman. You'll hit it off splendidly."

"How do you know?"

"Rich, too—fifty thousand pounds, they say. That doesn't often come with looks like hers. Come, now—don't look so grudging. I know what's good for you. You're going to need a good wife if you're going to impress your fine friends. I almost wish I could have her myself but she's really not my style."

His first sight of Lavinia was an overwhelming experience for James. Two years ago, when Amy Burke was married to a Dublin lawyer, he had suffered pain so unbearable that he wondered everyone around him could not feel it too. He said not a word, since it would have made him ridiculous, but the wound was still there, a little less raw lately. Now she was here before him again, it seemed to his first astonished look, the same smooth dark hair, the same pale skin and long, curled lashes, the same sweet, small size that had been one of the things he had loved most about Amy. Lavinia was more assured, which was to be expected with her wealthy English background. She looked at him directly, holding his eyes with hers for several seconds before drooping her head in the conventional young lady's way. He had seen that she liked him, with less of the reserve that had been drilled into Amy. Middleton's words had made a sharp impression. She might be exactly right for him. After all, Disraeli had launched himself like this and no one had thought the less of him. And Mrs. Taylor was very gracious, talking to him that very first evening as if he were an old friend who had her daughter's interests at heart.

"Poor child, no father to take care of her; it all falls on me, and I'm very inadequate. There are some things that only a man can do. He left her well provided for but that's not everything. The world today is full of pitfalls for a young girl, Mr. Fahy."

And she looked at him so frankly that he knew she did not include himself among them. She was taller than Lavinia, thin and elegant in a black dress with fine lace at the neck and sleeves. Lavinia's white dress was sewn with pearls on the bodice so that her breasts were outlined gently, as in a marble statue.

"She is a very religious girl, Mr. Fahy, very spiritual, though

175

one might not think it and it's unusual in young people. She was very affected by her father's death. Ah, yes, it broke her heart, poor girl. That's why I want her to be gay now, go to all the balls, dinners, parties."

"When— How—"

James found that with this lady there was no need ever to fear embarrassment.

"How kind of you to ask, how delicate. I can see how you feel. The war, Mr. Fahy, cholera, in the Crimea. So sad, and not even the body home—the heat, even a general—"

"How dreadful!"

"Yes, very dreadful, though not everyone appreciated it as you do. I've even had friends, if you can call them friends, who said that it saved— But we all have bad friends, Mr. Fahy, don't you think? For myself it's not so important, at my age, all finished, but for Lavinia it's important, only eighteen years old, already an orphan, though we must be grateful for what we have."

"Do you intend to stay for the season?"

"Yes, we have a suite of rooms. Not like home, but for Lavinia's sake I would do anything. Poor child, she knows how I long for my quiet garden but I've persuaded her to let me make the sacrifice." She gave a quick, bright glance around the drawing room. "And London is so good for one, so cheerful, meeting people, finding old friends, it will do me good, make me forget. Do you want to take Lavinia for an ice?"

He did, and found it remarkably understanding of Mrs. Taylor to have guessed it. This first evening he brought her back to her mother almost at once but said before he left them, "May I call tomorrow evening for a short time?"

"Of course, Mr. Fahy, very glad to see you, to know you better. So crowded here one can't talk, always better at home. Lavinia will be receiving a few guests at six, Lord Burtonfield, Mr. Kingston, a few others. She'll be pleased to have you come. Lavinia!"

"Yes, Mother. Mr. Fahy, I'll be very glad to see you tomorrow."

She was so demure, so well mannered, and yet there was something else about her, a kind of repressed sparkle that suggested she would flower when she left her mother. She would never have the grand style of the duchess but then James did not want a grand wife. He was slightly offended by Middleton's question as they walked away from the house.

"Well, how did it go? Did you make a conquest?"

"Really, I couldn't say. I've only just met the girl."

"One can always tell. They say the mother is ready for anything suitable because she's a little anxious about the girl's background—something funny about the father."

This was good news indeed. Anything funny about Lavinia's father would be well balanced by Master Fahy. No harm at all to have Mrs. Taylor just a little apologetic, though he wondered what it was—not debts or gambling, with that fortune. More likely a background in trade.

He went to the hotel suite where the Taylors lived and found that he was introduced at once as a very special friend. Slightly startled at first, he quickly took advantage of this to assume that he would be asked again.

Lavinia was very sweet to him and at the second visit her mother said, "Mr. Fahy, if you would be so good as to see that everyone gets something to drink, I can look after the tea with Lavinia. Drinks for the gentlemen are so difficult with no man in the family."

She was a lot less vague at home, and Lavinia shone gently, the center of a group of charming, well-dressed young men. James watched her from all angles those first days and quickly found that he was as much in love with her as he had ever been with Amy. It was different this time, much better, easier to deal with altogether. How right he had been to leave Ireland, where social distinctions were such a burden, where land counted for everything, where one's antecedents were known back as far as Cromwell. Soon he would be able to buy an estate in Ireland, a small one, where he would spend part of the year always. Lavinia would queen it in Ireland, with her elegant clothes and her slender figure and her quiet charm. He began to wonder how soon it would be decent to declare himself. The strain of never touching her except to kiss her hand, which anyone in the company was allowed to do, was becoming unbearable. He had never touched Amy either but a lot of water had flowed under the bridge since then. Middleton had taken him to a house where the girls were accommodating and on the whole clean, and even enjoyed teaching him all about the delights of bed. It was one of the things that had helped to cure him of his obsession for Amy and he felt a certain amount of gratitude and friendship toward Middleton for the experience. Some of the other customers at the house had not liked to see one so young and innocent among them, but since he had let his beard and whiskers grow, he looked older.

Walking home in the cold winter air, his hands burned with desire for Lavinia, to feel her breasts fit neatly into them, to stroke her thighs and press her whole body close to him. His

177

agony was pure joy, with every day bringing more and more proof that she loved him too. Mrs. Taylor was so gracious.

"Lord Burtonfield and our dear friend Mr. Fahy. Of course you know each other well. Now let us have a quiet evening together; the bad weather keeps people at home, with friends, dear friends, in winter, a great pleasure. Lavinia!"

"Yes, Mother."

"Do your imitation of the Duchess of Richmond for us. Have you seen this, Lord Burtonfield? It's so amusing. Mr. Fahy has seen it. He'll tell you how amusing it is."

James chuckled and said, "It certainly is."

Lavinia raised her voice several tones and gave off a long speech exactly in the manner of the duchess greeting her guests at her own drawing-room door. During it, James did not quite feel his usual enjoyment, perhaps because Lord Burtonfield did not seem too pleased. James wondered in alarm if the duchess and he were related but he rather thought not.

When they left the house together he said, "Lavinia has such a sense of fun. When she's on her best behavior, one would never guess it."

He did not like the curl of Lord Burtonfield's lip as he answered, "She did it far too well, I thought. I don't admire that kind of fun in young ladies."

James was stricken, and he ran to Walter Lawrence with his grievance.

"Such a snob! If it had not been the duchess he would have laughed, I'm sure. And who cares what he admires in young ladies? Oh, Walter, she's divine! I'm going to ask her mother's leave tomorrow to propose to her."

26

"Be careful, James," said Walter. "You're going a little too fast."

"How can you say that? You've never even met her." James sprang to his feet in indignation and glared at his friend.

Walter lay back in his chair and said calmly, "Perhaps that's why I have such a clear view of her. From what you tell me, she leaves a lot to be desired. May I suggest to you that you draw off for a while and see what happens?"

"I might lose her."

"You might, indeed, but your head would clear. You're in too much of a hurry."

"But I love the girl."

Walter did not answer for a minute and James watched him anxiously.

Presently Walter said, "One thing you can do, indeed you must do, if you are determined to propose, and that is to stipulate that a settlement is to be drawn up at once—if she accepts you—and all Lavinia's property settled on her from the day of the marriage."

"Talk about money! I couldn't possibly—"

"You'll have to. Otherwise they'll doubt your honesty. It's always done with an heiress. Her mother will know all about it and so will her lawyer. There's nothing improper in it. After the marriage, the property will be Lavinia's and then it will descend to Lavinia's and your children. Mrs. Taylor will have been provided for. I know all about it because my parents and grandparents had marriage settlements like that."

"In that case of course I'll broach the subject. Is it my business to broach it?"

"Yes, to the mother, of course. Lavinia is too young to have to think of such things. I'm worried about you, James." Walter's expression was indeed full of doubt. "You're in this very deep, I'm afraid. Where have the new suits come from?" He put a quick hand on James's sleeve. "You don't mind my asking, I hope. You know we all care a great deal about you. My mother always asks for you when she writes."

It was a bad moment but James got over it by saying as lightly as he could manage, "I broke the habit of a lifetime and went to a Solly Cohen off Soho Square. I had to be able to take Lavinia and her mother out to the theater and the opera, send her flowers and so on, and of course there were the suits." He wriggled his shoulders in embarrassment.

Walter said, "How much?"

"Two thousand pounds."

If he had not been standing on the fender, James would have felt very small indeed and yet it was a relief to tell someone about this burden.

"What security did you give?"

"I just told him my plans and he seemed to accept that."

Walter's expression was still kindly.

"Well, it can't be helped and perhaps there is no harm done. Drop in tomorrow night and tell me how things go."

James was silent at work the next day.

179

Middleton said, "Is the mistress's eyebrow giving you pain, Fahy? Everything should be fixed up by now. Don't waste time, my boy."

James did not tell him, of course, that the fatal day had come at last. It gave him a cold, dead feeling, not at all how he should have felt, and he knew the reason was his fear of making an almighty ass of himself.

Mrs. Taylor and Lavinia were both very helpful and it was not half as bad as he had expected. Lavinia blushed and went off to her room when James asked if he might speak to her mother alone. He even thought he saw a sensitive tear and he loved her for it, so that his tongue was loosened.

Mrs. Taylor said, "Ah, yes, I thought this might happen; it has to come. Young people must have their lives, too. We must all stand aside when the time comes. Very young she is but sensible, and so spiritual, Mr. Fahy, so unusual in a young person, never misses church on Sundays. Do you go to church, Mr. Fahy?"

"Yes," James said. "Yes, indeed, as often as possible."

"With Lavinia you will always go, Mr. Fahy; she will insist on it. But of course you haven't spoken to her yet, so do, do, yes, with my leave and blessing."

And she went out of the room and sent Lavinia in. Details of this kind of behavior in the upper classes were a constant source of interest to James, who always feared that the Irish version would appear *outré* in England. Copying Samuel in everything had been a great safeguard but this time it was of no use. Lavinia's sweet, soft face unnerved him so that it was a moment before he could get his tongue to move. Tears came into his own eyes. His habit of preparing his speeches came to his aid and he felt himself regain control. A good thing too that he had stopped padding up and down just before she came into the room. In his position, he would always have to be sure that he was the master.

He took her small white hand in his and felt her press his hand as if to give him courage. In a rush of happiness he lifted her hand to his lips and kissed it firmly saying, "Miss Taylor— Lavinia—I have your mother's leave to ask you—will you be my wife?" He felt himself blush but there was no help for that. He went on quickly. "I'm only at the beginning of my career and I know we'll do well together. That's what I have to offer you—my life and my work, and I love you, Lavinia."

Now his heart was in his mouth because the name he had almost said was Amy. It had been so near that he had appeared to stammer "A— A— Lavinia!" What an escape! It brought him to his senses. Amy was gone and it really was Lavinia he wanted, not just for her fortune but because she was so sweet and pure and pretty, and could enjoy life too. She was looking up at him now with a confiding air that made his blood rise, so that he had to restrain himself from seizing her then and there.

He spoke very softly and intensely. "Lavinia, what is your answer?"

"Yes, Mr. Fahy."

Her head was down again and he decided to risk taking her in his arms. She yielded herself to him at once, unmistakably tightening her grip on him so that he knew she loved him too.

Then she said softly, "I'll send Mother in."

And she fled from the room. James walked from the door to the window twenty times before Mrs. Taylor came in. His hands and feet were burning and there was a thudding in his chest as if he had backed a winner at the races. It was a miracle —that was the only word for it. As Middleton had said in his coarse way, such a girl with such a fortune was a rare combination. Poor innocent! She probably had no idea what love was but he would take good care of her. He had learned in the last year that he did not like to have to depend on sneaking visits to low houses, where his medical knowledge made him too nervous to enjoy himself freely. The other men were careless and gay because they had never seen a bad case of syphilis or G.P.I. as James had. He knew what girls to avoid too, though it was easy to get caught before the symptoms became visible. Middleton would soon be in trouble at the rate he was going.

When he heard the door open he whirled around and saw Mrs. Taylor coming toward him with her hands out to take his. He intended to be very friendly to her always, which was the right way to act toward one's mother-in-law.

Her thin, sharp face had a skull-like smile now as she said, "Lavinia has told me everything. How lucky you are, dear James. A girl like that is not every day, so young but full of character, yes, a sweet companion to you. A loss to me but I've been expecting it for so long. Her life must come first. When do you want to have the wedding?"

She had called him James for the first time, which gave him courage to say positively, leading her to a chair and seating her, "As soon as the business details can be arranged."

She was as gracious as ever, so that he was hardly embarrassed at all. The opportunity had been perfect, prepared for it as he had been by Walter, and she seemed to know just what he was talking about when he said, "The marriage settlement must be made first. Your lawyers will insist on that and we must have patience with them." Where had that heavenly phrase come from? He was really inspired today. "As soon as you possibly can, you should ask them to draw up the documents and after that we can go ahead with—with—"

"The wedding!" she said ecstatically.

"Sounds fairly satisfactory," Walter said in the evening. "I hope I didn't offend you with my caution."

"Of course not. I know you'll be pleased when you meet her. She's everything I want in my wife."

He had three weeks of the purest happiness before Walter began to bother him again.

"Time you got after Mrs. Taylor, James. She's had lots of time to see the lawyers."

"I'm sure she has seen them," James said warmly. "She has told me several times that she's going ahead with all kinds of preparations for the wedding."

"In that case there's no harm in asking her about it."

James was very reluctant to bring up the subject again but it was indeed very important, as Walter had pointed out. Since his engagement, money seemed to flow through his pockets much faster, with flowers every morning for Lavinia and little bouquets for her and for her mother every evening before the balls and parties that seemed unending. The sooner they had the wedding, the better all round. He loved Lavinia more and more every day, especially when she treated him as a source of all wisdom, looking up at him with her large, dark eyes melting with respect and love.

Before she appeared one evening, he said to her mother, "I hope we can have the wedding quite soon. I don't see why we should wait."

"Yes, why be always in mourning. You never knew him, of course. How happy he would be, always thinking of her future, how to provide for her, such a sweet girl, lovely companion—"

"Have you been to the lawyer, then?"

"These things take time, James. We must have a little patience, as you said yourself."

Suddenly she had stopped fluttering and her look was colder, so that James was silenced.

Late that night he said to Walter, "I felt such a brute, so mercenary, too. I hate talking to a lady about money."

"She's a woman of experience," Walter said. "Did she object to your talking about it?"

"Not exactly, but I could see she didn't like it."

"It was the right thing to do," Walter said firmly. "No one can afford to be so sensitive about money. That's very Irish too, of course."

When he saw Mrs. Taylor the next evening, she was full of her old charm, warmly smiling, coming forward and laying a motherly hand on his arm.

"I hope I didn't seem lacking in understanding. I know how it is with a young man in love. Of course you must go on with the wedding. Why wait for the lawyers? Old slow coaches, so cautious. Gave you my blessing. Her father if he were alive, Lavinia too, as soon as possible, a special license at once, three or four days."

James bounded into Walter's room to tell him. Walter's reply damped but did not extinguish him.

"Rather odd behavior, I must say. She knows well that these things must be settled well in advance, just as she knows you must get a license. See how she knew that? If I were you, I'd wait. There's something fishy about the whole affair. Have you ever met anyone who knew Mr. Taylor?"

"He was a general, I believe."

"Well, I don't believe it. I never heard of a General Taylor and no one else whom I've asked has heard of him either."

"Middleton vouched for them." Now James realized that he was the only person who had done so. They live in an expensive hotel. That must prove something."

"It could prove a colossal nerve."

"I don't want to quarrel with you," James said stiffly, "but I really can't allow you to speak of my fiancée and her mother in that way."

"Sorry, old boy. I'm only thinking of your good."

James accepted the apology and invited Walter to the wedding. There was no time to send invitations to his father and to Samuel and Alice, as he would like to have done, but they would go to Ireland on their honeymoon.

27

James took his usual cold bath on the morning fixed for the wedding. It was a clean, sharp spring morning. Yesterday he had seen crocuses in the park, a little mosaic of them that had lifted his heart into the highest range of happiness. His morning suit and top hat were ready from the night before. It was his last night alone and he had made sure that Murphy knew nothing of the wedding, else he might have insisted on a bachelor party with all the lewd jokes that James disliked so much.

As he finished dressing with trembling hands, he heard the door flung open at the foot of the stairs. That would be Walter arriving. He was bringing his own brougham to take James to the church—Protestant church, which would infuriate the Irish if they knew. He twitched more sharply at his tie and settled his hat before the glass, lifting his chin and looking down his nose with narrowed eyes. A pity Walter was so tall—it would show when he stood behind him in the church. There he was now, tapping on the door.

"Good morning, James. How do you feel?"

"Splendid. All ready."

A little too hearty, perhaps, but it was early in the morning for putting on a good show. Already he seemed to smell Lavinia's special scent, to feel her soft, clinging arms around him, to see her angelic white body uncovered for him. How would he ever get through the day?

Walter took his arm.

"Come along then."

He let himself be led downstairs and out through the gardens onto the street where he saw for the first time that it was a frosty morning. Steam rose from the horse's back and its breath smoked in the still air. A pink sky glowed behind bare trees etched in stillness. The grass was stiffly white. No wonder he had shivered as he left his room.

A few men were standing about, chatting to Walter's groom, who was holding the horse. James wished there had been no one there to see them go. He felt ridiculous now in these clothes, conspicuous, obviously on his way to his wedding. One of the loungers stepped over to him, a well-dressed man who could not possibly be a tout. James gave him a passing glance and then was horrified to find that the man laid a hand on his sleeve.

"Mr. James Fahy?"

"Yes. Well?"

The man was not put off by the impatient tone. He spoke clearly, "I have a warrant here for your arrest on the order of Mr. Oswald Goldwater of James Street, Soho, for a debt to the sum of two thousand pounds. I must ask you to come along with me, quietly if you please."

"Walter, what is this?" James gasped for breath. "Walter, tell this man to go to the devil. Walter!"

But Walter said, "I'm afraid you'll have to do as he says. You have no choice, and it's better to go quietly." He turned to the man and asked very politely, "Have you a cab handy?"

"Yes, sir. Around the corner, sir."

He whistled, actually whistled, to another of the loungers, who went off around the corner and returned followed by a cab whose driver might have been at a funeral for all the interest he took. Feeling horribly humiliated, almost on the edge of tears, hating his small size, which must make him look like a boy, James climbed into the cab. The only comfort was in Walter's kindly face at the window just before they drove off and his pleasant, unruffled voice saying, "Now, don't worry, James. I'll have you out of there in no time. This is only a temporary setback—just have patience."

"What are you going to do?"

"See Mrs. Taylor, of course. It will be no trouble to her to pay Mr. Goldwater. Keep your heart up! Drive on!"

While his captor was still clumsily climbing in at the other door, the driver, recognizing the authority in Walter's voice, whipped up his horse and they were off. The man fell across James's fine, clean striped trousers and righted himself apologetically.

"Now don't take on, sir. The young gentleman will settle everything, I'm sure."

James spoke not one word on the way to the sponging house, quite close by in Cursitor Street. He was deadly afraid. This above all was the last feeling he must show, since the bailiff would despise him for it. Frozen, with his eyes fixed like a lizard's, he sat upright, with his cane between his knees, while the cab rattled and bumped through the narrow street until it stopped at the far end. A servant opened the street door as they arrived and the bailiff got out at his side and ran around to help James down.

"This way, sir. Follow the man, if you please. Is Mr. Fahy's room ready, Bennet?"

"Yes, Mr. Moss. This way, sir."

Without looking to right or left, James walked briskly into the house, which was cleaner and better furnished than he had expected. A narrow hall was almost filled by a heavy mahogany table on which was a brass bowl containing an aspidistra. Somewhere in the back, he heard a clock strike ten. A shudder went through him. He must not break down, no matter what humiliations came. He followed the servant up the thinly carpeted stairs and across a dark landing to a dark door. The room beyond was quite bright by comparison, furnished like a lodginghouse with a brass bed and chipped furniture. The sight of the bed made James shudder again and he was glad to be left alone.

As Bennet went out he said civilly, "Dinner's at two, sir. I'll call you."

He would starve before he would eat that dinner. He spent ten minutes in futile tears followed by frantic grimaces of temper, all the more exhausting for being silent. Then he sat on the bed, his hands hanging between his knees and his shoulders drooping. Samuel would be kind, as always, but he would disapprove, and Samuel's disapproval had never been suffered by James. All his life he had managed to avoid this final torture, even when he was small, enduring his father's frequent beatings without question and in silence, in the privacy of that hell over the coach house, always making a point of appearing to Samuel as a person of cool control. All of that carefully built-up reputation would be finished when Samuel heard of his adventure. Goldwater had let him down badly. He hated him for it, so fiercely that he felt ill. Why could he not have waited, as he had said he would? Six months to a year, he had said, and he had seemed quite uninterested in getting his money back before that.

James was calmed by the necessity to think it out. He got off the bed and crossed to the window to look down into the street. A man with an Irish accent was shouting the sale of turnips from a basket and a bandy-legged lively cockney had wheeled his coffee stall almost directly under the window. Rubbish lay thick in the gutters and the cobbles ran with horse manure and dirty water spilled there by the householders. The house he was in seemed the best in the street. That was not saying much. The smell was nauseating, even with the window shut, and his weak stomach began to heave. He tried lying down and felt a little better. He wanted to discover whether he was locked in the room but could not bring himself to try the door handle. A nightmare vision of the Marshalsea prison rose up before him. There the debtors lay year after year, living on charity and unable to work off their debts, until some miracle rescued them. Worst of all was the disgrace. Unless he got out of this scrape at once, he was ruined. As it was, he might have to go to India after all. That would be better than going back to Ireland, at least.

When Bennet appeared to call him to dinner, he was sitting in a chair by the window.

"Go away," he said angrily. "I don't want anything."

"Come now, sir, don't take on so. The gentlemen always feel

186

like that at first but it's no use adding to your troubles. Many a one out there hasn't a good dinner waiting."

"Go away, I said."

"Now, don't be 'asty. It's roast beef and Yorkshire, the very best," the man said in a kindly, fatherly tone.

James said grudgingly, "Thank you, but I don't feel like it."

Encouraged, Bennet said, "You'll be the better of it, sir, and all the other gentlemen likes a bit of new company. Come on, do."

But at the mention of all the other gentlemen, James had closed his eyes in horror and despair. He lay against the tall back of the chair, whose plush upholstery felt like the skin of a dead mouse touching his ears. This was how Walter found him in the middle of the afternoon. When the door handle rattled, James made no move except to open his eyes. Walter stepped quickly into the room.

"James! You're as white as a sheet. It's not the end of the world. Here, have a drop to cheer you up—a good job I thought of bringing it. Come on, now. You're going to need it."

James swallowed two mouthfuls of brandy from the cap of Walter's silver flask held to his mouth, hating the waste of time until he would hear the news.

"Well? Well?" he said impatiently.

"I was at the Taylors'." Walter turned away so that James could not see his face. "The old one rounded on me like a fishwife. She's a harridan. And she has a vocabulary that suggests she was in the Crimea herself, with the Army. She must be an intelligent woman to have covered up so well."

James cowered, knowing that Walter would have spotted at once that she was not a lady. He said nothing, afraid that his voice would reveal too much.

"I told her you had made no attempt to deceive her and that all your friends can vouch for your honesty. She said— I don't want to repeat what she said. You've had a narrow escape, James."

"I was not going to marry the mother," James said sourly.

Walter might have been offended but he seemed to be as sympathetic as ever.

"I saw Lavinia," he went on in a low voice. "She was in her wedding dress. She is really a beautiful girl, James."

"Go on, for God's sake!" James said when he stopped there.

"She had hysterics, poor child. It was a fearful scene. Her mother accused her of misleading her, of telling her that you were rich and had a big estate in Ireland. She called her a

187

scheming little bitch and Lavinia—Lavinia said the same sort of thing to her. I said the amount was so small to them that there was no need for such a scene and the mother said, 'You bloody cock, we haven't a ha'penny between us either.' "

James crouched low in the armchair, though there was no avoiding the words that fell on him like blows. Walter had turned around now and was looking at him with abominable pity, taking out the flask again and saying as he took off the cap, "I told her that it was they who had deceived you but she said you had such an air of gentility that she was sure—she was sure—" Walter stopped and then said energetically, "James, for God's sake, see the funny side of it. She said she was sure you had a huge fortune and had to conceal the fact lest you might be the prey of money-grubbing nobodies. *I* laughed at that."

James muttered, "I'd have married her with nothing." He stood up, holding the unpleasantly upholstered chair back for support. "I'll go there now and tell her so."

"You can't do that," Walter said mildly. "You won't be allowed to leave here."

James leaned over the chair, glad now of something soft to hold. Amy was snatched from him and now Lavinia. It was unbearable. He would fight it—but not today, not until he had got out of this hole. He should have run away with her but she was too much under her mother's thumb. Besides, it had not seemed necessary. She was so sweet, so innocent, so like Amy, and she loved him, too. He was certain of that. Every look she turned to him showed it, every touch of her dear little hands, every word was sweet with her love.

He accepted another mouthful of brandy and then said, "That's enough of it, Walter. Please don't give me any more. I haven't thanked you. It must have been very unpleasant for you."

"Not at all. Please don't thank me." Walter looked less anxious, as if he thought they were near the end of the affair. He said, "We've still got to get you out of here."

"I can't raise two thousand pounds."

Samuel would give it to him, but how could he possibly ask Samuel? It would be a loan, and it would take him years to pay it off, but that was nothing to the shame of having to tell Samuel what a fool he was, an Irish gambler, a fortune hunter, a cheap social climber, rightly punished for his impertinence. James did not care what his father might think of him. Samuel was the important person. Samuel and Alice, and that stinking little cur Andy, who would be sure to hear of it.

"I'll see Goldwater," Walter said. "He can withdraw the charge and let you pay him off gradually, but it can hardly be arranged before tomorrow. You'll have to spend the night here, at least. It looks clean. You're not the first of my friends who has been in here. Now do cheer up—"

"That's what the manservant said when he called me to dinner."

"Did you eat well?"

"I didn't go down at all. I had no appetite."

"Now, this won't do. It's not the end of the world."

"Have you ever been in love, Walter?"

"Of course, but I was able to live my life at the same time."

"Then you were not in love."

"James, please! You must pull yourself together. You've had a narrow escape—they're an unprincipled pair of women and they were out for your blood. Can't you see that?"

James could see it but it did not reduce the pain of his loss. Even if he had discovered that Lavinia was a street woman, he would still have loved her. It was easy to see now that she had been in this thing with her mother but she, the essential Lavinia, was still the person he loved. Long after Walter had gone away, he sat in the tall-backed chair and dreamed about her, remembered words she had spoken, heard the very tones of her voice as if she were present and worst of all felt her young, soft body in his arms where she should have been tonight.

The room darkened and the cries in the street became even louder as the evening crowds assembled. A bunch of rude boys serenaded the windows of the sponging house and threw cabbage stumps at them.

James cowered inside, until Bennet came and drew the blinds, saying, "Now, Mr. Fahy, sir, I'm bringing you a nice tray of cold beef and pickles, since you won't come down. The gentlemen are having a bit of music tonight and a game of cards. Helps to pass the time. Won't you change your mind?"

But he would not, could not, bring himself to join them. He had not the smallest curiosity about them, and he only wished to avoid them and all they stood for. It was like being asked to join a happy party of devils in hell. He found he was hungry when the tray of food came, however, and he ate most of it. Bennet made up the fire so that the room looked almost cozy. Something in his manner suggested to James that he would accept a tip, and though he knew he would miss it later, he gave him five shillings.

Bennet pocketed the money smoothly and said, "Now, don't

fret any more, sir. You'll be out of here tomorrow by noon. It's all arranged."

"What is all arranged?"

"Why, the whole thing, sir. Mr. Lawrence arranged it with Mr. Goldwater and Mr. Moss. I shouldn't tell you but I can't bear to think of you lying awake all night. Mr. Lawrence had an awful job to find Mr. Goldwater. Now don't go telling that I split on them. Mr. Lawrence is a true friend of yours. Be sure to turn out the gas before you go to sleep, sir."

By morning, James had recovered his balance. Even though it was true that Walter was his friend, James intended to keep to his resolve and marry Lavinia. What did it matter whether she had money or not? She would be an asset to any man, and they would get on somehow. He wanted her so much, he cared nothing for money or position now. He would go back to medicine and they would settle in Dublin, where Samuel, with his connections, would help him. He would look after Lavinia, since her mother had failed to do it. He felt his senses return to something like normal and even wondered at himself for having collapsed so badly yesterday. Walter had taken a great deal on himself in interfering as he had done. It was very English of him to have cared so much for the truth and for the honesty of the Taylors, and to have thought that James would be grateful for being rescued from them. James would tell him this morning that while he appreciated his actions, still he intended to continue with his plans as if nothing had happened.

But when Walter came at eleven o'clock, the first thing he said was "They've gone, cleared out."

"Who?"

"The Taylors, without paying the bill. The manager had the impertinence to ask me for your address—thinking you would pay it. I sent him off with a flea in his ear. It was his business to get his money regularly. As a matter of fact, if he had demanded it, they would have been found out long ago and you would have been saved a lot of trouble. James, please don't take it so hard. Can't you see you were being led by the nose? Honesty is the first thing any man wants, indeed needs, in his wife, else she'll deceive him after they're married as she did before. That would never do for you. James! Look at me directly."

James turned to look at Walter and saw such kindness and understanding there that he could not bring himself to hate him.

Walter said, "That's better. I've been to Mr. Goldwater, too. I have a confession to make, James. I engineered all this because I got so uneasy after what you told me about Mrs. Taylor. It was not quite straightforward but the situation seemed desperate to me. I hope you'll forgive me."

"Of course," James whispered.

"Thank you. Mr. Goldwater says he'll trust you to pay up and he's extended the time to three years, which is very generous of him."

Now James was really able to look at Walter. Anything could happen in three years. He could think of nothing to say and he had to take Walter's hand in his and press it as an indication of his trust and gratitude.

Walter said, "Now, then! The sooner we're out of here, the better."

Still in his ridiculous clothes, James sat huddled in the tall-backed chair after Walter had gone downstairs until Bennet appeared with a suit of his clothes in a portmanteau.

"Thinks of everything, Mr. Lawrence does," Bennet said.

In the cab, James asked Walter, "Where do you suppose they've gone?"

"Heaven knows. The old lady will have planned it, you may be sure. Her kind have great resources and all she has to sell is her daughter. She'll turn up at Bath or Harrogate or perhaps somewhere in Europe—Brussels or Paris. That's more likely, now that I come to think of it, because England will be too hot for her when the hotel manager gets after her."

Walter said no more but James suddenly realized that if he had been married to Lavinia, the police would actually be after him now, as an accessory. Only Walter's foresight had saved him. As they drove out of smelly Cursitor Street into broader, cleaner streets, James felt the full, conscious joy of freedom.

28.

For a long time after they got back to Ireland, Alice lived on her memories of Paris, fed on them, drew life from them in endless daydreams where Morgan seemed to be actually present with her in her room. Not once but several times she had gone to his lodgings while Samuel was ill, fully reviving her old love and all the pain that went with it. She would never leave Samuel—they both knew that—and she would pay for all this in heartbreak at home. Sometimes in a flash of terror she knew how reckless she was in reviving such painful sensations.

Samuel saw that she was miserable and he attributed it to her pregnancy. She had not told him about this before leaving home lest the trip might be put off. Now he shamed her with attentions, making her rest, spending hours with her when he should have been in Galway at the mill, bringing her presents and treating her with unending patience. She was irritable, as bad as any lady, but she managed to control it with Samuel, though not with the children. By the time the baby was born she knew that she had thoroughly estranged Anna with her constant snapping. She tried to placate the child by telling her how pleased she was to have another girl, and that soon she and the infant Julia would be able to play together, and even that she should regard Julia as her own property. For a while this was successful but Julia proved to be such an uncomfortable personality that no one would want to own her. A difficult birth, she seemed to have been born suspicious and independent. She was a replica of Alice in appearance, large blue eyes, black hair and lively ways. Her hair curled more than Alice's did and there was a flash of wildness in her that Alice did not recognize as coming from herself. If she had not known that she was already pregnant in Paris, she would have thought that this must be Morgan's child.

News of Morgan came from time to time but he did not come himself. At first Alice expected him daily. Each morning she woke up in a glow of hope that somehow she would hear from him—he would be in Galway and he would send word by the Clifden mail car or he would send a messenger on horseback. Wheels in the driveway sent an agonizing shiver through her and she had to send at once to find out who it was. She had a maid of her own now, a Moycullen girl named Barbara Folan, who had been lady's maid to Mrs. Bates until the family went finally to England. Barbara's only business was to wait on Alice, to help her dress and to brush her hair and to run messages for her. She was always in the room seconds after the bell sounded.

"Who was that?" Alice would ask in her new, querulous voice. "I heard a horse come into the yard. Go down and see who it is and come back at once."

"Yes, Miss Alice."

And Barbara would go flying down the stairs, glad to have an excuse to go to the kitchen. Lying on the drawing-room sofa or on the chaise longue in her room, Alice would twitch with impatience until the girl came back, always with a disappointing story. She preferred the upper rooms at this time because they gave a better view over the surrounding countryside.

When Julia was almost three years old, four years after the visit to Paris, Alice heard slow, tired old hooves walk around by the side of the house and knew that Mike Sherwin had come. It was a dry September afternoon and Alice had spent a depressing morning with tenants near Moycullen and down by the lake at Glann, driving herself there and back in the tub trap. In every house, someone was dying or had died, of consumption as they said resignedly, and in every house a man sat like a stone on one hob while his wife rocked in agony on the other, weeping for a lost or dying child. Young people seemed to be the easiest victims. Alice was accustomed to find that a girl of sixteen whom she had last seen blooming with health and energy was now lying despondent in a corner of the kitchen, querulously turning away from her mother's offers of goat's milk and raw eggs and other unpalatable foods that were said to be cures. Worst to see was the terror on the faces of those who still had their health. It was the same expression she had seen when she was a child, in 1847, during the great hunger. In each of the five houses she had visited today, she had been followed when she left by a boy or a girl who had said, almost in the same words, "I'm for America. If I stay here, I'll be dead inside a year. I'll come over to the house to talk about it some evening. I don't want to say it in front of the old people."

She had told them what she knew about disinfecting the houses with whitewash, as her mother had done, but they seemed to have got the idea that it was impossible to live in Ireland at all. It was safer to go where the land was free and you were paid good money for your work, and where you would get a welcome from those who had gone already. This was the greatest draw, as well as the certainty that they would be able to send money home to buy food for the winter. The potatoes were bad again this year and food must come from somewhere.

Alice had washed thoroughly when she came in, soaping her hands several times and rinsing them with a sense almost of shame at her fear of having brought home the disease. She had recovered her health by now and her step was as light and as quick as when she came to Moycullen more than eight years ago.

The new housemaid, Nellie, came into the dining room. "It's Mike Sherwin, Miss Alice, and he wants to come in here. In Ballinahinch he always stays in the kitchen."

"In Moycullen he comes into the dining room," Alice said, but kindly.

Nellie said, shocked, "Does he eat here too?"

"He eats in the kitchen and then he comes to sit in the dining room. Does he want to see me at once?"

"Yes, ma'am."

"Then send him in."

The turf fire in the dining room was immense and she was grateful for its warmth. Since she had come in she had not been able to stop shivering. When Mike came in she seated him in his usual place, in one of the huge leather chairs that were turned hospitably toward the fire.

"It's like coming home," he said, "if I had a home, to come to your house. Tell me, ma'am, is Mr. Samuel well, and the children?"

"All very well, Mike, and how are you yourself?"

"I have the rheumatics and the old pony is spun out, I'm afraid. He goes so slow now, it takes an age to travel from one house to another and we do be hours on the road in all weathers."

"I thought he was slowing up," Alice said. "We have a young one that you can take. I bought him last week from Hernons in Oughterard, a sound pony, but they want the money to send Joe to Boston. I'll have to ask Samuel."

"It would be a blessing."

"What news have you, Mike? Where were you last?"

"East Galway, where the wind never stops blowing. It's a cold, hard country, only fit for sheep and that's all that's in it now. I was in Mayo before that, out to the west. The whole country is rising, if you were to judge by that part of it. One thing after another is making the people mad—the new schools are nearly the worst at this present moment. They've brought war into every house. I suppose you have the same here in Moycullen?"

"We have Master Fahy here in the house still but I've heard the people talking about the national school. They say some of the new teachers are very cross."

"It's this new plan about teaching English. Irish is to be stamped out—the language of Raftery and Barrett and Strong Thomas Costelloe and all the poets of Munster and Ulster and Leinster as well. The worst part of it is that the fathers and mothers are playing in with the teachers. Up in Mayo the teacher hangs a tally around every child's neck and when he goes home in the evening his own father and mother are putting a little mark on it for every word of Irish he speaks. The

194

next day, doesn't the teacher count the marks and gives him a blow for every one of them, as well as a few on his own account, you may be sure. The children are driven mad with it. I was talking there last week with a few lads from Erris and they told me they have a devil of a woman there. She'll have them all with good English in a year, she says, and she has one little lad mounted on the back of another with his breeches off and she caning him until the blood flows. 'Tis madness. And the girls, too, with their bottoms bare, God help us, and she belting hell out of them in the name of education. The men teachers are worse. There's one hero has a trick of loading the boys with slates and making them stand on one leg and then he starts with the cane wherever he can get a lick. I'm thinking the parents don't know the harm they're doing. All they want is for the children to learn English for when they go to America and that's where they're going as fast as they can. The big boys and the young men are in the Fenians, all panting for guns and pikes and drums to have a go at Queen Vic."

"Are all the parents marking the tally?"

"Not all. Some of the fathers are going wild when they see the condition of their children when they come home from school, and they're sending threats to give the teachers a taste of the same, but sure they know they'll never get justice if they lay a hand on them, only jail and transportation as rebels. It's a sad country, ma'am, and getting worse every day. I'm not a man for the gun. I like a quiet life and a chat and talk by the fire and meeting old friends like yourself, but lately I'm thinking the old ways are gone forever and we might as well start fighting in earnest."

If Mike Sherwin, the careful Mike, who lived on his wits and his smooth tongue, said such violent things, what were the real men saying and doing?

"I've heard some stories like that about Moycullen and Cappagh," she said, "but the parents aren't able to fight. They're too beaten down themselves."

She filled a pipe for Mike and sat with him for more than an hour before he said at last, "I met Morgan Connolly last week over near Castlebar."

Alice started forward in her chair and then leaned back deliberately as she asked, "Was he well?"

"Never better. He's walking from one townland to the next making speeches in every shebeen and public house to get recruits for the Irish Republican Brotherhood or the Fenians or whatever they call themselves. It's a dangerous game but so far he's getting away with it. I met a man that was at one of the

195

meetings and he says Morgan is a powerful talker. He told them how the land would belong to the people instead of to the landlords, and a whole lot about France and the way they do things there, and how we'll have a republic and a parliament with an Irish name, but in the end what got the recruits was when he shouted out: 'Is every man here ready to fight for Ireland?' He got a good answer to that."

"The police will be after him," Alice said in panic.

"They will," Mike said, "but he won't be the first nor the last they're after. He has good friends and he knows how to make himself scarce."

He might come to Moycullen. She would hide him in the attic, where he would be safer than with Father Kenny, Everyone knew he was a great friend of Father Kenny's but they wouldn't expect to find him at Samuel's house. She would see him every day.

When Samuel came back he showed less than his usual patience with Mike. He let him talk on for a while and then said quite brusquely, "Time for supper. I want to talk to you, Alice."

Mike went off to the kitchen at once and Alice said, "Weren't you a bit rough with him?"

"He's used to it. I have no time for peasant manners today."

Alice looked at him in alarm and astonishment. Samuel never spoke of peasants.

"What's the matter? Has something happened?"

"Jerome Burke is leaving, going to live all the year in Dublin. He's been threatened again and this time he says he can't stand any more. I called in there on my way home and he was in the drawing room banging the fire with the poker as he's done for years and looking half mad, to tell the truth."

"You've known he was like that for a long time. How was Lydia?"

"Lydia is always the same. Where were you today?"

"I took the trap over to Glann to see how they're getting on there. It's a dreadful sight, half the people sick or dying and everyone talking of going away."

"There's no living for them there, on the side of the mountain. Did you take meal?"

"Yes. Anna Donnellan is dead and the young sister, Kathleen, is in the bed now. The mother looks as if she'll go out of her mind. You'd think she was at least seventy, but if she's Kathleen's mother she can't be much over fifty. I told them—"

She paused and Samuel said more gently, "All right, they

needn't think of the rent. They haven't paid it for three years, anyway. They kept it up longer than most. Pat Donnellan insisted, as you know, Alice."

"I know well, Samuel. You were always good to them."

"Jerome says the Irish Republican Brotherhood is growing —that thing that was founded in Dublin in March. I think that's why he's clearing out. He says the whole of the west is in it and soon they'll be burning houses and hayricks and maiming cattle again."

"I don't think that's the sort of thing they're thinking of now. Mike was talking about it before you came. It sounds more like an army to me."

"An army?"

"Yes. He says they have regular drill and they get pikes made, and guns have come from America and from the Irish in England."

"God help them, what are they going to fight?"

"The Army of England, Mike says."

"It sounds mad."

"It's not as mad as lying down under the rule of the landlords."

"Perhaps they will really kill a few landlords, if that's the way they're talking. Jerome may be right to get out while he can."

"What kind of a threat was it?"

"A letter, in very good English, he said."

"Did he show it to you?"

"No. He had given it to the police. They've promised him protection. He said it had a quotation in French that he couldn't understand, though he was able to read French well once."

Alice turned away and gazed into the fire and then absentmindedly took up a sod of turf to put on it.

"Ring the bell for Andy," Samuel said. "You'll ruin the servants if you do that kind of work yourself."

"Samuel, I'd like to get rid of Andy."

"Why? In a way he's the best servant we have. He's always on hand and he keeps an eye on the whole household, though he's not a trained butler. Are the other servants complaining?"

"No. It's just that he's too watchful. He seems to be outside every door as I open it. I can't come in or out without his seeing me. I know he doesn't like me."

"Has he been insolent?"

"No."

"Then it doesn't matter," Samuel said irritably. "When will

you learn that it doesn't matter whether a servant likes you or not? Andy has been here since my father's time. He knows all about the house, who to let in, who to keep out. He looks after my clothes. He takes messages accurately. I don't like Andy, in fact, but I recognize his value."

"You don't have to live with him all day."

Deliberately she stood up and went to him, taking him by the arms and leaning against him. In a moment his arms were around her and he was pressing her to him, stroking her hair and her cheek, then burying his face in the hollow of her neck.

He said with a chuckle then, "Alice, I know what you're doing to me. I'd do almost anything you want but please leave me Andy a little longer. He can't do any harm in this house. We never do anything that can't be published in the whole parish."

"Then you have the same idea as I have, that he's a spy."

"He would be if there were anything to spy on, but things are so quiet now that there's nothing to fear."

"What about the threat to Jerome Burke?"

"There's nothing very new in that. He's a rotten landlord, even worse since he's been imitating Lord Lucan's antics in Castlebar—knocking every house whether the rent is paid or not and turning the people out to die on the roads. Improving the land, he calls it. I told him so today, as well as I could do safely, but it's no use now. Lord Lucan is his hero—the fine gentleman of the old school, and a military hero. He still thinks Lucan distinguished himself in the Crimea instead of making an ass of himself."

While he talked, Samuel walked jerkily around the room, picking up a book, moving a vase, arranging a curtain, while Alice watched him from the chair by the hearth. She had not rung for Andy and the fire had collapsed. The single lamp on the mantel gave a poor light in the wintry afternoon.

"Jerome will be no loss," she said. "Is he selling out?"

"He's hoping to get a buyer in Galway. It's within driving distance for a businessman. Fennell might buy it himself. I wouldn't fancy him as a neighbor." He came to sit by the dying fire, leaning his head against the tall back of the armchair. It was time for Alice to see the children before they went to bed but she made no move. "I suppose I care about Jerome's house because my father died there," he said at last. "It's not very reasonable but who is reasonable? I try to be but it's no use. If I didn't have you, Alice, there would be no sense in anything, and no reason to live at all."

29

No one could be found to buy Jerome Burke's house. Year after year it stood empty, and though Fennell came there periodically to look after it, Samuel could see how little by little it began to look deserted. Its white paint peeled and pads of grass appeared among the white gravel on the avenue. Cattle were put in to graze on the lawn and they quickly trampled the ground under the trees into a muddy morass. Sometimes Samuel crossed the fields and went through the wood to see what was happening, once finding that the cattle had broken into the flower garden by the side of the house and had browsed on Lydia's herbaceous border. This did not worry him in the least but he was distressed after an early autumn storm when he saw that the big yard gate was down, lying broken on the cobbles. That day he saw his own house in ruins, crows nesting in the chimneys, floors rotting away and the kitchen flags split by the winter frosts. He hurried home, hungry for the first sight of the lamplight and his own healthy children. Jerome's youngest two, the boy and the girl, were both sickly and long before they left Moycullen they both seemed to Samuel to have symptoms of tuberculosis.

Jerome had scorned the idea. "They're whiners, like their mother. They'll improve when I get them out of here into better company."

When Samuel had repeated this conversation to Alice she had said, "Kate told me they get the kitchen food and there's never enough. And two of the maids are sick with coughs but Jerome says they're not bad enough yet to send away. He has them on half wages because they can't do much. Lord God, Samuel, how was the likes of Jerome bred?"

The latest news was that the boy was dead and the girl was always in bed and couldn't last long. Alice wept for them, and so did Master Fahy, whose misfortune it was to love all his pupils. Samuel noticed, however, that though the servants in his own house said they were sorry and they had always liked the poor lad, there was a gleam of real pleasure in their eyes when they spoke of Jerome's loss.

On the day when he found the gate had fallen down, Samuel felt confused and angry. He sent for his own men to lift it back into place, though it was already dusk. They were sullen about it and Paddy said when they brought the horses home, "You shouldn't have touched it, Mr. Samuel. It was as good as a day's work to them to see it lying there and to know there was no one to right it."

"I couldn't bear to see it rot," Samuel said sharply.

"You nor anyone else won't be able to stop that rot, saving your presence," Paddy said. "If Mr. Burke hadn't gone of his own accord, he'd have got a helping hand some fine night."

"How do you know?"

"I hear all sorts of things."

Samuel could not question a servant on such a subject and he had to suffer his curiosity since he hesitated to question Alice either. Her easy way with the servants was sometimes an embarrassment but it meant that she knew what was going on better than he did. His father, the cold fish, had sacrificed this advantage by not marrying Mary. How could he have been such a fool as to let her go? Samuel remembered well how suddenly the life had gone out of the house, everything became disorderly and cold and dirty, bawdy jokes were told over meals, the servants began to quarrel and sometimes Samuel had come on them fighting with their fists. There had been no more of that after Alice came. The whole household seemed to sense that she would not stand for it. The women servants loved her after she got them all fitted out with crinolines, a stroke of genius that also kept Nellie Cooney, the dressmaker, busy for months.

Alice loved a new dress best of all things in the world, sharing her pleasure with Samuel in perfect confidence that he would enjoy it too. She had one that evening, ready to show him when he came back from seeing the men lift the gate. Barbara met him in the hall with a message that Miss Alice was waiting to see him in their bedroom. She was like a ship in full sail, her skirt extending for a yard at either side and at the back, making her waist look tiny.

Samuel said suspiciously, "Are your stays too tight?"

"No, no. Come and feel. You see, quite easy and natural."

The dress was made of fine blue wool, gathered closely at the waist and fitting tightly in the bodice. Alice's long neck, curved in pride to show off the dress, looked like the stalk of a flower. Samuel walked all around her in sheer delight, observing her from every angle.

She said, "Would you ever have believed that Nellie could make a dress like this? It's stiffened in the bodice and lined all through with plain silk. I love wearing it." And she twirled around as if she were at a ball.

Samuel said, "I wish I could show you off."

Alice took his hands and waltzed him around the room as she said, *"Ma tá sé in a raic, bíodh sé in a raic—cuir síos an scadán eile.* Do you know what that means, Sir Samuel?"

"No," he admitted. *"Scadán* is a herring. I've heard your father say it."

"Right. It means: 'If all is lost, all is lost—put down the other herring.' I was going to suggest that we have a party. Not our usual kind but one for the people."

"A tenants' ball?" Samuel asked with a lifted eyebrow. "I've been at some in England, with fat happy peasantry doing country dances, everyone well dressed and my lord and lady footing it with the best until six o'clock in the morning. Do you think our poor neighbors are in humor for that?"

"The worst way the people are, they like a bit of fun. I thought of having sports down by the lake. There's just time before the weather gets too cold. We could have all sorts of things—boat races and a tug of war and foot races. We could have supper for everyone and I could wear my dress and be with people we like for a change. Usually when I'm dressed up it's all spoiled because the people we're with are so horrible."

"Would you have no one but the tenants, then?"

"We could ask some of our own friends, too, and some of the nicer landlords. The Blakes, and the D'Arcys might come up the river in their boats, and we could ask the Kellys and Father Ned's brother, the one in Loughrea who hardly ever comes and the Goggins from Annadown. They have a fine boat now. And the Guinnesses, though it might be too far from Cong. Oh, Samuel, I love a party! Maybe I'm not getting old, after all."

"You'll never be old, if you live to be ninety. And if you want to have Father Ned, you'd better be careful what landlords you ask."

"Next to a party I love a fight," said Alice, but he knew she said it only to tease him.

He said in his measured way, "I hope we've reached the stage where discussion can take the place of war. I'll get Andy to see to it. We can hire a marquee in Galway and have trestle tables and benches and plenty of food for anyone who takes part in the sports. Plenty for everyone—why not?"

The day of the sports was warm and clear, with the lake as smooth as milk under a pale-blue sky. The leaves were turning, the chestnuts already curled and glowing red and orange, with patches of dark green persisting in their lower branches. Down by the lake, where the long fingers of land

201

stretched out into the water, in the early afternoon the people drew their boats in to moor them in safety on the shingle and walked through the woods to the long meadow that bordered the lake. Though his own tenants and servants and the Moycullen shopkeepers could be picked out at once by their good clothes and healthy looks, Samuel could see that the other country people were better dressed than they used to be. All the girls had bright ribbons, even if their dresses were worn, and most of the older women had clean cotton aprons over their red petticoats and faded dresses. He would ask Alice to take pieces of flowered cotton to the houses; dark blue with a pattern of small red and yellow flowers was the favorite. Alice would enjoy that. The children's pinafores were white cotton with flowers but theirs were mostly in rags, hanging unevenly and so ill-fitting that he could see they had been handed down through the whole family. Their feet were bare but it was not yet cold enough for this to matter. Indeed, it was a pleasure for them to run on the soft, smooth grass, cushioned with moss and beginning to warm in the autumn sun.

The men pleased Samuel most; they looked so much more determined than they had a few years ago. Each one as he arrived came over to him to greet him, to thank him for his hospitality and to say that it would be a great day.

Alice stood with him in her new dress, with a silver-gray woolen shawl because of the damp air. He could see how everyone admired her and he loved the courteous tones of her voice when she spoke in Irish to the Menloe and Annadown people, from the far side of the lake, who knew little English. Only Anna's behavior spoiled the warm feeling of closeness to the people. She stood by Alice, dressed in white starched cotton with a pinafore of white *broderie anglaise,* her long fair hair brushed neatly by the nurse, who kept the brush in her pocket and now and then smoothed out any hairs that were lifted in the breeze.

Samuel walked over to the nurse, who was standing at a respectful distance, and said quietly, "Better not to keep Anna too tidy. Let her run around and enjoy herself."

"Very good, sir," the nurse said disapprovingly. "But she likes to be neat—it's her nature."

He saw that Anna was looking with distaste at the poor children who were beginning to run and skip all over the field, playing tag in and out through the gathering crowd and shrieking like birds to one another. Her hand clutched Alice's skirt and she leaned against her as if she were afraid.

Samuel bent down to speak to her. "Why don't you run around with the other children? They'd like you to play with them."

She let go of her mother's skirt and moved a step or two away but a moment later she was back again with her face buried in the folds of cloth and tears of fright in her eyes. He decided to leave her, not to press her too hard, but it worried him that she had no wish at all to be with the other children. It was a small problem and he soon forgot it as he moved through the crowds. The marquee was up and the tables were erected and Kate was already carving cold bacon onto her biggest dishes. She covered the dishes with sheets then because supper was not to be until five o'clock, after the games.

He spoke with Kate for a moment and then went to where Andy was putting up a winning post for the foot races. Thomas and Julia were with him, shrieking advice at him until he turned in exasperation as Samuel approached and said sharply, "For pity's sake, will you stand out of the way!"

They scattered from Samuel, pretending to be afraid of him, though they were not at all.

Andy straightened up and said, "That will do. You'll have trouble today, sir, as I was telling you."

"What kind of trouble? Everyone looks very happy to me."

"Fennell came, after all."

"He wasn't invited."

"Who is to know that? I suppose he thought he'd need no invitation."

Samuel frowned, sorry that he had answered so fast, aware that Andy was watching him. It had not occurred to him that Fennell would come without an invitation. He must know how he was hated, as the agent of several other absentee landlords in the district besides Jerome Burke. The people held him directly responsible for the evictions and arrests and cattle drivings that had taken place since the owners of the estates had gone away. Samuel moved off to look for him, rehearsing how to explain politely that he should not have come.

The boat races were being started from the lake shore, seven boats, every one of them made from Samuel's timber in the workshop at Moycullen House. They were lighter than the Annadown boats, more suitable for fishing and certainly more capable of racing. Two oarsmen had a pair of oars in each. Master Fahy was the starter, walking up and down excitedly as he examined the boats, limping slightly from a rheumatic hip. He had an old brass-mounted pistol, loaded with a blank cartridge by Samuel himself, and the men were teasing him about it.

A young man named Batt Riordan, a tenant of Samuel's from the hills above Creevagh, called out, "On the warpath, Master! The west's awake at last!"

Seeing that Samuel had heard him, he moved into the crowd and tried to lose himself there. Samuel saw him talking to Kate's brother Fintan, who towered over most of his companions, and to Fintan's brother-in-law Pat Crehan. With a tremor of horror he recalled his father's death. The murderer had never been arrested. Fintan was rarely seen in the district but Andy had told Samuel lately that he was sleeping at Riordan's place since early summer. Though the police were still after him, the district was so hard to reach that it was not often raided. Neighbors were few since they were being emigrated systematically but Fintan and his like refused to go. Samuel had not pressed any of his tenants to leave but he heard every day in the club that emigration was the best solution for them.

"Too many of them on the land. Should never have been allowed. Get rid of them. Send them to a country where people are needed. Work for them all in America. Learn honest ways. Pay their way. That's what they need. Rotten habits they have. Debts everywhere. Living rent-free. Socialism on the doorstep. Heard a slogan about the land for the people. What next? Murder, arson, roguery a habit of life. Emigrate as many as will go and devil take the rest. Ruining the country. Ruining us all."

Fennell talked like this. It was thick-skinned of him to have come today—so much so that Samuel wondered if it were true. Then he saw him, his boots planted wide apart, watching the preparations for the boat race. He was a tall, strongly built man who looked as if he would be slow on his feet but in fact was as agile as a fox. He rode to hounds with the Galway Blazers and was always in at the kill. Samuel had given up hunting since his marriage because Alice could not accompany him, but he well remembered Fennell sitting his horse like a Roman emperor, reins drawn short, heels down, head up and with an expression of concentrated energy around his set mouth and eyes. In spite of his weight and age—he was in his late fifties—his back was straight at the end of a day of leaping the impossible Galway stone walls. His little fox's eyes missed nothing, seemed never to rest from their duty of guarding his employers' property, though he had a practice in Galway to attend to as well.

Fennell had seen him too and was calling out, "Afternoon,

Mr. Flaherty. Great day for this. Great idea. You should do it every year but a bit earlier to be sure of good weather. September is a dangerous month."

At that moment Master Fahy fired his pistol and the race began.

30

At once the multicolored crowd ran to the shore, cheering and hooting encouragement to the rowers, who worked as frantically as if they were racing from a hurricane.

Samuel turned to look, and seeing that everyone was occupied, he took Fennell's arm and said quietly, "You shouldn't be here. It's not safe."

Fennell gave his barking laugh.

"Safe? That would be a new word for me. If I thought of safety I'd be done for at once. Have you heard something?"

"A hint only, from a man who sees a Ribbonman behind every bush but he's sometimes right. That's why I didn't invite you."

Fennell raised his eyebrows and Samuel could not tell whether or not he was offended. Then he said, "I thought it was a free-for-all. No harm done, I hope."

"Of course not. I'm only thinking of the danger to yourself."

"Can't you be more specific?"

"No. But I've seen one or two people here who I know would like you out of the way. I hear a great many things."

To his amazement, Fennell's lip curled back to show his fox's teeth as he said, "Your wife, of course. She would know all about it."

"What are you suggesting?" Samuel felt his fists clench with rage.

Fennell shrugged and said, "Naturally you're in touch with the people through her. I don't suppose you'd hear much without her help."

"I'm on good terms with all my people," Samuel said furiously.

"But not good enough, surely, to hear when they're planning murder. I've had word of it myself, through my agents."

"Then why did you come?"

"To catch them out, if I can. I'll have a guard of four policemen on my way home. They plan to ambush me, I hear. They wouldn't dare to try it here in front of everyone. That's not their way."

"Are you armed?"

"With two pistols, and they know I'm a dead shot. I'd like to draw them. I'm tired of waiting. If I could catch a couple of them, make an exemple of them, hang them in Galway town, we might have peace for a while."

Hiding his disgust Samuel said, "I've never seen that do much good."

He wished Morgan were here to talk sense to the men. Morgan would never approve of the murder of Fennell. He was a man of honor, always defending the rights of the tenants but never believing in violence for its own sake, as Samuel knew from Alice. She heard these things from her own sources and she seemed always to know a great deal about Morgan and what he was doing.

The boats were turning at the tip of the point and would soon be back. Samuel felt a sudden longing for Alice, to have her to himself as he had had her in Paris, away from these terrible problems and scenes that were inescapable at home. Now and then he amused himself by speaking of Paris so as to enjoy her instant look of pure happiness. This day must be gone through, and a long evening after it, before he could be alone with her in their room, the only place where they had complete peace. Just to think of it brought him a moment of calm.

He found her at the marquee and immediately told her of his fears for Fennell.

"It won't be like that," she said. "Andy would like it so, to prove that all his spying was justified." Samuel was astonished at this but he let her go on. "The best time for shooting Fennell is after an eviction—that would make sense. It would be some use then. Otherwise they may as well leave the poor old devil alone."

"Is this a new way of doing things?"

"I don't know. I'm only thinking it might be like that. Oh, Samuel, I wish we could have this day free from murder and guns and killing!"

"Fintan is here."

"I saw him."

"Does Kate know?"

"She's so excited, I think she does."

Throughout the rest of the afternoon Samuel raged at his own stupidity in having held this meeting at all, knowing as he did from experience that it would be used for conspiracy. At races and sports meetings, even at Mass on Sundays—wherever a crowd was gathered together—plots were hatched and secret meetings were arranged. He knew that his anger showed on his face and that the people wondered at his grim expression while he announced the winners of the various events and awarded the prizes. These were very practical: a piece of bacon, a goose, two chickens, a bag of meal for porridge, a length of cloth, a jersey, socks, all chosen and prepared by Alice. The winners were in high good humor and their rivals were just able to curb their envy.

In the marquee, Samuel saw that Kate had arranged a special table for the gentry. It was decorated with streamers of smilax and ivy and had a white cloth from the house, as well as the best glass and china. Fennell was there, of course. Samuel assumed a smile of hospitality to cover the great anxiety that filled him. Alice came over to him and taking his arm led him outside.

"What's the matter? You look so wild. Has something happened?"

"I'm looking for Fintan and Batt Riordan."

"They left an hour ago. I saw them."

"Together?"

"Yes. Samuel, what are you thinking of?"

"I should have acted faster. Which way did they go?"

"There's only one way from here. Once they reached the Galway road they could go either way."

"Is Mrs. Fennell here?"

"No. He came alone."

"On horseback?"

"He's dressed for riding. Samuel, I saw the silver-mounted pistols sticking out of his breast pockets. They had a trial of him—"

"When?"

"A while back. I've just heard about it. They condemned him to death."

Samuel had heard of these trials that were held with a judge and jury and evidence heard on both sides. The victim's fate had usually been decided in advance and still they went through a long ceremony helped on with poteen to keep their spirits up. In this case, Alice said, lots were drawn for the executioner and the lot had fallen to Batt Riordan. He was authorized to get others to help him and he was expected to report from time to time on any attempts made on Fennell's life. There was no time to ask Alice who had told her all this. He felt murder in the air, all the worse for Fennell's stupid courage.

He said, "We could advise him to stay the night with us."

But he did not want his own tenants to see him sheltering Fennell. Besides, Alice said, it would do no good. Fennell's best chance was to stay in and around Galway.

"I've already spoken to him," Samuel said. "He laughed at me. Indeed he was quite rude. He told me he's having a guard of four policemen on the way home. It's no use my trying again."

"I'll talk to Father Ned," Alice said.

"Wouldn't Fennell be safer with a crowd, when all the people are going home?"

"Perhaps," she said doubtfully. "But he wouldn't want to travel with them."

She went weaving through the crowd, stopping here and there for a word with the people who were sitting at the long tables. At last he saw her with Father Kenny, looking at him with her usual amiable expression, as if she were merely chatting about the day's sport. They spoke for a minute or two and then Father Kenny, still smiling, moved toward the entrance. Samuel waited for him.

Father Kenny said in a low voice, "I'll try to catch up with the boys. They're going to be trapped."

Samuel accompanied him as far as the gate of the sports field, where Paddy had left the stableboy in charge of all the horses. While the boy was saddling Father Kenny's horse, Paddy himself came up and said, "You're going very early."

A strange look passed between them, making Samuel even more uneasy.

Father Kenny said, "I may be late already."

Paddy helped him to mount and tightened the girths with a sharp decisive tug.

Something in the gesture made Samuel say, "Saddle a horse for me too. I'm going with him,"

"You can't do that, sir," Paddy said quickly.

"Any horse will do," Samuel said, "Hurry."

With a helpless flap of his hands Paddy sent the boy to loosen a gray that belonged to D'Arcy, the best-looking animal in the line of tethered horses.

When he had mounted, Samuel looked down at Paddy and said sharply, "In ten minutes' time you can tell Miss Alice that I've gone with Father Kenny. If Mr. D'Arcy wants to go, give him my mare."

The boy opened the gate and they walked the horses out onto the rough lane that led from the sports field up to the sandy road to Galway. The gray was frisky, pleased at being let out, and he danced impatiently behind Father Kenny's bay. Where the lane emerged onto the road, to the Galway side of Moycullen House, they were able to ride side by side.

Father Kenny waited for Samuel and said, "This is a bad business. Alice says Fennell will be protected."

"Where do you come in?"

"God knows! I must look after my people."

"You seem to know a great many things," Samuel said angrily.

Father Kenny replied reasonably, even humorously, "They tell me a great many things, some I'd rather not know. The whole picture has changed. I'm surprised at this plan to shoot Fennell. With eighty thousand men in the Fenians they shouldn't feel the need to kill individual agents."

"Eighty thousand!"

"That's the figure I've heard. It seems true enough—every man I've asked has said he's in it."

Samuel had a sickening sensation of being surrounded by plots that concerned everyone except himself. But Alice often talked of the Fenians, making no secret of Morgan's being one of them, and she had talked once, very briefly, of the meeting to which Morgan had taken her in Paris where some of the leaders had been present. Samuel had not pressed her for details of this meeting but he hated the idea that there were two strata, living separately and thinking separately. The Flahertys had never lived like that, not even old George. He had always known what was happening, even when he had taken no part in it. He had never once contemplated leaving Moycullen as so many of their neighbors had done. A gentleman lives on his land, in his country house—that was old George's way—and he had instilled this principle in Samuel. The school, the workshops, the sawmills and flour mills, all were offshoots of the notion that the people must be cared for. When they failed in their rent, they were never given passage money to America unless they said first that they wanted to go. On many estates there was no choice. Indeed it was made to seem right, reasonable, benevolent, magnanimous on the landlord's part to give a ticket to America and a respectable outfit and a sovereign to be used on landing to defaulting tenants. Samuel knew that as far as the tenant was concerned, the landlord had grabbed his land, his God-given land, the sacred land of Ireland for which generations of Irishmen had fought and

209

sweated, for which any Irishman worth his salt was ready to die. When the landlord was an Englishman, living in England —the Duke of Devonshire, the Marquis of Bath and all the dozens of others like them who rarely visited their Irish estates —he was regarded with loathing, which had doubled in intensity since the great famine of '47. Now as he rode along, Samuel could see the silent fields on either side of the road, newly returned to grass and with occasional herds of sheep grazing them, right up to the walls of the ruined hovels that no one had bothered to demolish.

Father Kenny said, "I'd have thought you would have heard from Alice how strong the Fenians are now."

"I hardly believed her. What is it leading to? Another rebellion?"

"What else? Parliament will never give the people anything."

"Do you believe that?"

"I have to believe what I see. The Government is more oppressive than ever. Keep the people down, put them to work, keep them poor, teach them who are the masters, hang anyone who shows signs of fighting back. How long are the people to stand it? They have every right to rebel against impossible oppression, as they know very well. Every summer they go hungry for months until the new crop of potatoes comes in, while they hand over the corn to the landlords and see it shipped out of the country. How can men like Morgan Connolly put up with such treatment?"

"I haven't see Morgan for a long time. Where is he now?"

"On the run, as usual."

"I'd like to talk to Morgan. He has sense."

"Were you asked to join?"

"No. I couldn't join an oath-bound society. I'm glad I wasn't asked, since I'd have had to refuse."

"It's an army, Samuel."

"And I'm not a fighting man."

"Then why are you with me now?"

Father Kenny reined in his horse and Samuel followed suit. They faced each other, Samuel in astonishment at the priest's expression. He had never seen him like this before—fierce, uncompromising, angry, his lower lip jutting in a way that Samuel would have thought impossible, his dark-brown eyes burning in his thin face and his brows drawn under his wrinkled forehead.

"Well, why did you elect to come with me?" he repeated. "Where do you stand? These are desperate men. If you're not on their side, you'd better turn around this moment and go home. You saw the whole country turn out for Terence Bellew MacManus' funeral. You read the sermon that the Archbishop of New York preached over his body before it left America. It was a directive to rebellion in Ireland."

Samuel asked, "Where do *you* stand?"

"With my people."

"They're my people, too. You know that."

But even as he said it, he felt a shiver of fear go through him. These were the people who had murdered his father. How could he claim them as his own? That was more than ten years ago and still he did not feel that he had made any closer bond with them. Since his marriage, his rich neighbors had rarely confided their true feelings to him, so that he was isolated between the two classes. The children were probably suffering for this—the picture of Anna clinging to her mother's skirts came clearly to his mind.

Father Kenny shook his horse's reins and said, "Then we'd better hurry."

He looked like himself again, worn and hungry but calm. They rode through a defile between rough hills that rose high above the road. Stone walls on either side marked the edge of the Bates estate, now neglected and overgrown with fern and furze and ivy. Skinny pines were scattered on the hills, a melancholy organ for the September wind.

A movement among the pines caught Samuel's eye. In a low voice he said, "There's someone up there."

31

At once Father Kenny turned his horse onto the grassy verge of the road. Samuel followed. Ahead of them, the winding, rutted back avenue of the Bates estate was entered by a five-barred gate. They set their horses to the gate and cleared it.

Then Father Kenny said, "Get below the wall and wait for me. I'll go up the hill and find them."

In a moment he had slid to the ground and thrown the reins to Samuel, who had no choice but to walk both horses over to the high estate wall. He could see Father Kenny running up the hill, crouching as he went and skipping over the rough ground at an astonishing speed. Samuel dismounted and held both horses close to the bits, feeling the cold wind nipping him through the thin cloth of his jacket. He moved as near as possible to the wall for shelter. When next he looked up the hill, Father Kenny had disappeared over the top. Then into the deep silence came the sound of a large group of horses trotting together, coming from the direction of Moycullen.

Samuel's instinct was to keep close to the wall, concealed from the road. The two horses tossed their heads at the sound of the hooves on the sandy road. He spoke to them softly and put their noses together so that they could comfort each other. It sounded like at least eight horses, though by Fennell's account it should have been only five, thundering closer every moment, pounding in unison like drumbeats, creating an air of the tensest excitement. As the group of horsemen passed, Father Kenny's bay began to jerk at the bridle and lift his forefeet. The gray shivered in sympathy and then without warning let out a long whinny.

Twenty yards along the road the horses were halted with shouts. Samuel heard voices say, "Where's that horse? Did you hear it?"

"It's nothing," another said. "They'll always whinny when they hear horses passing."

"It sounded very near."

"It could be the assassins." That was Fennell's voice.

"Should we go and look, sir?"

Then they seemed to become more cautious and he could not hear what they were saying, but in a moment or two they trotted slowly off. Still he stayed close to the wall, shuddering at the thought of what he would have done if they had decided to investigate. He, a landlord, Flaherty of Moycullen, hiding by a wall, holding the horse of a rebel priest. He would have had some wriggling to do to prove that he was there to prevent crime. There was no end to the things that could happen to a man in this crazy country.

As soon as he was sure that Fennell and the policemen had rounded the next curve, Samuel hitched the two horses to the rusted gate and climbed the hill among the rocks and bushes, crouching as Father Kenny had done. At the top he lay on his belly, concealed as well as possible by a low furze bush, and scrutinized the scene below him. He could see the horsemen on the road, winding through the narrow valley. It was dark down there, shadowed by the hills, though the sky was still a faded blue. The horses were going in single file now, on the grass for silence. They disappeared for a full minute and then he saw them curve into view again and come to a stop. They reined in quickly, piling up in a ridiculous way, at a place where the demesne wall was low. He saw a confusion of men dismounting, throwing themselves over the wall, moving very fast. Then three other men were running, stopping, running again. One climbed the wall. There was a shot and the horses pranced in terror. Samuel dared not make the smallest move but lay as still as a rock on the hillside.

It had happened, then, after all. He watched while the policemen abandoned their proper work of catching the assassin and leaped out onto the road again to bend over the man who had fallen from his horse. While they were at this, the three men who had lain in wait for the cavalcade sprinted over the low brow of the next hill and disappeared in the direction of the lake.

Sick with horror, Samuel let his head subside gradually onto the grass. His neck was stiff and his eyes felt hot and sore. The grass was soothingly cool. He could not think clearly nor did it seem that he needed to, for the moment. What could he do? Whatever had happened down there was the concern of the policemen who had accompanied Fennell. Samuel could only wait to see what they would do next, whether they would decide to go on toward Galway or turn back to Moycullen. Just beyond the valley there was a stone house that had been inhabited by the Bateses' bailiff, a logical place for them to shelter. Sure enough, within a few minutes the whole group moved on in the direction of Galway. They went slowly, with three horses in the lead followed by two men awkwardly carrying the victim—dead or alive, it was impossible to say. Still he could not bring himself to move until he was aware that Father Kenny was back with their own horses. Samuel stood upright and went stumbling like a sleepwalker down the hill. He felt the priest grip his arm and shake him, saying, "What happened? Did you see? I was too late to stop them. I heard a shot. What was it? Wake up, man!"

"I saw it," Samuel said at last. He paused for a moment and then said firmly, "I think I know what happened. When they heard our horses, the men thought it was Fennell coming alone. They were surprised by the guard."

"Were they caught? Where are they now?"

"They shot Fennell, I think, and they've certainly got away."

"Where?"

"Toward the lake. They ran while the policemen went to help Fennell. That was intelligent of them but they were plainly seen. There's no doubt about that."

"How did they do it?"

"One of them got boldly up on the wall and fired. We'd better go home. There's no more to be done here."

"I've got to go to Fennell."

"So you have. I'd almost forgotten he's a Catholic." Foolishly he asked, "Must you really go?"

"Of course."

"I'll come with you."

"No. That would look suspicious. I can pass at any time—I could be on my way to another sick call—but you're giving a party today and everyone knows it. Some of the policemen are Catholics, too—they'll be expecting me."

Samuel opened the gate this time and they walked the horses out onto the road. He watched Father Kenny climb dispiritedly into the saddle, looking shabby and old, his graying hair unkempt in a way it would not have been a few years ago. He kicked the horse into a trot at once, however, and rode off briskly. Samuel galloped D'Arcy's gray along the grassy edge of the road home. At the turning to the lake, where the sports were, he glanced down to see if there was any sign of people leaving the field. It was all quiet. He wanted desperately to talk to Alice but the people probably knew what was afoot this afternoon and they would watch closely. Better to go home and wait for her there. But the horse had to be returned. There was nothing for it but to go back to the sports field. He slowed to a walk to cool the horse—all the better if D'Arcy did not know it had been out.

He had been gone more than an hour but the crowd seemed still the same. Paddy was waiting to take the horse, saying, "Where's the priest?"

"With Fennell."

"They got him?" The comment was hardly a question but then he asked urgently, "Did they get away?"

"Yes." Samuel slid wearily to the ground. "Does everyone here know all about it?"

"Not all, sir. Only a few. It's a bad business, I grant you, but that's how it had to be. You saw it all, I'm afraid, sir?"

"Yes, I saw it."

"Did you see the men's faces?"

"No, but I knew them by other things."

Paddy dropped his voice to say, "Don't let on you saw anything; don't let on you know who was there; don't name anyone."

"I won't name anyone, you may be sure. Was Miss Alice looking for me?"

"Yes. I told her you'd be back soon. That was a good half hour ago."

He went up to the marquee and knew by the curious way the people looked at him that he had been missed. He wondered if this had been connected with Fennell, whose departure with his escort must have been quite a spectacle. Still the long tables each had a double row of steadily eating men and women, picking slowly at the food, from politeness. The table for the gentry was surrounded, too, and Alice was there, holding a glass of claret while she talked to a landlord named Stokes from the northern part of the county. Samuel knew that this man was specially unpopular just now for having cleared his tenants off the land to make a deer park. Not only that: he had brought in Scottish gardeners to keep his new demesne, building them good houses of stone, which he had never done for the natives, and he had added the final insult by building a little Protestant church of cut stone next to the ruins of a medieval monastery that was a place of pilgrimage for Catholics from the whole of Connacht. He was unaware of the hatred he had aroused, talking affably to Alice about the improvements he had made on his estate, his tree planting and summerhouse building, and his new landing stage for the steam yacht that was the wonder of the county. He was a pleasantly mannered man, always courteous to Alice, which was more than could be said for some of the gentry here present.

Alice caught Samuel's eye and he saw her excuse herself to her guest before beginning to come toward him. He waited for her outside, where it was cold now with the damp feel of a late autumn evening. She was wearing her shawl tightly drawn around her, clutching it against her breast with one hand. He took her arm and led her away from the marquee.

"You had my message?" She nodded, gazing at him with eyes full of terror. "Yes, they shot Fennell," he said softly. "He fell off his horse. I saw it happen and I saw the men get away."

"Who were they?"

"Fintan, Batt Riordan, another man—I couldn't make out who it was."

"Morgan?"

"No. It couldn't have been Morgan. It was a smaller man."

The flash of joy in her eyes delighted him. She never wasted a moment, always leaping ahead, never afraid, never hanging back or wishing to save herself. This was how he had wanted her but lately he sometimes wondered if he had gone too far. She was his creation. He had taught her to be a fighter but today he had lost his own nerve.

"Alice," he said, taking her by the shoulders and holding

her firmly, as if she were trying to break away from him, "I'm going to buy a house in Dublin, after this. We can spend part of the year here—the children are not safe here—"

"No one would touch our children!"

"We can't risk it. I've made up my mind. It won't be at once —you'll get used to the idea, see that it has become necessary. I've no intention of being an absentee landlord but I must look after my family."

She looked at him strangely, as if she were wondering at his speaking of such things now.

He said gently, "I had to tell you at once. We'll talk about it later. Now we'll be back to our guests together so that no one will ask questions."

He steered her back into the marquee and almost at once the guests began to move away, first the gentry and then the poorer people. One in each little group of these made a short speech of thanks to Alice and Samuel.

"God bless your Honor and long life to you."

"God bless you, ma'am, and guard yourself and your family."

"May you live a hundred years."

32

A month after the shooting of Fennell, Morgan met Master Fahy by chance in Cong—his last visit for a long time, he said, as he had arranged to go to Dublin and write for James Stephens' new paper, which was to be called *The Irish People*.

"Remember to write good, grammatical English, Morgan," Fahy said anxiously. "Be sure not to disgrace your education."

"What's the news of James?" Morgan asked.

They were sitting in the hotel bar where Fahy was waiting to be picked up by Paddy and driven home to Moycullen. Knowing that Morgan was always liable to be watched, his arrival had flurried the old man greatly. The question about James distracted him from his fears.

"You know he gave up medicine?"

"I heard that."

"He went into the Civil Service and Lord Granville made a pet of him, promoted him over the heads of all sorts of senior people. Did you hear a story about his marriage?"

"Married? James? I'm delighted—"

"No, no," Fahy sighed. "I was told some cock-and-bull story about his being arrested for debt on the morning of his intended marriage but I don't believe it. You heard nothing about it?"

"Not a word."

"Then it's probably a jealous story. When people are very poor, Morgan, they take great note of other people's good fortune. James writes now that he's earning quite as much as if he had persevered with medicine. He has a special position in the Treasury, which he got because of his legal studies, and he has hopes of being made governor of some Crown Colony."

"Maybe they'll make him Lord Lieutenant of Ireland."

"God knows I don't like it either," Fahy said, "but it's none of my business. James seems to be lucky in his undertakings, more so than his father ever was. He talks of standing for Parliament. He has become a great talker—he talked us all into the ground the last time he was home—so perhaps it would be just the thing for him."

"He's very clever," Morgan said, sorry to hear Fahy's bitter tone. "If he gets elected, he'll put the case for Ireland well."

"You think so? I hope you're right. Are you coming to Moycullen?"

"Not in daylight. Is Andy there still?"

"Yes, looking more like a weasel every day. His ear is to every door. If I know when you're coming. I can keep him occupied and out of your way."

"Tonight?"

"Yes, though it won't be pleasure. He loves a game of cards with a glass of whiskey up in my place—thinks he's pumping me for information—and I suppose he may be enjoying himself in his own strange way." Fahy was peering at Morgan from under his heavy eyebrows, making no attempt to conceal his curiosity. "You've improved," he said decisively. "You're more of a man than when I saw you last. I used to think you were too soft to be a fighter, a bit of womanishness about you. Do come tonight. Samuel and Alice will be longing to see you."

"Is it true that Samuel has bought a place in Dublin?"

"Yes. He says he's going to keep both houses open all the time. He can afford it but it's a sellout all the same. It will look bad but he says he won't move a stick of furniture from Moycullen. He's having things made in Dublin for the new house, and it's to be called Moycullen House, too, so that the Moycullen people will be able to find him easily if they need him in Dublin. That was Alice's idea."

"How is she?"

217

"She's in good health, attending to everyone as usual." He paused, lifting his head to stare around the room, which contained besides themselves only two commercial travelers huddled over a jug of whiskey and a lawyer named Barron, from Ballinrobe, with an anxious client, conversing in whispers. "What's the news of Fintan and Batt?" he asked in a low voice. "Have they got away safely?"

"They're not out of the country yet but they've left these parts. Does everyone know who did it?"

"I heard the names the same evening, when I was told that Fennell was dead. I don't say everyone knows but they were seen by the policemen. There couldn't be much of a secret about that. I never heard the name of the third man. Who was he?"

"Master, I'm surprised at you!" Morgan said and Fahy looked abashed. He seemed to have shrunk in the last year or two, with a stoop to his shoulders that showed even while he sat at the table. His hands holding the glass of whiskey that Morgan had bought for him were thinned down to bone and vein, yellowish, with gray-blue nails. His eyes had sunk, his cheeks, too, and the bony line of his jaw showed clearly now the source of the determined appearance that he had used to dominate everyone since Morgan had known him. What age was he? Sixty-five? Seventy? Perhaps even seventy-five. The glint in his eye was as shrewd as ever, intelligent, uncompromising, signaling the danger of taking a short cut in one's logic with him. He would still be on to what he called half-thinking at once, as he had always been.

"I don't know myself who the third man was," Morgan said, to make amends for his rebuke. "The Brotherhood is taking care of them. I suppose they'll go to America if they can. Isn't it a strange thought that the Government sends all the informers to America and we send all our men on the run there, too? That will be a mixed country in years to come."

"It's an interesting speculation," Fahy said with another quick uneasy look around the room. "Where have you been, or can I ask that much?"

"I've been all over the country, north and south. I've heard the Reverend Hugh Hanna preach in Belfast. It was a marvelous sight, an outdoor meeting on the lawn of a big house, with at least five thousand people all shoulder to shoulder. I went with Fenian, a Presbyterian himself, who told me I'd never know how to make a recruiting speech until I'd heard Roaring Hugh."

"I'd give an ear to hear him," Fahy said eagerly. "How was he?"

"He seemed to draw the people with him, as if they were suddenly blinded and had to be led. He has a voice like thunder. He told the people that if they didn't repent at once, they were for the short drop into hell, but if they washed in the blood of Jesus Christ they were saved. It's a sort of Christianity, what every one of them had heard a thousand time before, but whatever spell he put on them, in half an hour there were a dozen of them standing up to confess their sins, promising to lead a good life in future, promising to shake off the devil. Then they fell on their knees, and dozens more did the same, and they all began to lament and wail and to say they were miserable sinners and to call on the mercy of God. They were like people in a fever. It nearly broke my own nerve to see it, they were so much in earnest, but it's an unhealthy thing, I'm sure."

"How did it end?"

"Hanna and a layman who was with him went down among the crowd and told the ones who were howling and sobbing that God would have mercy on them and they would be saved —that's a great word, and seemed to give them some comfort, the creatures."

"How were you affected?"

"It shook me," Morgan said, "but I was well taught not to trust to frail mortality." Fahy grinned with appreciation. "I did pity them, they were suffering so much, and then Hanna turned on to the Catholics. He said we are idolaters, blinded in ignorance by our priests, lambs straying away in the wilderness, and we'll never be good, contented members of the British Empire because we pay our first allegiance to the Pope of Rome. There was a lot of that, and then he reminded them of the Apprentice Boys of Derry who closed the city gates against King James. I think it would have been news to a lot of them that King James is dead more than a hundred and fifty years. They finished up with three cheers for King William but Hanna warned them that they must not think of their Roman Catholic brethren with hatred. He said we're lost sheep and must be brought back to the one true fold under the wise eye of one shepherd—Queen Victoria, I suppose—and if you see your brother wandering in darkness, it's your plain Christian duty to bring him back by all means in your power. Then they sang a hymn: 'I do believe, I will believe, that Jesus died for me.' "

219

"It's a bad business," Fahy said eargerly, lowering his voice still further. "Ten or twelve years ago it wasn't like that. We had Presbyterian ministers coming down here and addressing meetings of the League of North and South, telling us we're all Irishmen together and if we united we could beat the landlords. Then, when there was talk of repealing the Act of Union and having a parliament of our own in Dublin, they got the wind up for fear the Catholics would take over. Their own landlords told them that would happen, and that the bread would be taken out of their mouths and England would disown the whole lot of us and wouldn't buy any more of our goods and we'd all starve. Why did they believe them? That's what I could never understand. They know the landlords are liars—the truth isn't in them. It's as if the cats were telling the mice what's good for them and the mice believing them. Then the Cardinal condemned the Catholics for having anything to do with the Protestants and who was going to say out loud that we don't give a rap for what the Cardinal says, outside of his own job?"

"The Irish People is going to say it, if I've heard Stephens properly," Morgan said.

"They'll all be down on it then, the Castle and the bishops together."

"Stephens is a strange man," Morgan said. "Until lately he was always saying that a conspiracy should never have an organ and now he starts a paper."

"It will be a good paper, you think?"

"The plans are good, at least. God knows how long it will last. Stephens says we must make money out of it. There's mighty little coming from America now. We're all trained soldiers but we haven't any guns."

"Will the fight ever come?"

"It must come. What else are we drilling and training for?"

"What else, indeed? Isn't it a terrible thing when an old man wants fighting? There are some things you must fight for because it's not worthwhile being alive without them. Once you see the light of freedom, you must follow it wherever it leads you, never let go as long as you live. You must shut yourself off from every distraction and put yourself on the path that will lead to the vision you had when you were young."

"What is freedom?" Morgan asked softly, almost afraid to speak lest he might change this unusual mood in Fahy.

"Freedom is when the blind see and the lame walk and the poor have the gospel preached to them. Freedom is when those who hunger and thirst after justice get their fill, when poverty is not shameful, when families grow up in peace, when the police are the friends and servants of the people instead of spies and enemies." He stopped and gave a short, sour laugh. "You'll know we have a free country when an Irishman will say he's Irish without ducking his head at the same time to avoid a crack on the ear."

He was back to his usual tone. Through the window Morgan saw the carriage from Moycullen pull up at the hotel door. Paddy threw the reins on the horse's back and beckoned to one of the bystanders to hold the bit for him. A moment later he came into the bar. He stopped on the threshold and then came toward them.

"I hope I didn't keep you too long. You had good company." He took Morgan's hand and pressed it warmly but he did not address him. "Ready for the road, Master?"

Fahy heaved himself upright and stood unsteadily, stretching himself, before venturing to take a tottering step. Morgan was shocked at his frailty now and put out a hand to help him.

He withdrew it quickly when Fahy said, "Thanks be to God I'm still able to walk alone." In a more kindly tone he added, "I'm all right once I've taken a step or two. Old age is a stiff time of life."

33

When they had gone, Morgan sat for half an hour, quietly finishing his drink and wondering if he should risk doing as Fahy had suggested. She would be there. She was so much with him that he was sometimes afraid his mind was unbalanced. But love is an unbalance of the mind, an obsession, outside reason. It had led him to that crazy expedition to Aran where he had finally given himself over to Alice body and soul, tied himself into a net where he had been imprisoned ever since, so that every thought, word and action were automatically linked to her. That was love, torment and bliss at the same time, far stronger since her visit to Paris.

The memory of her in Paris sent a fire through him. She was near, and he had been invited, pressed to go to her house. Samuel—clean, handsome Samuel—would be there too. The fire receded but burned up again more strongly, almost unbearably, filling his throat with longing, making his scalp tingle and his hands shake. This was madness indeed, but what could he do? It was too strong for him. Fahy would go home with Paddy, talking about having seen Morgan, telling how he had looked, while Alice's blood would fly and burn as his did now, though she sat quietly pretending to be concerned only as she would be for any friend. While she listened, her eyes would close slowly and open again dreamily in ecstasy, as they had done in Paris, her hands would lie on the arms of her chair, she would lean back and feel his body press on hers, his hands explore her, his mouth laid on hers to make them one.

He stood up smoothly, as he had learned to do so as not to attract attention, and walking softly out of the bar went around by the side of the hotel to the place where he had tethered his horse and mounted. The horse's muzzle was wet, showing that he had been to the trough for a drink. There was nothing to delay him. A drizzle of rain began to fall as he left the village and lasted throughout the two hours' ride to Moycullen. Morgan knew a short cut across the mountain that brought him down before dark near Maam Cross. The wind was bitter there, cutting across the lake so that he had to pull the collar of his long riding cloak up around his ears. He had good boots, given to him only a month ago by the wife of a Fenian named John Moran in Westport—real riding boots that had belonged to her husband and that fitted Morgan perfectly. Moran was in jail in Galway, awaiting trial on a charge of conspiracy. His wife was a small fair-haired woman with a sharp sense of humor. As Morgan was the cause of her husband's arrest, she said, he was entitled to the boots. The trial had already been twice postponed for want of evidence but she was sure her husband would not be needing them for a long time.

The horse was hardy but he was lagging by the time the dim lights of Moycullen village were visible. Morgan's back and shoulders had begun to ache, weighted with the cloak which had soaked in the rain until it seemed a ton weight. His hands on the reins felt cramped, gripped in the wet leather of his gloves, held so fast that it was hardly possible to move the fingers, as he knew he should do from time to time.

A horse ridden through the village would bring everyone to their doors, so he took a devious route by the back of the church. Father Kenny's house had been raided twice in the search for him. There was no question of his going there even if he had wanted to delay. Once beyond the church he was able to come out on the main road again, keeping to the grassy verge where the horse's hooves were muffled, feeling the tightening of terror that always came now when he was near people who knew him and could inform on him. He made the tired horse trot, anxious to reach the shelter of Samuel's house —a good house, as the people said—where he would be hard to find even if there were a raid. For Morgan, the best kind of house was easy to escape from and had a few outbuildings attached to it, so that it could not be surrounded. He never went to his own little house in Cappagh now, he could so easily be trapped inside it.

When he rode into the yard at Moycullen House, Paddy was waiting for him by the gate. He took the horse, saying "Get inside, quick. Miss Alice has a change of clothes ready for you. The Master told her you might come and that little *spreallán* Andy is out of the way for the night. Captain, it's a cruel way to live!"

"Better than starvation," Morgan said cheerfully and ran for the back door of the house.

The heavy wet cloak dragged him down and his fine boots were slipping on the cobbles but they did not delay him much. He slid out of the cloak in the kitchen and sat on a stool while Kate pulled off the boots for him.

"Morgan, my son," she said to him in Irish, looking up at him anxiously, "you're like a drowned rat. I have a pair of stockings here for you and shoes, too, and there's a glass of whiskey waiting for you within."

She sent him up to her own room off the kitchen to change into some dry clothes of Samuel's while she warmed the stockings at the blazing range fire. When he came back she rubbed his feet between her hands, moaning to herself at the cold of them, bending her gray head low in her anxiety while she put the stockings and shoes on for him.

"God bless you, Kate. May you have a thousand sons and a hundred daughters, and the biggest of them no bigger than a rabbit."

He dodged away from her, out into the hall where a hanging lamp gave a soft light. A turf fire burned on the hearth here, an idea of Alice's, and it made the floor and the stair well glow with a rosy warmth. He noticed that she had put some beech leaves in a bowl on the mahogany table. A sickness of longing went through him, mixed with jealousy of Samuel, dangerously like hatred. At that moment the dining-room door opened and there was Samuel himself, springing forward to clasp him affectionately and lead him into the room.

"I thought I heard a horse come in. Alice, Morgan is here!"

"Morgan!"

Under Samuel's indulgent eyes she flew into his arms and laid her head on his breast, so that he smelled the sweetness of her hair. He held her tightly and then, after a moment, took her by the shoulders to look her over carefully. He lifted her hands one by one and turned them over, as if they were curios he was considering in a shop.

"They're so soft and white," he said.

She pulled them gently from him, recalling him to his senses and to Samuel's presence.

He laughed happily and said, "I haven't had very elegant company lately. Those soft hands reminded me of Paris."

"Such a night," Samuel said. "We've been listening for you since Fahy came home with the news that he'd seen you. He was so excited that it took a while to find out what had happened. How did you come?"

"Over the mountain to Maam. It's a dirty night, indeed, but it's so good to be here!"

Samuel was busy pouring some whiskey into a glass and then making punch with hot water from the brass kettle that stood on a tripod by the fire.

"This is Andy's job," he said, "but we gave him the evening off. I'm not as good at it as he is."

Morgan said, "I feel safer having it from you. Andy shouldn't be in this house, Samuel. He's dangerous."

"Alice tells me that but it might look worse to get rid of him. I've no excuse—he's a perfect servant."

"That's part of his trouble," Alice said. "Morgan, is that why you didn't come to see us? We've been longing for it."

She took the glass from Samuel and brought it to him, then stood close beside her husband to watch him take the first sip, holding Samuel's arm and leaning slightly against him. Morgan saw Samuel take her white hand in his, casually, as he waited for the answer to her question.

"It's dangerous for me to be here, even now with Andy out of the way. How many servants have you, Samuel?"

"Twenty-two, if you count the yardmen—that's not counting the farm, of course."

Among twenty-two Andy would be almost certain to have a crony but Morgan said, "Well, let's forget our troubles and be glad to be together again."

The wind roared in the chimney and whirled shrieking through the branches of the park trees. The dry, leafless wisteria rattled and tapped against the very window of the room. Now and then, a specially strong gust struck the house, making the dining-room door give a shudder, as if it were being assaulted from outside. The first time that this happened, Morgan crouched back against the cushions of his chair and saw

Alice watching him, her eyes filled with pity. He sat up deliberately, realizing what had caused the thundering sound, and said lightly, "I should have remembered that door. It was always the same in a storm."

But it was impossible not to turn his head in terror at a louder crack, until the whiskey soothed his nerves at last. Then he gave himself up to the comfort of the room—the blazing turf fire, set six feet from side to side, with its orange flames reflected on the brass fender and fire irons, the warm gold carpet with faded roses, the old shelves filled with dark-bound books that had so overawed him in his childhood, the brocade curtains that moved in the draft, glittering in the lamplight. He missed none of it, or the changes in Alice that he could see more clearly now. He made no secret of gazing at her, upright beside Samuel, her slim body barely touching the back of the sofa. She was quieter, sadder, older, of course—even for Alice, time had to pass. She was thirty-two, or near it. The new repose suited her, giving her authority and poise. It aroused a demon in Morgan, most unexpectedly, that he wanted her now for a different reason, to get the better of her. What right had she to look so cushioned and cosseted, with her white hands and her fine crinoline dress and her cashmere shawl? There would be satisfaction in rolling her in the heather now, far more than long ago.

"Why are you smiling like that?" she asked softly.

"Just thinking how far we've come in the last twelve years."

He was sorry then, because she looked downcast, having understood too much of what he had been thinking.

Samuel said, "Things are a little better now for all the people, though it's mostly money from America that keeps them going. I had hopes that they had given up Ribbonism, especially with all the sermons they hear against it—and then they shoot Fennell right under my nose."

"Would you have stopped it?"

"Of course. It was murder."

"Samuel, never say that to anyone else. It's dangerous talk. Father Kenny doesn't preach against it, I suppose?"

"Not directly. You know I was with him when it happened."

"I heard. I was sorry."

"Nonsense. It's my country too."

Brought up short, Morgan was silenced. Of course it was Samuel's country—his name was Irish and he lived where his people had lived for more than a thousand years. His ancestors had given hospitality to the traveling poets and storytellers before Christ was born.

"Master Fahy said you're going to have a paper," Samuel said. "Now, that's more what is needed. Educate the people properly and freedom will come in time."

"When they're educated, they'll see that they have to fight for freedom."

But it was no use talking to Samuel about fighting. Reasoned argument was the weapon he favored, a worn-out weapon in Morgan's opinion, an unreliable tool. Besides, not one of the three of them there present had behaved reasonably. They had been driven before violent winds of passion and anger. This was true of Samuel, too, for all his staid appearance and mild speeches. What courage he must have had to face his neighbors with a wife from the bogs and present her to them blandly as a lady! Morgan could not bring himself to point this out to Samuel—a little still remained of their early relationship, patron and serf, and, besides, he could not have said it in the presence of Alice herself.

The whiskey began to make him drowsy and he basked like a cat in the warmth of the fire and the presence of love. Would he ever again be with her as he longed to be now? Desire for her swirled through his body, almost unbearably. He knew that she was aware of it, sitting there so still and quiet, listening to Samuel talking about the state of the country as if with her full attention.

He closed his eyes to shut out the agonizing sight of her and Samuel said instantly, "Morgan, you must go to bed. We've been selfish in keeping you here so long. Alice, where is he to sleep?"

"In James's room," she said coolly and stood up. "I'll go to see about it. There's a fire there, Morgan, and Kate said she'd put your clothes to dry."

"I shouldn't stay. Someone may have got wind of my being here and told the police."

He began to struggle out of the comfortable chair but Alice said, "No one will come here. They'd never think you'd spend a night in this house when you're on the run. Now sit back there again until I come for you."

"It's true," Samuel said when she had gone out of the room. "You're safer here than anywhere you could reach tonight. Where would you go?"

"To Glann, perhaps, or Creevagh."

"There are no houses left in Creevagh now. It's winter, Morgan. You'd be out in that fearful weather all night."

"It wouldn't be the first time."

But he did not want to go, though it was torture to stay

here, too, to be conducted to the big warm room opposite hers, and to know that she was in there with Samuel. After they had left him, above the noise of the wind he heard their door close sharply. Fuddled with fatigue and whiskey, he imagined Samuel enjoying the delights that were denied to him, until tears of rage and shame prickled his eyelids.

Kate had dried his clothes and laid them by the fire. He put them on and lay down on the bed, covered only with an eiderdown. He could have four hours' sleep now, which would keep him going until timorrow evening when he would be out on the Burren of Clare, a safer place. A man named Keane—four hours—no more—four hours—Miltown Malbay—Mr. Stephens sent me—he should have told Paddy to leave the horse saddled—Alice would come and find his empty bed—four hours only—O Mary of Graces, Mother of the Son of God— he fell asleep suddenly, lapped in that childhood prayer.

It was still pitch-dark when he awoke. The fire glowed dimly but he had to light a candle to see the time by his pocket watch. Four o'clock—he had slept too long. A vague uneasy dream of horses heard trotting troubled him. Probably one of Samuel's horses was loose and had passed close by the house, but his scalp crawled with primitive terror. He examined the pockets of his riding cloak to make sure that his things were safe and put it around his shoulders. It was still warm from the fire, comforting him. Kate had folded the cloak so that the pistols were protected from the fire by several thicknesses of the cloth—an intelligent woman. Her thoughtfulness pleased him and lightened his humor. His shadow in the long cloak cut the room in half. He picked up the candle and held it high, taking one long look around before going to the door. The four-poster bed had been short for him but it would have fitted James very well. What a little cock he was! And how he would love being a colonial governor, lording it over bigger men, wearing a top hat and striped trousers, having everyone fall silent when he began to speak, out of respect for his position. One couldn't grudge it to him—and his heart was in the right place. As Morgan had told the Master, James would be a good friend of Ireland if he ever became powerful.

He opened the door cautiously, not to wake Samuel and Alice, and walked silently along the carpeted corridor toward the stairs. The blackness of the hall below worried him but when he went down he found it empty, of course. Since he had been on the run, two years now, he had never before slept in a big house. In the cottages where he stayed, there was usually a sentry, a member of the family, who kept watch all night so that he could sleep in peace. He passed through the dark kitchen like a shadow, aware of Kate in the little room above. Perhaps she was watching for him, though he could not have asked her to do it. The storm had almost blown itself out and all that was left of it was a mournful sighing of the wind around the corners of the house. In the flagged hallway beyond the kitchen, he started back in fright from the tall pump handle, thinking for a split second that it was a man. Exasperated with himself, he went to the back door and with his hand on the bolt blew out the candle, pinched the warm wick between his thumb and forefinger and slipped it into the pocket of his cloak. Then he opened the door.

He felt safer in the dark yard under the wet, windy sky. There were neither stars nor moon—a good night for traveling if you knew the road. He would chance the main road into Galway. There was no avoiding the town, since the river had to be crossed there, but he would skirt it as best he could on his way to the Clare road. Planning his route, he reached the stable at the far side of the yard and found to his delight that Paddy was there, having slept in the hayloft. He came down the ladder as soon as he heard the horse move on the cobbled floor.

"I thought you might come early," he said softly. "The horse is fed and watered and I mended the bit for you." He slung the saddle on the horse's back and tightened the girths. Morgan led the horse out slowly and mounted while Paddy went to the gate. A good man, Paddy, a true Fenian, quietly devoted to the cause. He was a B, Morgan knew. He would have liked to talk to Paddy but there was no time. He was at the big gate now, opening the narrow side of it for Morgan to pass through.

It had all worked so perfectly until now that the shock took Morgan's breath away. Suddenly they were both surrounded by men on horseback and on foot. A torch was lit and blazed up in the blackness, revealing what seemed to be a vast crowd of uniformed police and soldiers. Brass glinted and shone, horses' manes flew, hooves pranced, sparks from the torch were blown on the wind, yet no one shouted except Paddy, in Irish.

"Morgan, make a run for it! I'll hold them."

Morgan's horse lifted his forefeet, his one bad habit, which Morgan had been trying to cure for a year. At the same moment Paddy flung himself with astonishing ferocity on the men nearest to them, kicking, flailing with his arms, until a little circle was free around them. Holding the reins cruelly tight, in a way that he knew would infuriate the frantic horse, Morgan felt him rear up again to let out a savage whinny, beating the air with deadly hooves. He came down on all fours and then pranced again, so that the torch fell back and the whites of the soldiers' eyes showed in terror. Then they were flying out of the crowd into the blackness, the horse maddened into final rage by the volley of shots that followed them uselessly. The avenue gate was open and they fled across the lawn. Now Morgan was lying on the horse's neck, whispering endearments to him as if he were a woman in a temper, patting him, slackening the reins, keeping him to the heavy wet grass, until he was sure that he had regained control. At the road gate he turned sharply to the right, by the way he had come yesterday. Galway had to be avoided now and this meant skirting the top of the lake by Cong, not on the main road, which would be watched, but on one of the thousand small roads and tracks over the mountains that Morgan knew well. Five minutes beyond Moycullen he entered one of these tracks, leading toward the lake, and felt safer.

In the flare of the torch he thought he had seen Andy's face for a second. If this were so, he was in danger of being followed even here. But the whole debacle had taken place right under Samuel and Alice's window. They would come down at once and she would contrive to hold Andy, make him bring drinks for the officers, think of a dozen ways to keep him out of further mischief. He would not dare to disobey her, though he was certain to be dismissed now. And at the vision of her, Morgan was overwhelmed with great sadness, pressing down on his heart like a physical load, filling him with bitterness, and weariness of his miserable life. What was it that sent him flying along a wet country lane in the dark, while other men were at home in their houses with their wives and children around them? A stupid will-o'-the-wisp, a crazy dream of Stephens' that the people could be roused to some sense of their rights? Slowly now, as he rode through the mud and rain, realization came to him that but for Alice he would be a prosperous Boston businessman like his brother. It was a time of the night for fantasy—even for poetry: he would never be rid of his passion for Alice or for Ireland because he had see them both naked and helpless, when he was young.

PART
FOUR

34

Morgan could not go back to Moycullen after that night. Saddened by news of Paddy's arrest, he made his way to Dublin by a roundabout way and very slowly, arriving three weeks late for his new work on *The Irish People*. No one seemed surprised to see him when he came into the office in Parliament Street at three o'clock on a wet November afternoon. Stephens looked up from the table where he was peering at a mass of handwritten papers and scraps of printed material, his eyes keeping their usual expression of frowning concentration.

"Morgan? Just in time. Sort out these, for God's sake— French, Austrian, Italian, Prussian and so on. I'm sick of them. And the advertisements— We haven't many but there will be more as we get known. Have you eaten? Neither have I. Then there are three terrible poems to go in. Look at this advertisement—'Monte Video Dried Boneless Jerked Beef.' Does anyone know what jerked beef is? It's dried beef. Tautology everywhere. This is Miss Jane Hopper, who is going to write about fashions in Hamburg. Denis Mulcahy you know already. Just do every single thing he tells you. Publication day is Saturday the twenty-eighth. Now I'm going out."

And out he went, leaving Morgan to discover from Mulcahy what his work was to be. Miss Hopper followed Stephens, leaving them alone.

Mulcahy asked, "Have you found lodgings? When did you come?"

"An hour ago. I put up my horse at the City Mansion and said I'll stay there but I'll have to get rid of him if I'm going to be in Dublin."

"That will be easy. You'd better move to lodgings. There's a good house across the street, very convenient. The City Mansion is expensive—a shilling a night, I think, and another shilling for your breakfast. The lodgings are five shillings a week all found and you'll be near enough to get home for dinner. Morgan, it's good to see you."

Morgan had always liked Mulcahy, ever since they had met in Paris. He was a Tipperary man. His wild hair and beard and bushy eyebrows distracted attention from the happy, lively optimism of his eyes, so different from the defeated sadness of western eyes.

Morgan asked, "What is your job on the paper? Are you the editor?"

"Heavens, no. There are to be three editors—Mr. Luby, Mr. Kickham, when he comes back from America, and Mr. O'Leary—a blessed trinity so long as they agree. I'm the sub-editor and you're to be my assistant. O'Donovan Rossa is the business manager—he's good at that, from his shopkeeping in Skibbereen. We're quite well organized, in spite of Stephens' remarks."

"He did make it sound rather haphazard," Morgan said cautiously.

"Stephens has big ideas. He's going to marry Miss Hopper, by the way, which is rather off his usual preaching. You'll work with me," Mulcahy said, "and it's true that there is a lot of sorting of material to do. Stephens gets it from everywhere, God knows how. Use your discretion—I'll put in anything you recommend."

That first day Morgan found a gem that he knew would please Fahy back in Moycullen, a correspondence between Garibaldi and Victor Hugo, and he translated it and had it printed in the first issue. He could almost hear Fahy reading it out sonorously:

" 'Caprera, August 18, '63

Dear Friend,

I want another million of muskets for the Italians.

I am certain you will help me to collect the necessary funds.

The money will be placed in the hands of Signor Adriano Leniaro, our Treasurer.

Yours,
G. Garibaldi' "

And the reply:

" 'Dear Garibaldi,

I have been absent, which delayed my receipt of your letter and your receipt of my reply.

You will find enclosed my subscription. You may safely depend on the little that I am and the little I can do. I will, as you think it useful, seize the first opportunity to raise my voice.

233

You will need the million of muskets, you will need also, and above all, the million of arms, the million of hearts and the million of souls. They will come.

Your friend,
Victor Hugo' "

He wondered what the Moycullen people would make of Miss Hopper's item on Hamburg.

"The females of this city are in general of fair complexion and fine color . . . in general they wear short sleeves and very short petticoats . . . so many points of attraction to woo a bachelor from celibacy . . ."

He could imagine Fahy snorting impatiently over that one. More of interest would be the item on the earthquake in Turkey. Fahy would discourse on earthquakes for ten minutes before getting on to the main part of the paper, the political articles. He would deplore the literary style of those written by Stephens himself but he would love the open sedition: ". . . a noble race whose land may be occupied but never conquered. The chief auxiliaries of the law are Famine, Disease and Exodus. . . . Young men, not equal to those we have yet available in Ireland, have led, in the present American war, with valor and devotion never surpassed, through battles terrible beyond all precedent, the companies and regiments of the Federal armies. In spite, then, of any and all untoward issues of the past, our confidence in the national cause should remain rooted and strong. Let the people only strive, with might and main, to develop and rouse to vigorous life all the intelligence, energy and virtue they have amongst themselves—let them do this and they will soon find substitutes within their own ranks for the corrupt and craven classes that have abandoned the cause of their country. To this end, we say, let the people toil day and night. This is what is chiefly requisite in order to make Ireland an independent nation!"

A paragraph on Irish-American soldiers who fought at the battle of Gettysburg ended:

"General Mallon was also a true-souled Irishman. He commanded as Colonel of his regiment at Gettsyburg, after which battle he could muster only seventy men. Captains O'Shea and Downing, and Major Downing, underwent a long imprisonment in Cork Jail, in '58 and '59, on a charge of being United Irishmen, or belonging to an oath-bound society conspiring to destroy English government of Ireland. They belong to the Irish people, and while there exists a large supply of such material available, in England and Ireland, we must have trust in the ultimate success of the cause of our country."

Morgan took a copy of the first issue, wet from the press, to Kevin O'Doherty in Hume Street, where he had set up as a doctor.

Kevin said, "They won't let this go on for long."

Morgan shrugged.

"They won't have far to come for us. We're on the doorstep of the Castle. I think that if we survive the first weeks we'll be let alone. The organization is so strong now, both here and in England—"

"That might work either way. They'll hardly put up with such sedition, especially knowing the strength of the organization. They could decide to jump on you at once."

But they did not jump and the paper continued to appear week after week. Stephens soon went to America, to everyone's relief. From down the country, word came of raids and arrests on charges of being in possession of the paper, which was taken as enough proof of conspiracy, and still Mr. O'Leary and Mr. Luby and Mr. Kickham came quietly into the office every day, well dressed and respectable-looking, and suavely wrote their inflammatory pieces advocating insurrection.

Morgan became absorbed in the workings of the paper. The printers were all Brotherhood men from Kilkenny—John Haltigan, his son James, Fireball Martin and Edward Neville. Pagan O'Leary lived above the office in a little room at the back of the building.

"I'm a fighting man all my life," he said to Morgan, "and that's why I can't be a Christian in this Christian country. I worked it all out—I'm an Irishman. That's my religion. There were Irishmen in Ireland before Christianity was ever heard of. Look what they do to the Christians, or the Catholics if you like to call them that. The law of England is against them for wanting to live in peace in their own land, and the Catholic Church is against them for putting up a fight to keep the sod they stand on. That's a queer kind of religion, if you ask me, that will tell a man he's obliged to let the roof be knocked over his head. Archbishop Cullen has given instructions, plain as a pikestaff: anyone that reads *The Irish People* is not to get absolution from his sins, he can't get married, he can't even die in peace unless he tells a lie on his deathbed, saying he repents of belonging to the Fenians or reading *The Irish People*. What sort of religion is that? Fratres Feniores and Freemason Fratres are all the one. I couldn't live with a big stone like that around my neck so I've gone back to the old gods that were here long ago, that understood the people of Ireland—Lugh of the Long Arm and Angus Og and the Dagda Mor and Manannan Mac Lir. When I get to the other side, I'll find them standing alongside the Christian God and we'll have arguing and talking and comparing all night long, and I'm thinking Archbishop Cullen will come badly out of it."

"Will the Christian God be there?"

"Of course He will. Isn't He the father of all? When I was in America I learned to do without a bishop or a pope at my elbow every minute and hour of the day to tell me what to do. Cullen has the people tortured out of their lives, weighing up where they'll go when they die if they raise a hand to protect their homes and their wives and children."

The little room was furnished with a worn trestle table and two chairs. A battered iron bedstead stood on the bare boards in one corner. The light came from a single candle in a brass holder on the mantel. Pagan crouched low over the fire and stirred a small iron pot that was balanced on the coals, then quickly poured the contents into a pan. Steam shot into the air, circling Pagan's gray head and curling around his straggly beard. The candlelight swam in its fog.

Morgan chuckled and said, "You look like a druid, sure enough. What are you doing?"

"Making bullets to shoot the bastards. I can make pikes, too, but you need a proper foundry for that. We're setting up one soon, down the street. In the meantime every little helps, as the wren said when he peed in the sea. Bullets are better than pikes in these hard times, so long as you have the guns to put them in." He began to sieve his bullets out of the pan. "A fighting man is all I am, Morgan," he said almost apologetically. "That's why they're always sending me to swear in Irishmen in the army. I'm off again next week to Liverpool and Birmingham and Chester."

"Watch your step for God's sake, Pagan."

"You bet I will. I'm as fond of my skin as the next. But a strange thought is taking hold of me lately, a kind of dream, though I'm not always asleep when it comes on me. I see a crowd of us, maybe twenty, maybe more, in a cold, dark place where the sun never comes, a place we can never escape from no matter how we try. Maybe it's the hell that the Archbishop is always talking about, but that's a hot place, according to some, though I don't know how they know it. There are devils in my place, very attentive, full of ideas for new ways of torture. I suppose I'm getting old and scared, superstitious. Maybe I shouldn't talk of a thing like that to a young fellow."

Morgan shouted with laughter.

"I'm thirty-four this year, Pagan!"

Pagan squinted around at him from his crouched position on the hearth.

"You look like a child to me. That's another sign of getting old, though I'm not sixty yet. One thing is certain about that dream. I know there's no escape. We'll die in that place." His voice trailed away.

Morgan asked, "Were you ever in prison, Pagan?"

"A short spell. You think that's prison? I suppose you're right. Sure, that's a thing that will come to us all and we can only bear it when it comes."

This seemed to please him but the conversation left Morgan in a state of great depression. Of course he had been risking prison for years but Pagan's ugly little picture had put the prospect right under his nose. The leading articles in the paper always spoke of the rising as something in the far distant future but Morgan knew that this was a ploy to fool the authorities. There must be a rising, soon. Morgan talked of it to Alice when he went to her fine new house in Donnybrook on an afternoon in April, when the paper was almost six months old.

"The people are sick and tired of the faded stuff they get in *The Nation* and *The Irishman*. We're giving them the same but they know we mean business. Our plans are definite—the men will go mad if they see nothing for all their preparations. The money is coming in now and the guns, too. Alice! Put down that damned embroidery and look at me straight!" She laid it down on her lap and gazed at him directly. Her eyes were darker blue—was this possible? He complained, "You're far too good at embroidery. Do you like Dublin?"

She gave the right answer. "Of course—we see you so much more often. And it's good for the children."

"You've made the house beautiful."

It was a Georgian house, with a flight of steps leading to the door, built in a little park with an avenue of chestnut trees and a fine grassy lawn to separate it from the road. The long drawing room looked out on one side of the house, with French windows through which he could see great round beds of daffodils and tulips. It was a painful relief to come here from the center of the city.

He pressed her further. "But you—what do you want? Is this better for you than Moycullen?"

"It's what Samuel wants."

"That's no answer."

"It's what makes it right for me," she said sharply, and then she put out a hand and took his, saying, "I go where Samuel wants me to go, Morgan. I'd have stayed in Moycullen with my people, but I can't have what I want."

She stopped abruptly and he knew she was remembering another occasion when she had said the same thing. Usually her friendly correctness and above all the presence of Samuel defeated him but now he felt desire for her go swirling through him from the touch of her hand. She took it from him gently, pretending to begin on her embroidery again, saying, "The people feel deserted. It's no use telling them we'll be away for only part of the year. Old Mrs. Molloy said when we were leaving for Christmas: 'Sure ye must be going with the other gentry—how could we keep ye? I'll pray for the children every day.' I'll remember that to the day I die. It was the kind of thing she'd say if we were going to America. They're in despair, I know, especially the women."

She bent over the embroidery again and Morgan said, "If we're arrested you must keep their hearts up, keep up the fighting spirit; I can see you doing it—the people will trust you—they always speak well of you."

"Do they?"

That had pleased her.

"Of course they do. They say you would feed the whole county if you could. Do the poor people of Dublin come to you?"

"There's a crowd at the back door every day about dinner time. I used to think city people would never starve but it's just as bad here, and worse."

"And the Moycullen people—do they come to Dublin?"

"Sometimes, on their way to England. And Mike Sherwin came last week. He drove all the way from Galway, to see how we're fixed, he said. It did my heart good to see him, just where you're sitting. He has the pony we gave him, still going strong. He stayed a week and said he'll be back soon."

"What news had he?"

"That the Fenians are powerful and everyone is singing 'The Rising of the Moon.' He says there's talk of fighting everywhere. Does it make sense, Morgan?"

"Great sense. If we don't fight now, we can never hope for help again from America. I only hope things are as good as Mike says they are. Kickham says the time is ripe and Martin—"

"It's easy for the like of Martin to talk. He has his fine house in Boston and his fine clothes and plenty to eat. If you ask me, he has forgotten what it was like to go hungry from morning till night—"

"He has never forgotten! How can you say that? Martin is always generous."

"He never liked me," she said inconsequently, still intent on her embroidery. "Is he coming again soon?"

"He'll come in the summer. I suppose I'll meet him in Father Ned's house, if I can get there. The paper takes most of my time. There will be more American officers this year, too, drilling the men. Mr. Luby doesn't want them—he says we can do our own drilling—but then the Americans are so anxious to come and see for themselves that something is being done. They'll pay for it dearly, Mr. Luby says, but that doesn't seem to bother them. And you can see that the people respect them for having been in real battles already. Americans want to fight a war the way a football match is played. The Irish way is to snipe from behind rocks and bushes, which hasn't worked out too well so far. We may as well try the American way now. Where are the children?" he asked suddenly, sick of the topic of war.

Alice rang for them and they came in a few minutes. They were all fond of Morgan. Anna sat on a footstool by Alice, looking nervously upward at him. She was tall for twelve, slender like her mother but without her bloom.

Thomas sat down politely at a distance for half a minute and then plunged forward to ask urgently, "Have you brought the paper? Is it in your pocket?"

He reached into Morgan's pocket and rummaged, pulling out the folded *Irish People* in a moment. Julia was already sitting firmly on Morgan's knee and she crouched against him as if in fright. Thomas retreated slowly to his chair, already absorbed in the front page.

Alice complained, "He has no manners. Thomas! You should talk to Morgan first. Put down that paper."

He let it trail from his hand and smiled genially at Morgan but a moment later he had lifted it again and was trying to read out of the corner of his eye,

Morgan said, "Let him be, Alice. He has done his duty by me. Julia, my pet, you've grown again. You're almost too heavy for me."

She snuggled against him like a puppy, saying, "If you came often enough you wouldn't notice. Where have you been?"

"Working."

"Even on Sunday?"

239

"Sometimes on Sunday too."

"That's a sin."

"I hadn't thought of that."

"You should come here on Sundays. Mama, ask him to come every Sunday!"

"Will you, Morgan?"

"Of course."

He saw her eyes light up with joy, sending a flashing signal to him as clear as words. He held her gaze while a marvelous intelligence passed between them, all the more painful because it must never again be expressed. The presence of the children restrained him, making him conceal his helpless anger. He saw himself in a slightly ridiculous position, the odd man out, the devoted friend of the family, everyone's uncle, with no rights, conscious of the possibility that he was sometimes unwelcome. He had seen bachelors in this situation in Cappagh, their girl married to another man, themselves unable to leave her presence, always to be found in the third chair, a laughingstock for all comers, an obvious object of pity. The picture made him squirm and hold the child tighter to him. He hated Alice's capacity for continuing the pantomime, as if she were not the same woman who had lain in his arms in Paris, who knew she obsessed his thoughts day and night. She seemed even to be savoring the situation quietly, appreciating it, as if it were almost as good as the real thing.

"Please come. It's no earthly use being angry," she said cryptically for the children's benefit. Julia twisted around to look up at him quickly and then settled down again, reassured. Alice gave a short sigh, as if something had been dealt with, but he saw that she was suffering. Well, let her suffer. Why should it all be on his side? But immediately he pitied her and knew that the whole cycle had started again. Would he never again be at peace?

"Where is Samuel?" he asked abruptly.

"In Galway. He's coming back tonight on the train. He's going to open an office for the mill in Dublin. He wants to talk to you about it."

Morgan brightened the moment he heard that Samuel was away, and while she went to change her dress for dinner he set out on a tour of the house and garden with the children, each showing him a special feature. Julia's was a hedge of miniature roses and an apple tree with a bird's nest in it. Anna's was her own elegant bedroom, with flowered curtains and a view over the lawn, and a collection of dolls that Samuel had given her at various times. Thomas' was his own gray pony and the coach house, with carriages and traps and a phaeton and racks for harness and saddles.

"We have a governess now instead of Nurse," he said with a satisfied chuckle. "I got rid of her."

"*You* did?"

"Yes. Pushed her downstairs. She used to spank the girls with a hairbrush." Morgan saw Anna blush and turn aside. "She was afraid of me. I asked Papa to get rid of her but he wouldn't, so in the end I had to do it myself. It didn't hurt her much. I got an awful hiding from Papa afterward but it was well worth it. I couldn't sit down for a week, but then I cured and she was gone."

Morgan nodded, speechless.

Thomas said, "I'm the best at Latin and Greek in the school. I'm to go to Papa's old school in the autumn."

"Where?"

"Stonyhurst. Somewhere in England."

"Will you like that?"

"Probably. I'd like to see the world."

And this was Alice's son! Morgan could hear the tones of her voice in his, and he had a way of lifting his chin that was a replica of hers when she was angry. Julia's confiding hand in his reminded him of Alice, too, accepting his love without question. Only Anna seemed ill at ease, but when he tried to make her talk freely, she just looked at him hopelessly and stammered, so that he turned away from her out of pity.

He had dinner alone with Alice that night, watching her soft white hands in the candlelight while she poured wine for him and then set the decanter near the fire to warm for Samuel, who was to come at ten o'clock. He saw her face light up when the carriage wheels sounded on the gravel and smelled the stronger whiff of the scent she wore as she walked quickly past him to the hall to greet her husband. He followed, and saw her run into Samuel's arms.

35

All through that summer and the following winter Morgan went to Samuel's house every Sunday, as he had promised, each time finding the subsequent pain almost unbearable. Still he could not bring himself to give up the visits. They were an essential relief from the monstrous world he lived in, dominated by the strange genius of Stephens. When he came back from America in August, everyone tried to argue him into sharing his power, at least with the American Fenians who were sending the money that kept the paper going, but Stephens would not yield to anyone.

"I live in Ireland," he said. "I know our situation. Americans come and go. In this country, division of authority has always proved fatal. Our good friends in America will understand that. I explained it to them in Troy and Philadelphia and Louisville and Nashville and Detroit and Washington—in all your great cities where Irishmen have settled and still think of home. Their earnings will make our freedom possible. Your skill will teach our men the use of arms."

So he talked on and Morgan saw the two American generals who had come to Ireland look at each other uneasily.

Then General Kerwin said, "Mr. Stephens, we learned democracy in America. We don't like to take dictation from one person—nothing personal, you understand—it's the principle of the thing. You say you don't want to divide authority in the movement but you seem to us to be in danger of splitting the whole country. Surely that's much worse. What about all the good Irishmen who don't belong to the Brotherhood—the nationalist parliamentarians—can't we have their support too?"

"If they want to come in with us, they can do as we direct."

In May of 1865 Morgan was sent down to Mayo to call on George Henry Moore.

"Remember he's a landlord," Stephens said. "You can never trust a landlord, even when he looks like a nationalist. They're all the same when it comes to saving their own skins, keeping their hold on the land. They call it 'peaceful agitation by parliamentary means' but it's just cowardice. Not that Moore is a coward—but I don't trust him and I never will."

Morgan found Moore at home, in his great gray barrack of a house at Carnacon in Mayo. All the countryside around seemed gray or white, reflecting a gray-white sky full of rain clouds. He was let in by an untidy manservant and left to wait in a fine drawing room whose long windows looked out on the gravel in front of the house. A soughing wind blew the turf smoke out into the room. The walls and the molded stucco ceiling were already yellowed from many years of this treatment. Through the windows he watched the driver who had brought him from the station walk his horse, shivering and twitching with the cold, around to the stable yard. In the field below the house, hawthorn glittered and the chestnut trees were in full leaf.

He turned from the window when Moore came into the room, a weather-beaten, rocky, white-haired man with sad eyes, wearing a velvet smoking jacket, carrying a book in his hand with a finger among its pages to keep the place.

"Mr. Connolly? It's cold here—come into my workroom." As Morgan followed him toward the back of the house he turned suddenly to say, "Duffy and O'Donovan were here, I suppose you know."

He led Morgan into a smaller room which was certainly warmer. The walls were lined with bookshelves and the desk was littered with disordered papers, except for the part where he had been working. A collie bitch was spread on the hearthrug, her nose in her paws, and her sad, watchful eyes slewed toward the door as they came in. Mr. Moore sat down, carefully avoiding the dog, gesturing Morgan to the second armchair.

Morgan said, "Yes, they've reported back to Dublin and Mr. Stephens wants you to come to a conference."

"Conferences, conferences! What do they do for this godforsaken country? They're better than pikes, I suppose, but it's—let me see—fifteen years since we had the Tenant Right League, in '50. What has happened since? Conferences, jobbery, more conferences. What's going on in Dublin, young man?"

"O'Donovan Rossa is not much of a man for conferences, Mr. Moore."

Moore chuckled and said, "A regular firebrand, that fellow. I liked him. I had to believe in him—there's nothing of the peasant in him. He's all intelligence but what a fighter! Are they determined on that? I needn't ask—they made it very plain."

"We are determined but we need the help of everyone—"

"You don't exactly woo the landed gentry," Moore said dryly. "I seem to remember a statement in *The Irish People* that 'the elite of property will be an obstacle in the people's way—' " He reached over the desk and picked up a copy of the paper. "Here it is: '. . . an obstacle which no false delicacy must prevent us from trampling upon, if need be.' This article suggests that we be swept into the sea. It's a fine piece of rhetoric: 'In the darkest hour of her dark history the people were true to Ireland. Whoever were false, they never were. Whoever denied her, they never did. When she was betrayed and scourged and spat upon, the hands that lovingly supported her familiar form were the blistered hands of labor. Oh, brave toilers, surely it is reserved for you alone to lift her

243

to her place among the nations.' That doesn't leave much room for people like me, don't you think, Mr. Connolly?"

"Very few people like you read *The Irish People*. That was written by John O'Leary. His hands are not blistered with labor but he believes in giving the people a better opinion of themselves. He was not altogether against the National League a couple of years ago but he thinks, like the rest of us, that peaceful agitation will never work."

"Is that your view?"

"Yes. You know your own neighbors. They think of nothing but whiskey and fox hunting and point-to-point races. Their own dogs have more thoughts than they have at this stage. We can hope for nothing whatever from them, and they turn and snarl like dogs when they feel themselves threatened. You are respected, educated, traveled. The Americans are asking to have you in their counsels."

"What would my position be?"

"Not an active one—rather a talking one. After the rising, we'll need representatives, men who know how to explain our motives to the world—"

"After the rising?"

"It's inevitable. This year, next year—the time will come."

"And you'll die for Ireland?"

"I will if necessary but I hope it won't come to that."

Moore's eyes sparkled with amusement at this reply but in a moment he sobered and said, "It's not a matter for joking. I'm an old man. I've worked all my adult life for Ireland in spite of what O'Leary says. I did what I could for my tenants during the great famine and since then, and they're as ragged as ever, God help them. If I didn't give them work here at Moore Hall, they wouldn't see a shilling from year's end to year's end. What will your rising do for them? There will be hangings and transportations and imprisonments and evictions, wives and children left homeless, roofs thrown down, cattle and sheep stolen, even murder and rape, for all we know. Can't the people be spared? They always seem to come out of it worse in the end. Now the poorest can go to America and in time there will be room for the rest. Revolutions should be slow, otherwise one generation pays for all the generations to come."

"The poor have their responsibilities, too. The sooner the revolution comes, the better. Will you come to Dublin?"

"Will O'Donovan Rossa be there?"

"Certainly."

"Then I'll come. That man interests me. I have never seen an Irishman quite like him before."

Afterward Morgan realized that Moore had not talked about Stephens at all and when they met it was obvious that they would never agree. Moore automatically took the lead, as the older man, the landlord, the Member of Parliament used to being heard.

O'Donovan Rossa whispered in Morgan's ear, "Stephens will eat him. In another second Moore will call him 'my man.' Watch Stephens bristle!"

Stephens eyelids had narrowed in the way they all recognized and he turned his head sideways to look at Moore, as if he were nearsighted, which he was not.

"Good of you to come at such short notice, Mr. Moore," he said, paying no attention to Moore's remarks about cooperation and division of effort for the common good. "Now, what we want you to do is simple. You have prestige, of a kind. You're a good speaker. We need you to go to America and speak at the Fenian centers, explain our needs, collect money. We can do nothing without money. Later we'll need men but that won't be your part. All you need do is study the texts of the speeches I made in America in the winter of '63—Morgan will give them to you—and follow substantially the same pattern."

Moore said after a short pause, "I was under a misapprehension. I thought this was to be a conference—that was the word Mr. Connolly used. Now I see I have just been summoned for orders. I'm sorry, gentlemen, this is not possible. It's too long since I learned to think for myself and I find I don't agree with your policies enough to follow them without further discussion." He stopped and seemed to wait for a reply but Stephens had turned aside. Moore went on after a moment. "I disagree fundamentally with the idea of begging our way to an Irish parliament by going cap in hand to America—"

That stung an answer from O'Leary.

"It's not begging, not by any means. We get funds from Irish people, born in Ireland, who know they can't opt out of their responsibility to the country just by crossing the Atlantic. They give willingly."

"Perhaps so, but it's not my line of country and I'm too old to change. I think I'm too old to tour America for any cause, by the way. That's a job for a young man." He dropped his gaze unhappily but only for a moment. His habit of making up his mind quickly, no doubt acquired in parliamentary debates, asserted itself now, and looking around deliberately from one of them to the next he said, "I abhor divison among Irishmen. I am not going to withdraw my support from your effort. You may count on me absolutely, for anything within my power, but not for a rising in arms."

That was his last word. The conference had taken place in the clean, mahogany-furnished office of Mr. Denieffe's tailoring shop in South Anne Street and Mr. Moore was escorted courteously to the street by him, as if he were a customer.

After they had gone, O'Leary said tolerantly, "It's just as well. If we run into trouble, as we certainly shall, he'd be a drag on us."

"It would be a lovely scandal, though," O'Donovan Rossa said regretfully, "to have a landlord in the rising."

"Only if he had staying power, and I doubt that, especially at his age. They're all the same," Stephens said. "Well, we've made our gesture and it hasn't worked out badly. I still think that the fewer of Moore's type of Irishman we have, the better for the movement. He's a parliamentarian and that's what he'll be until the day he dies. So let him be. In the presence of our American friends I can say I'm glad we failed to impress him with our ideas. If we divide our councils, we fail once more. He would never have agreed with our policy of total war. It's written on his face."

The Americans had not liked the reference to begging.

"He's too arrogant," they said. "His accent, his voice, everything about him is sickening."

"As Irish landlords go, he's a lamb," Morgan said but it was no use.

Stephens smiled coldly. "I knew it wouldn't work," he said. "A landlord is always a landlord."

36

Morgan stayed late in his office one Friday evening in the middle of September. Gold sunlight still drifted through the dusty third-floor window at the back of the house and his lungs were full of dry, dusty air tainted with ink. A distant chestnut tree, just visible over the wall of a garden in Dame Street, reminded him of the approach of autumn, with its gold-tinged, drying leaves. To be in Paris now! Smells of leaves and flowers and trodden grass, and the tangy smell of the Seine, seemed to seep into the room. Vividly he lived it all still, feeling the warmth of sun-soaked doorways, tasting the sour wine, the crusty bread. Autumn was a good time in Paris.

He straightened his shoulders and reached for a bundle of clippings that had come in that morning. A door clanged—Jerry O'Farrell going home after sweeping up the debris that always cluttered the floors on publication day. A copy of the paper lay on Morgan's desk, O'Leary at his most urbane in the editorial:

"Nothing would please us better than to keep clear of the vexed question of 'priests in politics' if we could do so without injury to the cause we are endeavoring to serve. But the question was forced upon us. We saw clearly that the people should be taught to distinguish between the priest as a minister of religion and the priest as a politician before they could be got to advance one step on the road to independence. The people for whom God created it must get this island into their own hands —our only hope is in revolution."

O'Leary seemed never to tire of it all, or to suffer the agonizing doubts and moods that attacked Morgan periodically. He came in every day, neat and sure of himself, as if he were going to work in a good old family business. He had been just the same in Paris, walking deliberately from one bookshop to another, quietly picking up what he needed.

Morgan had a nervous sensation that Pagan O'Leary was at his elbow but when he turned quickly of course there was no one. Pagan was in jail, arrested almost a year ago in Athlone while he was attempting to recruit a soldier to the Fenians. Realizing that he had not read a line, Morgan put down the clippings and tidied them neatly into a pile. Better to come in fresh in the morning. It would be quiet then, since Mulcahy was away in Tipperary, and he would have the office to himself. Pierce Nagle would hardly come around on Saturday, the slackest day, the paper gone out and no real work to be done until Monday. Morgan disliked Nagle's habit of coming to the door without warning, looking as if he needed something that was not there and then going away silently. If he were a spy, as Mulcahy had suggested last week, there was nothing he could find out that was not public information. His job was to fold and pack the papers ready to take out but he had taken on one or two other tasks as well, without being asked, which gave him a right to go all over the building. He was the most willing messenger, never known to growl that he was too busy. He would even run to your lodgings for a book or a paper you had forgotten, though lately he was not often asked to do this kind of errand. Morgan's own view was that it was better to keep an eye on Nagle than to get rid of him and perhaps not identify the new spy when he arrived, as he certainly would.

He was groping his way down the dusky stairs when he heard a rumbling of voices from the street outside. It was no more than the usual sounds of traffic and yet it sent a *frisson* of terror up his spine and the back of his head. He darted into Mr. O'Leary's office, which overlooked the street from the second floor and looking down from the window there, he took in the strange scene. As he watched, he felt a sensation of despair, a kind of slackness, spread throughout his body. From his position at the window he could see that both ends of Parliament Street were blocked by solid ranks of policemen, their dark uniforms making an unbroken mass in the gloom. Outside the office there was a group of about twenty constables with several high-ranking officers in their gold-laced uniforms, and behind them a silent, shuffling crowd of people from the houses around. He recognized young Pat O'Toole from the sweetshop at the corner, his face bent whitely backward to look up into the determined faces of the men.

Before the first blow struck on the door, James Haltigan was at Morgan's elbow whispering, "I heard them from above. We're in a trap. Ned and Fireball have been out at the back but the police are around there, too. We're surrounded, Morgan."

A minute later, the other two men were in the room, going silently to the window first and then turning expectantly to Morgan.

He said, "This is the day, boys. We'll keep our dignity as soldiers as long as we're allowed. No unnecessary talk. We won't be alone, you may be sure."

They heard the lock give way and a clatter of heavy boots into the stone-floored hall below, shouts of officers and doors opened with a slam against the wall, boots pounding on the stairs and then a pair of policemen blocked the doorway.

One of them called out, "This way! There's some of them here!"

There was a rush forward and Morgan found himself grasped by a policeman on either arm, while the others were seized in the same way. The men who held him were shaking with excitement, squeezing his arms painfully so that he turned to them and said, "Don't be afraid—I won't hurt you."

An officer came to the door and barked, "How many have you got there?"

"Four, sir."

"Take them outside—no, just down to the hall. Turn out this room first."

As he was hustled out, Morgan saw another officer sit at John O'Leary's desk and begin to shuffle through the bundles of papers in the drawers while the first one said, "Everything is to come with us—leave nothing behind."

Standing in the hall during the next hour he saw the men pass and repass, carrying the drawers of the desks which they were using as trays for the papers. At one point the double doors were opened wide and the entire printing press was hauled out and loaded onto a waiting float.

Fireball cursed as he saw the rough treatment his machine was getting but Morgan said quietly, "You won't be needing it, I think. This lot means business. Look the other way."

"And they're Irishmen!" Fireball said with a sob of rage. "That makes it worse, and ten times worse. The curse of Cromwell on them—may they never die until the house falls in on top of them!"

Morgan was still Connemara man enough to feel shocked at this. He said, "God help them, they know no better."

"They do know better—they should know better," Fireball muttered over and over furiously.

Long before the search was ended, all four of them were marched outside, through the waiting crowd. As they appeared, a voice from the back sang in a high, wavering tenor, much too fast, as if he expected to be forcibly silenced:

" 'Yet thank God e'en still are beating hearts in manhood's burning noon
Who would follow in their footsteps at the rising of the moon!' "

Morgan tried to see who was there but the words had trailed off and the singer had probably slid into the middle of the crowd to avoid discovery. There could be no hope of finding out who he was but the policemen became very uneasy and they sent one pushing his way through the crowd, asking, "Who was that? Who sang that song? Who was it, then?"

A derisive voice called out, "Brian Boru!"

The howl of laughter infuriated the policemen but there was nothing they could do. They rushed the four prisoners away, pushing them roughly along by the shoulders, up to the end of the street, into the Castle, right across and out through the Lower Castle Yard to the police station in Chancery Lane. A thin sergeant sat at the long chipped desk that ran across the back of the hall.

"What are the charges?" he asked foolishly, goggling.

"Time enough for charges tomorrow. Get them locked up in the usual way—we're sick of them."

"But I have no room!"

"Make room, you sod! What do you think you have—a hotel!"

"Whose orders?" asked the unfortunate sergeant.

"The Privy Council's. Do you want it in writing?"

They swung out of the office, leaving the sergeant to summon his own men to take the prisoners into a larger room next door where they were ordered to strip off their clothes.

Fireball modestly turned his back, saying "What I suffer for you, Ireland!"

But none of the rest were in humor for jokes. They had become perfectly silent, and Morgan found that a second stage had begun, where silence seemed like a defense. He watched while one of the searchers went through his pockets, took several papers from them and laid them on the table. A second man took the trousers and cut off all but one of the buttons before handing him back his clothes. He began to recall the contents of his room, which would certainly be searched tonight too. From the way the arrests had been made, the determined wrecking of the offices, it seemed likely that they were going to be brought to trial. He felt a sudden rush of affection for the men who were with him.

"This way, this way," one of the searchers shouted, a redhaired, foxy-looking constable named Muldoon, who had never once raised his eyes to look into their faces. He opened a second door and herded them into an adjoining room, where familiar voices greeted them.

"It's Morgan and Fireball. Who else is with you?"

"Constable, I protest. I demand to be released! I'm a citizen of Boston. My Government will protest. Captain James Murphy of the 69th Regiment, now living in Boston—" one of the prisoners had begun to call out as soon as the door was opened.

Muldoon clapped the door shut without replying and Murphy turned to the others, saying, "Clods! Clowns! The whole lot of them! They can't do this to me."

"They can do anything they please."

That was O'Donovan Rossa. There was no sign of James Stephens but his father-in-law, George Hopper, was there, silent as usual.

O'Donovan Rossa grasped Morgan's hand and said in a low voice, "First time in, I think, Morgan? This is part of the fight, don't forget. The like of us that had a hard life when we were young—we'll be able for more than most. Don't lose heart—that's my best advice."

"You seem very sure we're in for a bad time."

"We're not in for our health. With any luck, they'll keep us together. Here comes some more."

Others were thrust into the room in twos and threes. Morgan went over to speak to them but the constables on guard chose that moment to start enforcing silence. By this time there were twenty men in the room, their faces ghostly in the greenish flare of the gaslight.

About midnight the door opened abruptly and the sergeant said testily, "Get some of them out of here—those lunatics seem to arresting half of Dublin. Get them into the cells—any place—"

Morgan, O'Donovan Rossa, Hopper and a man named O'Clohessy were hustled out, back through the room where they had been searched, where yet another group was standing naked now, down some dark steps, along an evil-smelling passageway soft with dirt, into a tiny room that appeared to be a lavatory. The thought crossed Morgan's mind that they were to be allowed to use the lavatory before being taken to the cells, but as the last of them was pushed inside and the door was locked, he realized that this was a cell. It was no more than seven feet square, furnished with nothing but a stool. Panic shot through him but he squeezed it down deliberately.

O'Donovan Rossa said, "Well, boys, here's as good an example as you'll get of Her Majesty's justice. Make yourselves at home and just pray that we won't be here a week."

Mr. Hopper, being the oldest, was given the stool, while the other three folded themselves down onto the floor. There was little talk, not even O'Donovan Rossa being buoyant enough to ignore the stench of the filthy lavatory.

O'Clohessy said plaintively once, "If I had my penknife I could have that lock off in two shakes."

"That's why they took it away from you, sonny," O'Donovan Rossa said.

Light came through the grille in the door from a gas jet in the corridor outside. They rested their heads against the walls and dozed but agonizing dreams tortured Morgan so that he woke again and again, cramped and shivering. He stood up now and then, stretching to his full height, feeling the hair on the top of his head brush the low ceiling. Sometimes there was a clatter at the end of the passageway when more men were hustled past, but no one else entered their part of the building.

Toward morning, daylight drifted in through a small air hole, the size of one brick, high up in the wall. The white faces of his companions looked desperately tired, especially that of Mr. Hopper, who was wide awake, lying against the wall in a heap, as if he had been thrown there. O'Donovan Rossa, the old lag, was asleep on his side on the floor and while Morgan watched he opened his eyes quickly, as a dog does, and looked around.

His eye caught Morgan's and he said softly, "I was dreaming of a little wood near Rosscarbery, in the last of the summer, just before the leaves turn—a sweet place. Ah, well, memory is for comfort in strange places."

"I'd be better without dreams."

"No. They're cheats but they keep a necessary part of us alive until better times come. I was to go to America today and my wife was to go to Cork. She's a strong woman, Morgan, but there are things no woman should have to bear. Seven months from now she will have another child and I won't be there to do a hand's turn for her."

"We're not condemned yet," Morgan said, not knowing how to console him.

"We will be. It's easy to tell by the way they're going about it. They'll get plenty of support in high places. Archbishop Cullen will be glad to have us out of the way and so will many another that's less honest. I could do with a bit to eat."

He stood up to stretch himself. O'Clohessy moaned in his sleep and rubbed his shoulder repeatedly against the wall like an animal, to find an easier position. The movement woke him so that he sat up, and they all remained silent for a long time while the light increased slightly as the sun moved around. At eight o'clock four bowls of porridge and four hunks of bread were pushed in through the partly opened doorway.

O'Donovan Rossa sang out, "Wait, if you please! We demand a lawyer and some information!"

But the door clanged shut and they were alone again. They ate the food as best they could, not knowing when the next lot would come, and then the time went slowly by until noon. For Morgan, the hell of those first hours at the police station made all that followed seem at least endurable. Any change was welcome, and when they were summoned from the disgusting cell, they moved eagerly out into the dark corridor as if it were a garden. Muldoon was on duty again, shepherding them through the entrance hall, where a different sergeant now sat at the desk, into a long black van drawn by two horses. The van was backed right up against the door so that they were inside and the door was slammed shut before they saw that it was already almost full. John O'Leary was there, collected and calm as usual, making way for O'Donovan Rossa beside him on the bench, as if they were meeting in the bar of a hotel. He had spent the night in the College Street police station with Pierce Nagle and James O'Connor, in a cleaner, more savory cell than Morgan's. In the presence of Muldoon and three other constables who traveled with them, they could not say much, and besides the journey was too short.

37

Within a few minutes the van stopped and they were unloaded and marched up some steps into a large building.

O'Leary said as they went in, "It's the Commissioner's office. This means they're nervous."

They were herded into a small courtroom and were crowded somehow, all twenty-eight of them, into the dock. A file of six constables stood at either end. After a long wait, two magistrates strolled in and sat on the bench with their heads close together, talking earnestly.

One looked up after a minute and said, "Open a window, for God's sake. It's suffocating."

He turned back to his colleague and went on with the conversation, which was inaudible because of the incessant shuffling of the prisoners' feet.

John O'Leary murmured, "The Chief Magistrate—what an honor! No point in our saying anything now, Mr. O'Donovan?"

O'Donovan Rossa shook his head and O'Leary, who had taken a corner place to the front of the dock, folded his arms in a characteristic gesture that all the men recognized. Tired and dispirited as they were, they made an effort to straighten their backs and look soldierly. Not even Captain Murphy of Boston spoke and all their eyes were fixed on O'Leary.

The door opened and Mr. Barry, the prosecuting counsel, in his wig and gown, came in, bowed to the bench and sat down. Two men of the G Division read out the prisoners' names, and while the litany went on, O'Donovan Rossa turned his eyes upward and gave a sigh.

Chief Magistrate Stronge said, "Will that prisoner kindly respect the court!"

O'Donovan Rossa's chuckle was echoed by several of the prisoners and Stronge said, "Can't you control them, Smollen? Dawson! They're in your charge. Finish that list quickly!"

When every man had answered to his name, Barry stood up and addressed the court.

"Mr. Stronge, Mr. MacDermott, we have a charge of conspiracy against these men, perhaps a charge of treason. The conspiracy is to overthrow the Government of this island, with a plot to hand over all property to the lower orders. We have much evidence to bring, which you will understand will take time to assemble." He paused and MacDermott bowed with an air of solemn understanding. Barry went on. "These are desperate men of known bad character. They cannot be allowed to go free. I am asking therefore that they be remanded in custody."

He sat down, his chin in the air, and watched while the magistrates consulted with each other.

Then Stronge said carelessly, "Remanded in custody for a week. The prisoners may be removed."

Stronge, MacDermott and Barry left the courtroom together. Standing silently in the dock, the men were aware that their captors were agitated in an odd way. They appeared to be at a loss what to do next. The two G Division men, Smollen and Dawson, and a superintendent named Ryan went in and out several times, each time consulting with the guards.

On one of these visits, O'Donovan Rossa leaned over the bar of the dock and said softly, "Mr. Smollen, sir, I have a reasonable request to make. As I was coming in, I saw my wife at the door outside. I'd like to speak a few words to her."

"No. No visitors allowed."

"She's with child, Mr. Smollen. It would be a decent, charitable act to let me have a few words with her in her condition."

"I said, no visitors. That's enough."

For a second it seemed that O'Donovan Rossa would argue further but then he closed his mouth tightly and turned aside. Seconds later, however, he was glaring angrily toward the other end of the dock as a small, quiet woman was led in to speak to Nagle. He started to call out to Smollen again and then seemed to abandon the idea.

Almost an hour later, an agonizing, boring, foot-shuffling hour, the gates of the dock were opened at either end and the entire force of their guards herded them out. Morgan was in front with O'Donovan Rossa, the first two to emerge from the double doors onto the steps, where they stood in amazement at the sight of the crowd surrounding the prison van. It was backed up to the steps, ready to receive them, its doors already swinging open, and the horses were tossing their heads in fright at the noise of the crowd. A short, sharp cheer went up. Four policemen forced their way through to the group that had cheered, seizing two men each and hauling them up the steps and thence into the building. Other policemen moved in from the back of the crowd and eddies of struggling men could be seen here and there. By now the rest of the prisoners had come out and Morgan was forced down to a lower step, from which he no longer had a view over the heads of the people.

It was then that he saw Alice, wedged in the crowd, trying to force her way to the van, her fur-trimmed mantle pulled awry. She was calling out to him.

"Morgan, Morgan!"

People made way for her, helped her forward, while she reached out with her hands toward him. Craftily, he made no sudden move but edged to the lowest step so that when she reached it he was there to take her hands for one glorious moment while a fire of pain coursed through him. Abruptly he was dragged away and hurled into the van, where he sat in a stupor, looking at his hands as if they had been used to perform a miracle. All through the journey to Richmond jail, the vision of her was constantly before his eyes, so that he scarcely heard the cheers of the crowd or noticed the bumping and shaking of the van until it stopped and they were taken out, hustled into the main hall of the jail and lined up to be registered.

Morgan stood beside O'Donovan Rossa, who glanced at him anxiously now and then as if he feared he would not be equal to the coming ordeal. This brought him to his senses. Mr. O'Leary and Mr. Luby were at his other side.

A hungry-looking official in a rumpled black uniform sat before them at a table. He looked at O'Donovan Rossa and said, "Your name."

"Jeremiah O'Donovan Rossa."

"Your occupation."

"Merchant."

"Religion."

"Irish Catholic."

The official looked up, annoyed.

"No jokes, mind. Are you Roman Catholic?"

"No, sir. Irish Catholic."

"There is no such denomination. You must register as a Roman Catholic."

"But I'm not Roman. I'm Irish."

"Sign here, under Roman Catholic, or it will be the worse for you."

"I will not sign a lie. I'm an Irish Catholic and I'll go to the chapel under that label."

"I'll put you down as an atheist, refusing to adhere to any religion. Next, please."

The next was John O'Leary, who continued the comedy, and he was followed by Morgan and then by Mr. Luby.

As they were led away, O'Donovan Rossa said, "I wonder how the Fireball is getting on."

"Silence!"

After that a half-life began, a kind of existence that seemed impossible to take seriously because it had so little to do with reasonable daily life as Morgan had known it until now. He was put in a cell alone, a flagged, bare room that at first sight seemed quite large because it was the same size as the cell he had shared with three others last night. He had a stool to sit on and a board attached to the wall for a table and for twenty-three hours a day his thoughts to amuse him. The twenty-fourth hour was spent in the yard, at exercise, eyes rigidly in front by orders, distanced six paces from his fellow prisoners, who were apparently docile and obedient, even O'Donovan Rossa keeping the rules that were shouted at intervals. He was allowed to buy his food, which meant that he did not have to work, and fortunately the little money he had at the time of his arrest was adequate for the trays of grayish material sent in by the official caterers to the prison every day.

On Sundays the other men were taken to the chapel to hear Mass but O'Donovan Rossa, O'Leary, Luby and Morgan were left in their cells. Morgan felt this as the cruelest deprivation of all, worse than his solitude, worse than being cut off from his companions. If Father Kenny knew where he was, he would get in somehow to see him. But they were allowed no visitors and the Castle would be sure to take advantage of the Archbishop's warning to the priests that they were not to encourage the Fenians in any way. Some priests had even interpreted this as a direction to inform on them and had used information received in Confession to send word to the Castle of Fenians in their parishes. Morgan knew of one of these in Kerry, and the nice question of whether he was to be shot as an informer was agitating the Fenian councils at the last meetings. He wondered what would happen now, whether the mass arrests would mean that this miserable traitor would go scot free.

Shocked at himself, he realized that anger burst within him at intervals, irrational, murderous anger that left him exhausted and frightened in an unfamiliar way. Sometimes when the jailer came around and the doors were open, the urbane voice of John O'Leary reached him, asking to have a glass of wine with his dinner or to be given back his pipe and tobacco. These requests were refused and no arguments were allowed, but Morgan found that he was calmer after he had overheard the conversations. O'Leary was so much more self-sufficient, so much more balanced than Morgan, whose youth spent running wild over the rocks of Connemara was poor training for confinement.

He dared not think of Alice after the first pitch-dark night when he had conjured her up so powerfully that he could feel her soft breasts in his hands and her soft thighs under his, and he had seemed to plunge himself into her body with the greed of starvation, coming to himself later in a half-crazed condition that made the hateful walls press closer and the ceiling seem to descend on top of him.

Toward the end of the week he began to adjust to this life, finding that the day divided into periods of more or less misery according to the amount of light in his cell. Light became an obsession with him, a love object to be watched and courted and lamented as it came and went. He tried to make a game of remembering sayings concerning light: "The light of heaven to your soul," a blessing; "A light in her eye," of a girl in love; but there were not enough of them to keep him diverted for long.

The end of the week's remand was a cruel disappointment. Instead of being taken to the court, on Saturday morning they were summoned to the great hall where they had been received on the first day. The Chief Magistrate was there, with Barry, the prosecuting counsel, who scarcely glanced at them as he repeated the charge of conspiracy and made a formal request for another remand.

O'Donovan Rossa livened things up by remarking, "It's on your side the conspiracy is, not ours."

The names were called again and then they were back in the cells, hearing as they filed upstairs the laughter of the visiting gentlemen at some joke of their own.

The day of the Magistrate's Court was the last Saturday of September, a warm, damp day with the air, even in the middle of Dublin, full of the nostalgic smells of fading leaves and grass and moist earth. Coming out of the prison the men blinked in the sunlight and were almost grateful for the shelter of the dark van that was waiting for them. A squadron of mounted police was there to escort them, and a constable sat in the van by the side of each prisoner. The men were livelier than usual, since something was moving at last, and O'Donovan Rossa had a glint of battle in his eye that made Morgan smile in spite of himself. He made sure to sit near him, his only chance to speak to him in two weeks. The constables looked uncertain but did not interfere.

"My wife has been in to see me," O'Donovan Rossa said. "We were allowed to speak loud and clear in the presence of the prison Governor—not much room for secrets there."

"How is she?"

"She told me she's well but I could tell by her looks that it was a lie. God help her, what can she say, to keep my heart up? She told me there are wild stories in the newspapers about us and the terrible things we were planning. It's a campaign to condemn us in advance. That's not news—solitary confinement for two weeks before the trial begins at all is the proof of it."

"We're to be charged with high treason, according to the Governor."

"It looks like it, and I can tell you I don't like the thought. If they want to hang us, it will have to be high treason nowadays. I went through the whole process in my imagination a few nights ago, and it's a good cure for the terror of it, though I can't say I liked it." Morgan shivered. The other said, almost casually, "I wonder where they're taking us this time."

It was Dublin Castle again, as they found when the van was opened in the Lower Castle Yard. They stepped down into what seemed a small army of police and were quickly marched into the courtroom, which was already full of spectators. Their hungry eyes were immediately turned on the prisoners, reminding Morgan of a pack of hounds waiting for the signal to take off. The Commissioner of Police was there in his splendid uniform, and several high-ranking officers of the Army. There was not a friendly face among them all. Stronge and MacDermott and three or four finely dressed men were already on the bench.

The prisoners were hustled into the dock, which was too small to hold them all now that their number had increased. While the police were arranging some of them to stand beside the dock, the guard at the courtroom door came forward and said, "Mr. Stronge, there are two ladies at the door, the wife of the prisoner O'Donovan Rossa and a Miss O'Leary. They want to come in."

"I've given instructions that the public is not to be admitted to come in."

"Very well, sir."

Mr. Stronge seemed put out at the interruption and seeing this the officials hustled their juniors with short, sharp barks. At last Barry, the prosecuting counsel, stood up and all talk stopped while the spectators leaned eagerly forward. A good showman, Barry lifted his head and breathed heavily once or twice before beginning in a slow threatening tone.

"I appear on behalf of the Crown. The prisoners, as you are already aware from the sworn information laid before the magistrates, are charged with a very serious offense—a charge no less than that of being members of a treasonable association, and active for the furtherance of that association, which has for its object the subversion of the Queen's authority in this country and the substitution for it of some form of government, the device, I suppose, of the members of this confederacy." He waved a contemptuous hand toward the prisoners. "The existence of this association has excited a considerable deal of public attention and in some quarters of the country some degree of anxiety and, I may say, alarm." He allowed himself a patronizing smile. "Of course anxiety and alarm not arising from any apprehension that the force and authority of the law would not be sufficient easily to crush any such attempt, but anxiety felt for the mischief that the existence in the country of such an association would produce amongst certain classes of the people by disturbing their minds from peaceful and lawful pursuits, and above all, anxiety for the consequences that their participation in this society must bring upon the foolish and misguided persons who are made the victims of reckless adventurers or, perhaps more, of designing knaves."

He swung his head upward, as if he expected applause. After a short pause he went on, in measured sentences, while the whole court listened avidly. Describing the conspiracy he said, "It is socialism in its most wicked and pernicious phase. The lower classes were taught to believe that they might expect a redistribution of the property, real and personal, of the country. They were taught to believe that the law by which any man possessed more property than another was unjust and wicked, and the plan of operation, as will be found to have been suggested, is horrible to conceive. The operations of this revolution, as it is called, were to be commenced by an indiscriminate massacre—by the assassination of all those above the lower classes, including the Roman Catholic clergy."

At this, O'Leary and O'Donovan Rossa looked at each other and smiled incredulously.

Barry raised his voice a tone. "The clergy, against whom their animosity appears from their writings to be especially directed, by reason of the opposition that those clergymen thought it right as Christian ministers, as Irishmen and as men of peace and honor to give to the projects in question."

Morgan watched the faces of the audience while Barry described, accurately, the organization of the Fenians—the Head Centers, the A's, B's, C's and D's, and the close tie that existed with America. God help them, how frightened they looked! And how was it possible to live on the land of Ireland and be so unconscious of what was happening all around them? Perhaps it could happen in Dublin households, where one need never rub shoulders with a real Irishman, where nurses and grooms and footmen stood between the family and reality. He must warn Alice of this danger—and like a wasp sting, realization came to him that he might never have the opportunity. Alice! Were the others thinking of their wives and children? John O'Leary was a confirmed bachelor but O'Donovan Rossa had a big family of boys who must be constantly in his mind now. There were gasps of horror as Barry described the pikes that had been made at home and the guns that had been bought in America, and looks of loathing were turned on the prisoners.

At last Mr. Stronge said, "The prisoners may have counsel for the defense."

O'Donovan Rossa snorted with contempt. "I'd rather defend myself, gentlemen. At least I'll know then that I'm in fair hands."

And John O'Leary said, "I also am alarmed for the fairness of this court when I see how the very name of Irish nationalism arouses such fears in the hearts of our judges. Yet this fear is justified if it is caused by reflection on the long history of oppression of our country and the certainty that retribution will come someday . . ."

Morgan was astonished that he was allowed to go on with this for several minutes before MacDermott ruled him out of order, rather uneasily, as if some of the jabs had found their mark.

When the witnesses were called at last, Pierce Nagle was the first, looking pitiably nervous but giving his evidence with conviction. He had joined the Fenians in Ballyboe, Clonmel, several years ago, he said, and he knew Denis Mulcahy, who was a neighbor of his. He had been engaged a year and a half ago by the G Division, which paid him regularly to bring information.

"One of the twelve, like Judas, and about as much information to give," said O'Donovan Rossa loudly.

"Silence! The prisoner will be silent!"

"If he is, it will be for the first time in his life!" said O'Donovan Rossa hotly, but he shut his mouth tightly.

Nagle was shaking but after a whispered consultation with Superintendent Ryan he went on with his evidence, glancing at the dock every few seconds as if he expected to be jumped on by all the prisoners at once. He was shown letters about the manufacture of pikes, which were always called "rods," and he recognized these and even described the flag of the new state, which was to have four stripes representing the four provinces and thirty-two stars representing the thirty-two counties. By the time he had finished, the courtroom was deadly silent and his high-pitched dreary voice had got under everyone's skin.

At last they were on their way back in the van and O'Donovan Rossa said, "Nagle hadn't much to tell, indeed, but it's all one to those judges of ours. They can convict or acquit by law without any trouble, just as they please. We'd better conspire together before Monday's hearing, since we look like being tried for conspiracy."

But they were not allowed to meet again or to consult with one another. At the prison they were quickly marched to their cells and locked in, and next morning, when they went out to exercise, they found that O'Donovan Rossa was not with them. From that day onward, he was given his statutory hour's exercise in a different yard from the rest of them, and the guards in the van prohibited them from speaking on their way to the court.

38

Two months passed in slow, deadly days, some enlivened by useless talks with the solicitor, strangely named Lawless, who had agreed to act for them. They were allowed to meet Lawless together, in the presence of the warders, but as some of these were Fenians it was often possible to pass on whispered news to one another. Early in October, less than a month after the big haul, Mulcahy was arrested and then one day there was James Stephens among them too. He had spent the time in the suburbs of Dublin, in Sandymount, by the sea, but had been discovered and arrested with three others. He seemed distant and preoccupied, as if the fraternity of their common plight did not affect him. Three days later he was taken to court and came back looking almost smug. He had been committed for trial, and the Undersecretary, old Sir Thomas Aiskew Larcom, had been on the bench with Mr. Stronge.

"Quite an honor, but of course the trial won't arise," he said, and would explain no more.

A week or so later he escaped from the prison.

"Self-centered, as always," John O'Leary said bitterly. "No understanding of the need for cooperation at the top level, no thought for the effect of this on the rest of us."

The immediate effect was that the warder who had helped him, a Fenian named Byrne, was arrested and brought to trial, and the other prisoners were watched more strictly than ever, especially Kickham, Duffy and Brophy, who had been Stephens' companions in the hide-out in Sandymount.

Lawless came hurrying in one evening to say that a Special Commission had been set up to try the Fenians, the first since the rebellion of 1848.

"The judges are Keogh and Fitzgerald," he said. "They're hand-picked."

O'Leary said, his eyebrows lifting in astonishment, "Surely not Keogh!"

"I'm afraid so." Lawless shifted uneasily in his chair and avoided O'Leary's eyes in embarrassment, as if he had been responsible. "We hope to have Mr. Butt and Mr. Dowse for the defense, and we already have Mr. Sidney. They'll do the best they can for you but they won't be able to challenge the selection of the judges at any stage."

"But Keogh has been our sworn enemy for years. Everyone knows that he's madly antinationalist—and his personal reputation—"

"I know, I know, but once the decision is made it will be presumed to have been made after proper investigation. Fitzgerald is a member of the Privy Council that ordered the arrests—his appointment is improper, too. It seems they don't care what anyone thinks so long as—"

"So long as they manage to convict us with some show of law. It couldn't be done without the help of Irishmen."

"The trouble is made worse by the press campaign. I've never seen anything so disgraceful. Stronge just says it's natural for the press to take an interest. The Archbishop's pastoral is another story. That's a horse of a different color." He looked at their glum faces as if he had just made a new, original joke and then scrabbled in his briefcase, taking out a newspaper. "He had no right to attack you while you're awaiting trial. We may be able to do something about that. Here, for instance, he clearly says that you're all irreligious, don't go to the chapel in jail, are out to destroy the faith of the people and intended to seize all property and exterminate the gentry and the Catholic clergy and have the poor people reading Voltaire—"

"Voltaire!" O'Leary snorted. "If they could read their own names, it wouldn't be a bad start."

"And he says you want to set up socialism. He condemns the managers of *The Irish People* wholesale, says the public authorities deserve the thanks and gratitude of all who love Ireland."

"It's a mandate to go ahead and destroy us," O'Donovan Rossa said. "Nothing could be clearer. But we can make a fine bang before we go."

"It sounds too crazy—"

"No one will believe it—"

"At this rate one couldn't found a new political party—"

"He sees a socialist behind every bush—"

The growls stopped when Lawless said, "There's more. He goes on about Mazzini and Garibaldi and the French Revolution, condemns secret societies—that's nothing new—and here he says that this will finish Fenianism and probably after a short time we shall hear no more about it."

"What can you do about it?" O'Leary demanded.

"A libel action against *The Freeman's Journal* for publishing it before the trials open. That won't make him love you more but it should silence him. It won't stop the damage that has been done already."

Morgan found that he could not interest himself in legal games, important though they might be. O'Leary had the kind of intricate, complicated mind that appreciated such things and O'Donovan Rossa saw a chance of acting the gadfly, a role he always enjoyed, but anyone could see that all they hoped for was some harassment and delaying tactics. The Archbishop was silenced, as Lawless had predicted, but the newspapers continued their slanders, more carefully worded, right up to the day of the trial.

Monday, November 27, was the opening day. In the morning, Philpot, the chief warder, came around at eight o'clock to see that all the prisoners were present and ready to go. He assembled them in the main hall and Mr. Marquis, the Governor of the prison, went over the list with him while the warders lined them up in double rows. The officials looked relieved, almost grateful, when they found that all forty-six prisoners were present. All the prison staff, from the Governor down, were in trouble since Stephens' escape, with an investigating committee on their backs for hours every day. There was a rumor that the Fenians would soon be moved to Kilmainham, which had a reputation for never losing a prisoner.

When the inspection was over, the great doors were opened and the men were ordered outside. They moved heavily now, weak from bad food and lack of exercise. Mr. Denieffe looked sick and old, and so did Mr. Hopper, but John O'Leary was almost dapper, even without his buttons and his collar and tie. In the yard they found an escort of dragoons and mounted policemen waiting to accompany the prison van, as well as several constables who traveled inside. They set off with a great clatter, the wheels of the van jerking over the rough cobbles. As they approached the river, gusts of wind struck the sides of the van, rocking it and whining around its corners. Then they felt the whole cavalcade slow up. The men inside could hear the murmurs of a large crowd, though it was barely nine o'clock. The horses' hooves seemed louder as they danced their way through the narrow streets.

There was a pause after the van came to a halt. Morgan felt a sickening excitement in his throat. The men were very quiet, not turning or looking at one another.

The doors opened suddenly and a voice shouted, "Out, and inside at once!"

They found that they were not in Green Street but in the smaller one, Halston Street, to the side of the courthouse. As the first man appeared on the steps of the van, a great cheer rose from the waiting crowd and was carried flying off in the wind. They were all hustled out, with hurrying hands on their shoulders, but O'Donovan Rossa could not be prevented from sending a delighted grin of recognition, like the flash of a lighthouse, around the nearest faces. Then the people were pushed back by the cavalry and a detachment of soldiers and police took up positions on guard around the courthouse. The doors shut behind the prisoners but they could hear shouts and the trampling of horses as they were taken into the building and down the stairs to the waiting room.

"That was a good crowd," John O'Leary said. "It's a full-dress affair. They're nervous, all right. They're even afraid to use the front door."

Sitting with the others on a long bench in the underground room, to which little sound penetrated, a sense of dullness, which might have been terror, replaced the former excitement, and Morgan marveled at Mr. O'Leary's quiet manner and tone of voice as he chatted with O'Donovan Rossa and James O'Connor about the possible course of the trial. It would not be slow, he said, as the Commission was to move on to Cork when it had finished with Dublin, but since the charge was now definitely one of high treason, they would have to go carefully. The other prisoners were silent, seeming to listen to Mr. O'Leary as one might listen to a running stream or to bird songs, soothed by the sound of the words rather than by their meaning.

After an hour in which the greasy benches and the dark-brown walls seemed to become every moment more aggressive, a stir and a rumble of voices suggested that the courtroom was filling up, but it was almost eleven o'clock before the prisoners were summoned. They went up the stairs in double file, led by John O'Leary and Thomas Luby followed by O'Donovan Rossa and Charles O'Connell. Morgan tried to improve the shambling gait of the men, ridiculously clutching their trousers at the waist.

"No need for us to slouch—shoulders straight, not too military but not apologetic either."

At first sight the courtroom seemed to be crammed with police, row upon row of uniforms in the seats allotted to the general public, but when he had recovered from the first blast of those hostile eyes and the shock of the tiny involuntary hiss that went up at their first appearance, Morgan was able to make out that there were some civilians, too, and lifting his eyes to the gallery he saw a small group of women together in the front row. The eyes of all the prisoners were on that group. Alice was there, wearing a hat with curled feathers, and Mrs. Luby, as well as Mrs. O'Donovan Rossa and Ellen O'Leary, Mrs. Hopper and some others whom he did not recognize.

Lawless had said that for the preliminary hearing all the prisoners were to be in court together, but afterward they would be summoned in smaller numbers or singly. Now as many as would fit were crowded into the dock and the rest stood on the floor beside it. Morgan was close to John O'Leary, who had at once taken up his place at the head of the line, as the leader of the group. That should have been Stephens' place.

Morgan heard several voices whispering anxiously.

"Which is Stephens?"

"Has he been captured?"

"What does he look like?"

"Is he there?"

The court clerk called on the public to rise and the judges were ushered in by the High Sheriff and the Lord Mayor of Dublin. The four Queen's counsel for the prosecution were at a table below the judges and counsel for the defense were just under the dock. At the reporters' table, which faced the judges, the artist from the *Illustrated London News,* who had been making quick sketches of the prisoners, laid down his papers and stood up with the rest, but his eyes wandered over the room as if he were memorizing the scene. Mr. Butt's square jaw and firm mouth were reassuring but Morgan found himself irritated by his deference to the court.

When the judges were seated on the bench, everyone except the prisoners sat down. There was a rustling pause and a sense of anticlimax. Then the Clerk of the Crown stood up and read the writ for the holding of the Commission in a threadbare voice, as if he knew all legal formalities were a farce. He was a little weasel-faced man named Geale, who looked as if he had never had enough fresh air. He seemed more interested when he began to swear in the Grand Jury.

Morgan examined those twenty-three men closely—Joseph Casson, the foreman, Joseph Wilson, Edmund Kinahan, Alfred Alexander, William Foot—such extraordinary names, but he couldn't remember them all—Fox, Findlater, Bagot, Graham. Where would they go and what would they do when they had finished with him? Alice was watching them, too, and as the last was sworn and took his place in the box, Morgan caught her eye and saw there, in this terrible place where it was useless to him, the naked love that she had concealed for so many years. It startled him as if she had called out to him. A moment later he was filled with a sense of fatigue with the whole hopeless business of living, so overwhelming that he almost welcomed the nearness of death.

The charges were being read out.

"High treason by compassing, devising and conspiring, within the last three years, with the members of a secret society called the Fenian Brotherhood, in England, Ireland and America, of which society they are members, to levy war against the Queen in Ireland, subvert her royal authority and establish an independent republic: John O'Leary, Thomas Clarke Luby, James O'Connor, Jeremiah O'Donovan Rossa,

Christopher Manus O'Keeffe, Martin Hanley Carcy, George Archdeacon, Patrick Scally, James Quigley, John Fottrell, Michael O'Boyle, Michael Moore and Patrick Hayburne."

Listening for his name, Morgan was surprised that it was not in that lot. The next one was read.

"Charged with being a member of the Fenian Brotherhood and conspiring with the members of the said society to levy war against the Queen in Ireland and establish a republic: George Augustine F. Gillis."

Morgan's turn came in a charge of "printing and publishing and uttering treasonable articles in a paper called *The Irish People*, thereby conspiring to levy war against the Queen and moving foreigners to invade Ireland." There was a charge against another Connachtman for doing the same "in a paper called the *Connacht Patriot*." Morgan stole a glance at his companions in the dock and saw that they were very quiet. He concentrated on keeping his own expression calm but feared that he had already betrayed himself. Heavy beards were a help to some of the others, but Morgan had long ago tired of his beard and now wore only side whiskers.

When charges against all the prisoners had been read, the judges conferred together and then Keogh began his address.

"Mr. Foreman and gentlemen of the Grand Jury of the City of Dublin, you have heard Her Majesty's special commission read, commanding my learned brother and myself to take immediate steps . . ."

The language was the language of the law but Keogh's malignance showed as he told the jury that it was well known that a conspiracy had been afoot for several years past to set up an independent republic in Ireland, a conspiracy that spread throughout the country to all classes, and even to America, where money and guns had been collected and sent to Ireland. The charge was now of treason felony, he said, and it would succeed if it could be proved that the men in the dock had held meetings, bought arms, collected money for a treasonable purpose, administered oaths or manufactured weapons. After that speech it hardly seemed worthwhile going on with the trial. John O'Leary was holding himself in check with difficulty and O'Donovan Rossa was glaring furiously, but both had agreed with Mr. Butt that they would not interrupt no matter what the judges said.

The air in the courtroom was foul with tension. Mr. Butt had made an angry movement or two in the beginning of the speech but had then sunk into silence. When he had finished with the statement that the object of British law is not retaliation, Keogh announced that the court would adjourn for three hours while the jury deliberated. Then he and Fitzgerald left the bench. The jury filed out of its box and was ushered out of the court, and then the prisoners were ordered below, the policemen yapping at their heels lest they make any attempt to speak to their friends. There was time only for a brief glance at Alice and Morgan had an odd impression that she had grown smaller in the course of the morning, as if he were already being carried away from her to a great distance. Weariness and hunger were the cause of this, he supposed, the same as affected all the men, who spoke little as they munched the lumps of dry bread that had been provided for them.

Presently O'Donovan Rossa said, "It was the sorry day I promised Mr. Butt to keep silent but I'm a man of my word. What I wouldn't give to have a slap off that Judge Keogh! A greasy old bastard, if ever there was one. Treason felony it is now, and I think I know why."

"You think they're *afraid* to hang us?"

Several of the men leaned forward to hear the answer to John O'Leary's question.

O'Donovan Rossa laughed sourly.

"Perhaps, but I doubt if we've reached that stage yet. More likely they haven't enough evidence. Nagle's word wouldn't be enough. They need two informers and this time for some reason they don't seem to have them. I must say I'm surprised —we're never short of informers in Ireland."

"It's no longer the safe job it used to be," Morgan suggested.

"True enough, a good many of them would be afraid to go into court now, afraid to show themselves. They don't mind in the least going up to the back door of the barracks in the dark of the night, whispering names, but that's no use in court. Hearsay isn't evidence. I have a mind to conduct my own case this time."

"Mr. Butt won't like it."

"No. I'd be sorry for that but I have a feeling that they're out to get us this time and if that's the way, even a good lawyer won't do much for us." He sprang to his feet and raised his voice. "The fight is on. This is not a trial. It's our business to fight in the gap of danger, as we always knew we'd have to fight some day. We had an idea that it would be a battlefield but we're not going to get the chance of that, if I'm any judge. Then we must make this our battlefield, yes, and the prison, too, since that's where we're going to be landed. I say to every man here that it's his duty as a Fenian and an Irishman to stand up to the humiliations and insults that will certainly be our share in prison. Don't give in to them sheepishly. Remember you're Irishmen, part of a great old nation, one that walked this land before the dawn of history. We swore to liberate our country, to fight for the poor and the lowly and the downtrodden who once were kings—"

By this time he was standing on a bench, facing the other prisoners, his speech in full flight, as if he were addressing a public meeting. The astonished constables came to life, perhaps at the sight of the shining eyes of the prisoners, who had been so apathetic a moment before.

The sergeant called out, "Silence, you! Sit down!"

He advanced threateningly, signaling to the nearest constables to close in on O'Donovan Rossa, who had sat down at once, having made his point quite well enough. Morgan saw O'Leary put on the judicious expression he wore during any debate when he was about to give his view, and his voice was as measured and quiet as usual.

"I don't agree with you, Jerry. We're in the hands of our enemies now and we should behave with dignity, the dignity of soldiers. That's what I advise."

Pagan O'Leary, who had been brought from jail to face additional charges, said quietly to Morgan, "This is the dark hell that I told you about. I never heard that a man could fight in hell. I'm going to be quiet now, as Mr. O'Leary says." And he lowered his head like a donkey on a wet day and seemed to begin his imprisonment in earnest from that moment onward.

Cold seeped into their bones and Morgan moved about to relieve it. Time crept so slowly that he began to long for the court to reassemble, for anything at all to happen that would break through the wall of depression brought on by Pagan's last words. Where was Alice now? From his position in the dock below the gallery, he had seen some twittering, feathery ladies give disapproving looks at the group of sad women in the front row. Perhaps they were all together now in some nearby hotel coffeeroom, enduring the grimy tablecloths and greasy food in a common fraternity.

By this time, Martin would surely have heard of his arrest. Nora would cry—he was glad that she had married, after all, though Mike Heffernan was a clod if ever there was one. Martin said Mike loved Nora. Now with the world so strangely narrowed down, love was the greatest thing in it, the anchor, the fixed star, the lighthouse. Several times lately it had occurred to him that Samuel knew quite well how much he loved

Alice and sympathized with his predicament. There was nothing humiliating to Morgan in this; on the contrary, it seemed to draw him toward Samuel, as if all three of them were combined in a family of love. Was this a monstrous idea? Without warning, that terrible letter he wrote after his visit to Aran entered his mind and sat there like a little devil to torment him. Samuel would have a very different view of him if he knew the source of that letter or the reason why it was written. Morgan squirmed as he had not done for years and was relieved when the door opened and they were summoned to go back to the court.

He noticed that an easier atmosphere had replaced the tension of the morning, as if the lawyers and the public had already become accustomed to the situation and were at home in it. In the gallery, the women were leaning forward in positions whose familiarity angered him. The dull afternoon light filled the windows so that they looked as if they were painted over, and the judges' faces looked ghastly. In the dock, the Fenians seemed to have lost whatever courage they had assumed in the morning, except for John O'Leary and O'Donovan Rossa. The weasel-faced Geale was looking them over impatiently, seeming to blame them for delaying the business of the court, though they had been the last to be summoned. He waited until they were all in position and then lifted a hand in signal to Judge Keogh, who said immediately, "The court is open. Gentlemen of the jury, have you reached a decision?"

"Yes, your Lordship."

"What is it?"

"We have found a true bill against the prisoner Thomas Clarke Luby."

A murmur went around the court, as if the news were unexpected.

The judge said, "Silence in the court. Let the prisoner Thomas Clarke Luby be put forward."

Mr. Butt stood up and said, "My Lord, I object. I'll need a copy of the indictment, since the charges have been reduced without notice to me."

Keogh looked for a second exactly like a dog whose dinner has been removed from under his nose but he said, "Very well, Mr. Butt, you may have it."

"Thank you, my Lord, and I must have until tomorrow to look it over."

"Nonsense—that's not necessary."

"I contend that it is necessary, and that it was improper to alter the charges without notifying me."

"The charges are reduced, not altered."

"It's the same thing."

"Attorney General, what do you say?"

"I object."

"Why?"

"It will hold up the proceedings—there are a great many prisoners."

"And they must get justice."

Angry voices called out, "Shame! Withdraw!"

The judge said, "The court will adjourn for an hour to consider the question and in the meantime the Grand Jury may continue to deliberate on the next prisoners."

Incredibly, they were being led out again, down the stairs that led directly from the dock to the vile room that Morgan had already come to hate. He found that his hands were shaking with a primitive emotion that must somehow be controlled at once if he were to survive. Then he saw a tear shine momentarily on the cheek of one of the men, a young Mayoman named Muldowney, a great, strong, healthy fellow, who always until now had seemed full of humor and courage. While he watched, the man put his head in his hands and seemed to quiet himself deliberately. Morgan was so deeply moved that he had to go over and lay his hand on Muldowney's shoulder and speak to him in Irish.

"Lift up your heart, my son. We'll go in together, whatever happens."

"It's a poor thing to fall into the hands of the gentry," Muldowney answered in Irish. "They're out to destroy us."

"A man can't be destroyed except by God. Have patience and we'll rise again when the bright day comes."

Muldowney looked up at him with gratitude, straightening his back like a newly watered plant, and Morgan found that he himself had taken courage from his own half-believed words. All around him, the men looked so tired and hungry now that even their hair and their clothes seemed more limp. This time the wait was short and within an hour they were being led up the dirty stairs again into the darkened courtroom. The jurymen looked uneasy and tired, too, seeming cramped in their box, which was barely large enough to hold them.

Casson answered Judge Keogh's question quickly. "We have found true bills against the prisoners O'Leary, Kickham, Hopper, O'Donovan Rossa, O'Connor and Moore."

Keogh stretched his arms out and drew them in again, like a man relieved of some long tension. In unmistakably triumphant tones he said, "Very well, Mr. Butt, you have had time to consider the indictment against Thomas Clarke Luby."

"I want until tomorrow, my Lord."

"The court has decided to go on. Let the first prisoner be put forward to be arraigned."

Mr. Butt sat down, looking put out but apparently accepting the situation.

Geale called out, "Thomas Clarke Luby!"

A flutter among the policemen resulted in Mr. Luby's being ushered out of the dock to stand by himself on the floor below. Morgan guessed that it would have been more correct to take all the prisoners except Luby downstairs again but the guards were taking a short cut. The charges against Luby seemed to have complicated themselves since they had first been announced in the morning. Geale's voice droned on and on, with references to drilling, buying arms, conspiring, subverting, oath-taking and publishing incitements to rebellion.

At last he had finished and Mr. Luby looked at him coolly as if to ask: "Is that all?" To the question whether he would plead guilty or not guilty, he answered in a clear, strong voice, "Not guilty."

Immediately Mr. Butt was on his feet, saying, "It's five o'clock, my Lord. I suggest an adjournment until tomorrow."

"Adjourned until ten o'clock tomorrow morning," Keogh said, and immediately a hubbub broke out in the court.

The prisoners were kept in the dock until the court was empty and then were hustled directly out into the entry off Halston Street where the prison van was waiting, surrounded by a huge escort of hussars with drawn sabers, as well as some mounted police. Beyond them could be seen the crowd in Green Street waiting for the spectacle.

"Lord God!" said O'Donovan Rossa softly. "The might of England is gathered against us and no mistake!"

The idea seemed to exhilarate him but Morgan heard a threat of death in the sound of the trotting hooves that accompanied them back to the prison. They were locked in immediately, so that there was no more opportunity for talk, even if they had not all been too weary for it.

39

The trial of Luby took four days but not all of the court's time was devoted to him. Other prisoners were brought up, among them Morgan, to be arraigned after the Grand Jury had found true bills against them. The dreary underground room in Green Street became horribly familiar to them while they waited for hours in case they might be called into court. Each day the prison van had to be escorted by an armed guard, and clearly the authorities wanted to make one job of this excursion.

Luby came and went, giving them news of what was happening. On the first morning, Mr. Butt spent three hours in challenging the members of the jury as each name came up— one was too old, one was not resident in Dublin, one knew some of the prisoners. In all eighty men were called before twelve could be sworn in.

"Keogh is furious," Luby said. "If this goes on, the Commission will be sitting until kingdom come. And in spite of Mr. Butt's efforts, the final selection is not very appetizing."

On the second day he said, "Nagle is cockier now. It seems the poor fellow was badly paid for his work, only sixty pounds a year. They had a glorious letter of Stephens' in evidence today: 'This is the year of action—the flag of Ireland, the flag of the Republic, must be raised.' You remember that letter?"

"Yes," John O'Leary said. "I didn't agree with sending it in the first place. How did Nagle get hold of it?"

"Stole it from Power, it seems, when he was taking it down the country to read at meetings of the Head Centers. What is it that makes a spy—money, conviction, excitement?"

"Money or fear," John O'Leary said contemptuously. "In Nagle's case it was money—he actually offered himself."

"Keogh was purring over the letter," Luby said. "One can see how they wish they had Stephens on trial for writing it. Not half as good having only me."

That evening, after they had been taken back to Richmond, they were ordered out after supper and transferred through the dark city to Kilmainham Jail. The great cut-stone building was oppressive and the cells into which they were put were colder and darker than those they had left. In the morning, Mr. Price, the Governor, went with them to the court.

Luby suggested, "He's anxious to make sure we're properly guarded."

"It's not anxiety at all," O'Donovan Rossa said, "but excitement. Now that we're in Kilmainham he has a right to a ringside seat."

But it was obvious that everyone was nervous, even the officers of the Fifth Dragoon Guards who escorted the van, closely watching as the prisoners got in and out lest there should be a sudden attempt at rescue.

On Saturday, Luby's trial ended. Morgan was in court that day, hoping that he could be called by counsel for the defense of John O'Leary, whose case was begun the same morning, so as not to waste time. He was placed on a bench just inside the door that led from the courtroom to the main hall of the building, which gave him a side view of the gallery. She was there, as usual, and across the ocean of the courtroom they gazed at each other with sadness and understanding. John O'Leary's sister had been given a special concession, a seat by the dock, so that she was near enough to give her brother courage and a breath of her love. Morgan had no rights over Alice —she was neither his wife nor his sister, not even his mistress.

Before one o'clock the jury retired to consider its verdict on Luby and John O'Leary was put forward. The long game of swearing in a jury for him began. When the court went into recess for luncheon only one had been sworn, David Mac-Birney, the foreman, who had a shop on Aston's Quay.

Downstairs Mr. O'Leary said, "In spite of myself I'm excited, as if I thought there could be some chance of survival. Strange, isn't it? Of course the Government that packed the bench won't fail to see to the jury. Everyone knows what is coming. That's why we're no longer allowed to buy our own food. They're anticipating the pleasure of feeding us on prison diet."

There was something especially displeasing in seeing him tear off hunks of the gray bread and put it in his mouth. Morgan and O'Donovan Rossa were used to rough ways but not this elegant townsman with his fine black beard and luminous eyes, and his gentle, cultivated voice.

At half-past two they were summoned back to the courtroom and Mr. O'Leary resumed his place in the dock. Mr. Butt had just challenged the next prospective juror called when a constable went to the door and then came back and whispered to the Clerk of the Crown.

Geale's little head seemed to twitch with nervousness as he

said to the judges, "My Lords, the jury is ready to give its verdict."

Judge Fitzgerald said, "Let them come in, then."

Geale squeaked, "Put forward Thomas Clarke Luby!"

Luby got up from his seat beside Morgan on the witness's bench and went toward the dock, standing aside while John O'Leary stepped down. The jurors' boots crossing the bare boards clattered and ground in the silence. The faces of the public had the dead look of people confronting inescapable danger, even the officials seemed to be overawed at last by their ceremony. Morgan felt his heart pounding and was grateful when John O'Leary sat close beside him, fixing his eyes calmly on the jury.

Geale called the names of the jurors and each stood for a moment to answer. Then he said, "Gentlemen, have you agreed on your verdict?"

The foreman stood up, his chest puffed forward with self-importance, which seemed, however, to be mixed with fear of the situation in which he found himself. His voice quavered as he replied, "We have. We say the prisoner is guilty on all counts."

Muttering voices became an uproar and died away suddenly as the Attorney General stood up to say with practiced casualness, "I pray sentence." He sat down, eying the two judges, who now had their heads together.

Then Fitzgerald said, "We will retire for a few minutes."

During that quarter hour, Morgan burned with longing for Alice as he had not done since he had taken her for the first time in Aran. Here in this stuffy room he remembered the cry of the curlew and the agelong wait on the doorstep of the Husseys' house, and then the final fulfillment of their love in the great cool bedroom upstairs. If she had come with him then, where would they be now? Perhaps in the little house in Cappagh, or over in the strange city of Boston, which he had never seen. It would not matter so long as they were together. His turn had not come yet but already he felt in Luby's trial the force that would tear him away from her, this time forever. At the back of his mind had always been the idea that he would have her again someday, in spite of Samuel. Would hope live through the horrors that lay before him? Perhaps, but Pagan had said they would die in that hell of his dream, and now old superstitions of his childhood seemed reasonable and important. A crazy idea came to him that if now, by a miracle, he were set free, Alice's principles and scruples would

275

be as easily dissolved as they had been in Paris and she would lie with him again. The happiness that this brought him was interrupted by the return of Keogh and Fitzgerald. Silence fell on the courtroom as they took their places on the bench.

Geale said then, "Thomas Clarke Luby, you have been found guilty of the crime of treason felony by compassing, devising and conspiring, within the last three years, with the members of a secret society called the Fenian Brotherhood, in England, Ireland and America, of which society you are a member, to levy war against the Queen in Ireland, subvert her royal authority and establish an independent republic. What have you to say?"

Luby had not expected this chance but after the first hesitation he used it to give a measured description of the Fenian Brotherhood and the reasons for its existence. He could not be stopped at once—after all, he had been invited to speak—but after a few minutes Judge Keogh said, "I am very reluctant to interrupt you."

Luby bowed as if this were permission to continue and the judges had to sit fuming for a further five minutes while he went on with his discourse, Keogh especially becoming more agitated with every moment that passed.

Then he said again, "Mr. Luby, I do not wish to interrupt you."

This time Luby answered, "I have almost finished. I believe nothing can ever save Ireland except independence and I believe all other attempts to ameliorate the condition of Ireland are mere temporary expedients and makeshifts. That is all I have to say."

He stood calmly while Keogh spoke for several minutes and the officials shifted from foot to foot, embarrassed, looking at one another uneasily. Keogh said that war was evil and peace desirable for the development of the country so that industry and agriculture could go forward. At first his tone was solemn and sententious but gradually the words were coming a little too fast. Then he broke off. There was a pause in which everyone sat so still that a fly buzzing high on the wall could be heard as it landed and took off again.

Keogh shuffled some papers before him but had no need to read them. He looked up suddenly and said, "Thomas Clarke Luby, the sentence of the court is that you be detained in penal servitude for a period of twenty years." Again there was a dead pause before he turned his shoulder quickly to the court and said sharply, "Remove the prisoner."

On that first day, Luby was taken downstairs to the waiting

room where O'Donovan Rossa and Michael Moore and several others were sitting in case they might be called. It was the only time this happened. Four days later, when John O'Leary was given the same sentence, he was taken away at once in a special van to Mountjoy Jail. Michael Moore, the pikemaker, came next, with what now appeared the short sentence of ten years, and then it was Morgan's turn. He and Moore were stopgaps, people of small importance who could be quickly disposed of before O'Donovan Rossa's trial could begin.

"I'll give them a run for their money," O'Donovan Rossa said. "They won't forget me in a hurry. I told them that Price stole the papers that I need for my defense and they could see the gentlemen of the press writing it all down. Keogh must be longing for the old days when they didn't have to worry about keeping up the good name of British justice."

"Mr. Butt is displeased."

"I don't think he is, Morgan. He can see we haven't a dog's chance and he's willing enough for me to have a go at them. They have good evidence against yourself, I think."

"Yes, a prosecutor's dream. They found my books in my lodgings—Macauley's *Field Fortifications,* MacDougal's *Theory of War,* Jervis' *Field Operations.* Any two of those would be enough."

"Will you speak when you're condemned?"

"Yes." Morgan accepted his fate at that moment, hearing it from O'Donovan Rossa's lips.

The speech, when his time came, was short and clear.

"I have been found guilty and I know now that my sentence will be a long one, though perhaps not as long as my two seniors who have gone before me. I wish it could be as long if it could prove me their equal in guilt, as you call it. To me, that would mean their equal in charity. It is not easy to give up the relative security that a little education can give in Ireland, the comforts of home and family, and go out on the hills and through the countryside to urge and encourage my fellow countrymen to ask for what by British law is already theirs in theory. You say that under British law all men are equal. I say that in Ireland British law is a farce, a sad betrayal of all the things that are the pride of the British nation. Everyone is free in Ireland except the Irish. There is justice in Ireland for everyone except the Irish. When I was a child I saw my people die in their hundreds, in a way that would have aroused anger and protest if it had been not people but animals that were dying. You may say that times are better now. I say, and my seniors who have just been condemned by you say, that they are not better. As well throw a bone to a dying dog as the help that is given now to this dying nation. One word or one action of mine, one man enlisted by me in the Fenian Brotherhood, would make what I must suffer now worthwhile."

Keogh leaned forward to say, "You may not think so later."

"A man cannot live in shame," said Morgan. "If I had lived my life without striking one blow for the betterment of my country, it would be better not to have lived at all. We have been accused of wishing to massacre our own priests. That anyone should take this charge seriously is so ridiculous that it proves the futility of this court. I say keep British justice for England—let us have Irish justice in Ireland when our country is free."

At this several people in the gallery began to clap their hands but he could not make out who they were. Samuel was with Alice, as he had been every day since the beginning of Morgan's trial. He slipped his arm around her shoulders so that she could lean against him while Keogh pronounced sentence.

"Morgan Patrick Connolly, the sentence of the court is that you be detained in penal servitude for a period of ten years. Remove the prisoner."

Smoothly now, accustomed to their task, two constables came forward and took him by either arm, almost as if he were an invalid who could not climb down from the dock alone. Glancing around at the gallery, he saw that she was no longer there. Within two minutes of his condemnation, he had passed through the door into the side entry from Halston Street where a prison van was waiting with an escort of cavalry, with drawn sabers, and mounted police. A crowd was watching from the gateway, pressed against the courthouse walls to be out of the way of the trampling horses. Samuel and Alice were there in front, both of them, but between was the barricade of soldiers to make sure that they could not speak. Weak with hunger and shock, Morgan moved in a daze down the steps, feeling his way as if he were blind, then up the three iron steps into the van, the only prisoner now. He had one moment of sour amusement when no less than ten constables climbed in after him, to sit there sweating, like big-game hunters who have captured a live bear to bring home to a circus.

40

The prison van was driven at a furious pace, surrounded by the galloping horses of the cavalry and police. Inside, Morgan and the constables were rocked from side to side, deafened by the clattering hooves on the cobblestones. His teeth rattled with the vibration of the wretched vehicle, whose springs had long since worn out on this same rough journey, and during the twenty minutes that it took to reach Mountjoy Jail, it seemed that his brain was being reduced to a useless pulp. It was over at last, the van came to a halt and the doors were flung open. He climbed out shakily and found himself directly at the foot of the steps that led into the prison. Soldiers were still running to take their places in a double file through which he was to enter, and his own escort of policemen circled him around as well. The solemnity of it brought him to his senses. It would be unseemly to look terrified. With a straight face he walked up the steps, as if he were a distinguished visitor.

The ceremony finished abruptly at the door. He was quickly pushed into a room where two warders were waiting. Their faces showed no sign of humanity or interest. One said, "Take off your clothes."

Without a word, Morgan removed his jacket and shirt and trousers, hesitated a moment before pulling off his vest and long woolen underpants, and stood, uneasily naked, in his socks and shoes.

"Go on," said the same warder.

He stooped to obey and felt two pairs of hands pull at his buttocks. In a raging fury he jerked upward, flinging the disgusting hands aside, and heard the granite voice say, "If you resist, we're entitled to knock you down."

He glared into the hard gray eyes and then submitted stiffly to the search. They had clothes ready for him, rough gray jacket and trousers and waistcoat, and woolen underwear, and shoes and socks, both too small. When he pointed out that his feet would not fit into the shoes, the second warder's expression softened for a split second and then he said, "I'll see if there's anything bigger."

There was, among the several pairs of shoes in a cabinet by the door, and Morgan put them on with disproportionate gratitude, but when he looked again at the warder's face it was as blank as before. With disdain at himself, he realized that he had hoped for friendship.

When he was dressed, they took him to the registry office next to the reception room.

"Height: six feet one inch; hair: black, curled; eyes: blue; nose: prominent; mouth: average."

That was Morgan Patrick Connolly at the moment of entering Mountjoy Jail, still his own man. He could not help being curious about their system. Without comment they led him through darkening passages, into a great hall, up an iron stairway onto a semicircular gallery with many doors and into a small, dark cell. The winter afternoon light was almost gone and in the passages yellowish gas jets flared in the drafts. The cell was intolerably crowded by the three of them, soon augmented by two more, the barber and his mate.

"Sit on the stool," the first warder commanded.

He obeyed, oppressed by the figures towering over him. The barber cut off his hair and side whiskers, yanking with the blunt scissors to improve their cutting power. His mate held the candle and the warders watched as impartially as if it were a sheepshearing. The mate produced a bowl of cold water and some soap, and the barber flipped open a razor from his pocket and shaved him briskly and excruciatingly. Then, bleeding from a number of small cuts, they led him downstairs again to photograph him, a placard containing his name pinned to his chest.

"Keep still. Look straight ahead," said the warder.

Was he a Dublin man? Surely only a city could produce such inhumanity, yet he had a look of the country about him, poor devil. Once, long ago, perhaps he was different, walking in sunny fields, bringing home cows, digging, planting, longing for city life.

In the next few minutes, while the warder read the prison rules, Morgan was filled with such pity for him that it almost diverted him from his own fear and humiliation. The dead voice read on and on, rules against speaking, sitting, lying down, addressing prison officers, rules about exercise, work, washing, letter writing.

"So I'm allowed to write a letter on my reception," he said. "Then I'll write it now, if you please."

"No. A special ruling has come that Fenian prisoners are not to be allowed to write letters until further instructions."

Ridiculously, this setback infuriated him beyond what he could bear.

"So we're getting special treatment already—" he burst out.

"Any impertinence to a prison officer is liable to be punished with a period of solitary confinement on a diet of bread and water," the warder intoned. "Look to your front!" Morgan stiffened. "Forward!"

He was marched out into the passage and was conducted back to his cell with cries of "To the left! To the right! Look to your front!" The warders followed, the first one waving his club as if he feared that Morgan would attempt to escape. At the cell the warder called out "Halt!" His companion unlocked the door and then Morgan was inside, alone for the first time, free to look over his new quarters.

It was a little, narrow room with a table and stool, a narrow bed, a tin mug and spoon, and a lavatory. Dim light came from a small gas jet. It would be necessary to be calm, deliberate in everything he did, never hysterical nor impetuous. He had little enough practice in restraint—already he had felt spasms of fury run through him, exhausting and useless. Bitter-cold air came through the high barred aperture that served as a window. It was pitch-dark out there now, and horribly silent. He stood in the middle of the cell, breathing slowly and rhythmically, forcing himself to realize that this was part of a military operation, an expected setback, remembering the others who had been in jail more than once and seemed to take it as a matter of course. Before they arrived, he must reach a presentable state of mind so as not to disgrace the whole Brotherhood.

He whirled around as the trap door opened suddenly. He had heard no sound of footsteps. A strange warder was outside, a triangular yellow face under a peaked cap and a grating voice that said, "Hold out your mug!"

He did so, and the warder poured it full of milk, then thrust a lump of bread into Morgan's hand and clapped the trap door shut again.

The sight of the food cheered him, and he discovered that he had had an unconscious fear that he would be starved to death. Working his way through the bread he considered how many a wretched family in Connemara would be thankful to have a meal like this, how often he had eaten no better at home in Cappagh. But he quickly found that it would not do to think of Cappagh or indeed of any family, no matter how wretched, sitting down to eat together. He shut his eyes as the walls seemed to press in on him and oddly the words of a Connemara song came to him, a love song, intense and sad,

bringing with them the smell of turf smoke blown high on a
starry night.

> "Donal Og, if you cross the ocean,
> Take me with you and don't forget me,
> And you'll have a gift every fair and market-day,
> And a Grecian princess to share your bed with you.
> Late last night the dog betrayed you,
> And the snipe called out from the marshy bog to you,
> A bird alone, through the forest ranging—
> May you have no partner until I come to you."

The Irish words were softly sibilant. He began to murmur the
song to himself but had to stop when his throat closed with
sorrow and his eyes were wet with tears. This was not going to
be his comfort.

Warmed with the food, he lay down on the bed with his
hands behind his head. Scarcely had he begun to relax when
the trap door clattered open and the warder's voice said,
"Take off your clothes!"

Morgan roused himself to obey. When he was naked, the
warder said, "Give me your clothes."

"What do I wear in bed? It's a cold night—it's December."

"Any disobedience will be punished with a period of bread-
and-water diet. Put out your light."

Morgan handed the bundle of clothes out through the trap
door and turned off the gaslight. The cold was gnawing at him
already. He found the bed and lay down, drawing up the
blankets, grateful that there were two of them. A dizziness in
his head presaged sleep, to his surprise, and he found himself
longing for the relief it would give him. Even the cold seemed
less and he began to savor the ease in store. But in a moment
he was shocked into wakefulness by the clatter of the trap
door, a bull's-eye lantern filled the cell with light for perhaps
half a minute and the trap door was banged shut again. He
lay quivering in the darkness. It was a trick, he supposed, to
catch him if he had been disobeying rules. But what could he
do? Dig his way out? File away the bars of the window with
the tin spoon? It was absurd—and he had been seen to be as
quiet as a mouse in bed. Again he began to relax into sleep,
and again at the moment of its arrival the trap door clattered,
the lantern shone on his face and the trap door shut again. So
it went on throughout the night. He slept, of course, as one
might sleep in a train, his hands over his face, hearing himself
moan as he was cruelly awakened over and over again, despis-

ing himself for his weakness in not being better able to suffer this new torture, yet never answering impatiently when the warder called out, "Connolly! Show your face!"

Half conscious, he would roll on his back, ridiculously happy if the warder's inspection coincided with the shouts of the soldier guards who were placed outside his cell and who called out to each other at intervals.

"All right, there?"

"All right!"

During the two weeks that he spent in Mountjoy he could feel the vitality drain out of him. He lived for the daily hour of exercise, when he was taken out with the others and was placed in a metal cage to walk in a circle. The bitter cold wind was voiced by the thin cries of the sea gulls that swooped and circled inland, expecting storms. The prisoners were made to walk six feet apart, eyes in front, never speaking to one another, watched by a dozen warders and twenty soldiers with long-barreled guns at the ready. O'Leary, Luby and Moore were there, as well as the Haltigans and Kickham, limping energetically to keep up the pace, and then one day Pagan appeared. Morgan longed to go to him but it was impossible. The others communicated with their eyes but Pagan never raised his head at all.

There was no sign of O'Donovan Rossa or any news of what had become of him. Even when they were taken to the chapel for Sunday Mass they could not discover whether he was present because they were all placed in narrow cubicles from which they could see only the backs of shaven heads. Morgan had been visited by the chaplain, a Kilkenny man named Father Cody, who seemed determined to avoid all discussion. It was strange to sit and listen to him recommending resignation and prayer without any reference to the reason for Morgan's imprisonment, and Morgan found that he was angered at Mass by the sound of the priest's voice reciting the lovely Latin prayers that seemed so incongruous in this dark and evil place. Bitterly he prayed for forgiveness, for himself as well as for them.

He had kept careful count of the days, so he knew it was two days before Christmas when he was awakened very early in the morning by the warder with the lantern calling out, "Get out of bed!"

Morgan rolled out on the floor. The warder shoved his bundle of clothes through the trap door, saying, "Dress quickly. Hold out your mug." He filled it and handed in a piece of bread.

"Eat quickly."

"Why?"

Of course there was no answer. The warder went off, leaving the trap door open and a dim light seeped into the cell from the passage. Morgan pulled on his clothes in a daze and as he finished his miserable breakfast the door clanged open and four men walked in. Their silence had an ugly flavor so that he felt fear in his throat, but one of them seized his hand, felt his pulse, dropped the hand and said three words: "Fit to travel."

Then they were gone, all four of them, and he could hear the door of the cell next to his own being slammed open.

Within a few minutes the warder was at the door again. "Outside. To your left. To your right. Look straight ahead."

He was taken downstairs and was placed in line with five other prisoners, all listless and dull, all looking straight ahead, all quite silent, until suddenly he heard O'Donovan Rossa's voice sing out.

"Luby!"

At once all the prisoners turned to look squarely at one another for one delighted second before the chief warder ordered, "Look to your front!"

They straightened and obeyed but Morgan had felt a warm spurt go through him at the closeness of his friends, especially of the unconquerable O'Donovan Rossa.

A moment later they were being handcuffed in a row. Morgan found himself attached to Pagan O'Leary on one side and to O'Donovan Rossa on the other. Beyond O'Donovan Rossa was Luby. The warder snapped on the irons roughly.

O'Donovan Rossa said sharply, "They're too small for my hand—you're breaking the bone—Jesus!"

"You can put up with it. We're in a hurry."

"Move along there!" said another.

The doors were opened and a blast of cold air filled the hall. At the foot of the steps the van was waiting and they were hustled inside, with six warders to guard them. The door was closed and they clattered off, with even at that early hour the usual escort of cavalry with drawn swords.

Beside him Morgan heard O'Donovan Rossa moan with pain and he said to the chief warder, "Can you do nothing for him? Why should he be bound so tightly?"

"It's not my business. I have no spare handcuffs."

But he lifted his lantern and shone the light on O'Donovan Rossa's hand, from which the blood was dripping. Morgan heard a gasp and saw the light glitter on tears that rolled down the cheeks of his own guard, silently watching.

The chief warder said, "I can do nothing, I tell you!"

The van rocked and rattled along for an hour, swaying them together and away, rolling them about sickeningly. At last it stopped and they could hear the shouts of the cavalry officer mixed with many other excited voices. The door swung open and they stumbled out, tripping on the steps, hampered by their bonds. They were on the pier at Kingstown.

Again Morgan marveled at the ceremony with which each of their movements was accompanied—this time a double file of soldiers in red coats and, oddest of all, the same detectives from Dublin Castle who had broken into the offices of *The Irish People* and had arrested him and his companions three months ago.

41

Morgan was only a short time in Pentonville before he realized fully that it was intended that they should die in prison, as Pagan had said, or go mad. The journey to Holyhead by sea and the long train journey to London had not proved this, since the zeal of the guards could be explained by nervousness, the starvation by inefficiency. He had even thought that they would have more detached jailers in England, and especially a taste of the British justice that was so lacking in Ireland. It was apparent at once, however, that they were not to have the treatment of ordinary prisoners. On the very steps of the prison, derisive voices called out, "Get up there, Paddy!"

O'Donovan Rossa glowered and raised his manacled fists an inch, then dropped them again. Morgan's heart was pounding with mixed anger and terror as he felt his hand go up with O'Donovan Rossa's. Then he saw the tough mouth harden and the eyes narrow, and throughout the next half hour, during which they were stripped and searched, O'Donovan Rossa made no resistance or any reply to the obscene remarks and handling of their naked bodies. Only once he spoke, to ask if they could have underwear, which they had had in Ireland.

"The doctor says you need no underwear," the warder said, and laughed in his face.

One by one they were led away to different wards of the prison. That first night Morgan found that not only his clothes but every movable article in his cell had to be put outside every night. He lay shivering in his narrow bed hour after hour, waiting for some natural warmth to travel through him, but the cold wind whistled under the drafty door and penetrated the thin blankets so that sleep was impossible. He dozed at last, exhausted, to be awakened at six o'clock by a warder who went along the corridor with a lamp to light the gas in each cell.

He was given back his clothes and a breakfast consisting of cocoa and bread. Cleaning his cell under the exact instructions from the warder became a valuable entertainment in the midst of the long day of boredom. Dinner came at twelve o'clock, cheese and bread, and supper of bread and porridge at five. It was Sunday but the warder said there was no religious service for Catholics yet at Pentonville. Morgan envied the other prisoners, who at least had the diversion of a march to the chapel, and that Sunday and the following day, which was Christmas Day, seemed to narrow his world and his wishes into a tiny, mean circle.

Tuesday was the first working day. At nine o'clock his cell door was opened and he was ordered outside, down the stairs to the great central hall of the prison. One by one the others appeared, and then with great ceremony the Governor, Farquharson, was announced. The warders seemed to tremble like sergeants in the presence of a general, feeling that they will be blamed for any sign of bad discipline among the privates. The prisoners were made to stand to attention, with their caps off, and each warder watched his own prisoners closely. The Governor solemnly read the rules, which seemed to be the same as they had been in Ireland, including the proviso that the Fenians could not write letters on their arrival.

After all the prisoners had been weighed and measured, O'Donovan Rossa was taken away quickly and kept out of sight and sound of the rest of them. It was his own doing, indeed, since he seemed incapable of making himself negative as the others did. When the warder called out his weight to be written on his chart, O'Donovan Rossa said loudly, "Twenty pounds lost since I was arrested!"

Besides, he kept tossing remarks to the other prisoners.

"An early sight of hell, boys. Hell open to sinners—look at the poor little devils in charge of us—"

Each time he was shouted and cuffed into silence. Morgan found himself storing his few casual words for future comfort. Later, when they were taken out to be exercised for an hour, O'Donovan Rossa was not there, but Morgan had glimpsed him as he was being marched in another direction. It was impossible to imagine him submitting to the search of his clothes and body, which took place at the cell door every day before exercise began, the warder's hands feeling over every inch of his body.

Twice weekly Morgan had to turn out the whole cell, and he was stripped naked and searched as he had been on the day he came. Everywhere the warders came in pairs, obviously to watch each other. There was to be no question of fraternizing or sympathizing with the Fenians. Two even came with the meals, one opening the trap door, which fell inward and formed a platform on which the tin dish was placed, and the other just standing by with his eye on his mate. When at last a chaplain came from Millbank to say Mass for them, they were taken downstairs into a wet cellar where some building work was going on, and there they sat on their stools, a yard or so away from one another, with a warder armed with a club at each corner, lifting it threateningly at any sign of a prisoner turning his head to left or right. Morgan talked with the chaplain, who had an Italian name. He would not budge beyond his instructions. He was to bring spiritual comfort, not news, and he would not say how things were in Ireland or whether anything was being done for the prisoners' wives and children.

He asked Morgan, "Are you married?"

"No."

"Then you have no reason to know—and you have something to be thankful for."

But he looked guilty then, as if even the comment were an indiscretion. Still his visit was a diversion and Morgan enjoyed arguing against his exhortations to give up the Fenian oath.

"Long before there was an oath, I had sworn to myself to fight for the freedom of my country. The God I know won't hold that against me."

"To justify a revolution, you must have extreme oppression and reasonable hope of success."

"Have you ever been in Ireland?"

"No," the priest said warily, suspecting a trap.

"You may take it from me that there is extreme oppression," Morgan said, "and we had only begun to develop our organization. A little more and we'd have had reasonable hope of success. That stipulation doesn't make much sense unless you interpret it properly. A revolutionary organization doesn't spring into existence—it takes time."

"How much schooling have you had?"

"Enough to get me to the Sorbonne for two years."

"Aha! I thought so. The French influence is obvious. You must pray for resignation."

"Resignation has been the ruin of Ireland."

"I will pray for you."

"Thank you very much."

But his tone was friendly enough and he seemed genuinely worried about Morgan's soul.

One Sunday Morgan found that the makeshift chapel was crowded with a new lot of crop-haired prisoners. His place was directly in front of O'Donovan Rossa, and sure enough, no sooner had Mass begun than he heard among the voices that were accompanying the priest in the Confiteor Rossa's beginning to question his companion on one side, in a muttering drone that matched exactly the tone of the prayer.

"Who are you?"

Quickly the other answered in the same way.

"James O'Connor."

"Where is Stephens?"

"Paris."

"Is there going to be a fight?"

"Yes. Not yet."

"Who came with you?"

"Kickham, Dillon, Mulcahy, Lynch, Duggan—"

Morgan could not make out all the names. In a moment a sharp sound of boots on the stone floor and a scuffle behind him indicated that one of the warders had observed something unusual and he could hear an angry voice whisper. "Give that up, you. Get back there—right to the back."

He did not turn his head while O'Donovan Rossa was hustled away but stared fixedly to his front, and then mocked himself bitterly at this proof that he was indeed a prisoner now, and a slave.

In May he was transferred to Millbank, a foot of clanking chain between his ankles and the long end of the chain held in his hands, four warders to guard him. As he walked into the prison from the van, a drunken soldier in his red coat staggered against him, saying, "God pity you, you poor bastard!"

The warder in front shouted, "Get away, you, or I'll have you arrested!"

The soldier tottered away, ludicrously placing one foot in the way of the other, and Morgan continued at a snail's pace to drag himself up the steps.

The Millbank warders seemed themselves oppressed by the misery of their jail, silent, sour, unhealthy. His cell was flagged, quite bare except for the plank bed and a bucket with a cover which served as his stool. On this he was obliged to sit for ten hours every day picking oakum, raveling the rock-hard hemp with his fingers, bent low, never speaking a word and never allowed to stand up or walk except during the exercise hour and during the daily visit to the chapel. As the summer went on, his back and chest developed pains that were somewhat relieved by hunching his shoulders together and downward. With the advent of autumn, the cold numbed his whole body, cementing it into this stooped position. Becoming aware of this, he practiced stretching his back deliberately at intervals and tried always to walk straight and soldierly, when he was permitted to walk at all.

It was at Millbank that he noticed a lightness in his head, a floating sensation that he attributed to the wretched food more than to the lack of air. Westminster Tower clock, chiming every quarter hour, day and night, seemed to measure out the days and years ahead with insane cruelty, forcing him to listen as they nibbled his life away. Prayers to an unknown, almost unremembered God were simplified to the first prayer of his childhood.

"Our Father who art in heaven, hallowed be Thy name. Thy kingdom come, Thy will be done—Thy will be done—Thy will be done on earth, as it is in heaven. Give us this day our daily bread. And forgive us our trespasses, as we forgive them —as we forgive them who trespass against us. And lead us not into temptation, but deliver us from evil—deliver us—deliver us from evil."

In November he was taken to Dartmoor. The change of prison was welcome merely because it would bring a change of scene, new things to learn, new faces, however hateful, and more company, since the prisoners worked in gangs instead of in isolation as they did in Millbank and Pentonville. He traveled there by train with Muldowney and two men from Cork named Kelleher and Duggan. All four were padlocked to a long chain that ran through their handcuffs. Heavily guarded they were driven to the station in the early morning. Throughout the long journey they talked to one another freely, as they had talked to no human being for a year.

Their guards were uncertain of their duties but at last one said, "God damn it, talk, then! You won't talk much from now on. Silence at the stations, though, or we might be in the soup."

Muldowney had news of O'Donovan Rossa from Portland, that his fighting spirit was as strong as ever and he was continually baiting his jailers. He saw loopholes in their rules and took advantage of them, and reported the warders for using insulting language to him when they objected.

"He's the greatest fighter of us all," Kelleher said, "but they won't stop till they break him."

"Mr. O'Leary doesn't always agree with him," Muldowney said. "He says we must remember John Mitchel, who submitted to prison discipline, but O'Donovan Rossa says times have changed. He's hardly ever out of trouble—always on bread and water and solitary confinement. But he comes back as good as ever. He's like a granite rock."

"Portland?" Morgan said, and longed to ask Muldowney how he had got his news. "That's where the stone quarries are."

"Yes." Muldowney gazed at him and added in Irish, "One of the warders there is sympathetic to us. He was transferred to our prison and told me all this last week."

"Cut out that slang!" one of the guards shouted. "Speak English or not at all."

"They shouldn't be allowed to speak at all," said another.

"How can we stop them?" the first one said. "I'll be glad when we get there."

"Never mind," Morgan said soothingly. "We won't let you down."

The guards relaxed. For years that conversation remained in Morgan's armory of defense against the insults and humiliations that became part of his life. Dartmoor prison cells were seven feet by four, with slate floors and ceilings and no windows, erected in tiers that opened on to a central hall. The air was foul and the prison food was so filthy that he could not even apply his usual standard of whether it would have been gladly eaten by the starving Irish in the days of the great famine. And it was here that he reached the lowest point of his whole life, where he came seriously to wonder whether, after all, the human race was not so hopelessly vile that it was a waste of time to make an effort to improve it, even in his own small, poor island. A Connemara man, a farmer, a fisherman, here in Dartmoor he was harnessed like a horse to a cart with seven others and made to drag loads of stones and coal about the prison grounds. His body shrank together with loathing, his mouth dried up, nausea filled his stomach as it did at the sight of the beetles in his food, yet his feet moved, his head and shoulder went into the collar and he pressed forward to pull the load while the last trace of charity toward his enemies seeped out of his heart.

PART
FIVE

42

After Morgan's arrest and conviction Alice found that she
could not forget the picture of him as he stood in the dock. It
kept coming back to her painfully and forcibly at odd hours of
the day and night, so that she lost track of what she was doing
and fell into a dream that nearly drove her to madness. She
heard his voice making his last speech, she saw his hands on
the rail, the fingers slightly spread, those hands that had held
her and made her love him as she could never love anyone else
in this life. At night she responded passionately to Samuel's
lovemaking but the man who was with her was Morgan. She
drowned in him, moaning softly to herself with terror in her
heart lest she might say Morgan's name. Samuel seemed to
understand her grief, going out each day to try to get some
news of the Fenians, trying to arrange for her to visit Morgan
in Mountjoy Jail, escorting her to Green Street to listen to
O'Donovan Rossa bait his judges and be condemned by them.

At one of these sessions he met Jerome Burke, who said,
"Taking an interest, Flaherty? You a rebel now?"

Samuel smiled and said, "What about you?"

"Here on business. Nasty affair, all this."

"Yes. It affects us all."

Jerome snorted and said, "It certainly doesn't affect me. That
fellow O'Donovan who's in the dock these days—he seems an
impertinent type. Doesn't know his place. Perhaps you can tell
me why they call him Rossa. Even the court clerk calls him
that, though it sounds like a nickname. What does it stand
for?"

"It's the only way of distinguishing which Jeremiah O'Donovan he is," Samuel explained, "there are so many of that name
in west Cork. He comes from Rosscarbery, Alice tells me."

"She ought to know. How is she?"

"Very distressed. One of the prisoners is a close friend of
ours. Perhaps you remember him. Morgan Connolly. He came
to the school for a while when he was a boy."

Jerome sighed. "No. I never took much notice of children.
How is he doing?"

"He's been given ten years, not the worst."

"Ten years!"

"How is Amy?"

"Very well. Always pregnant, of course. Keeps women quiet. Nice little children, healthier than mine ever were. Amy does things her own way, takes no notice of her mother's advice, and I must say she's successful."

"And Lydia?"

"No worse than usual. Visiting Amy keeps her amused, which suits me. Saves me from having to take her around, take her driving in the park, leaving cards, taking tea—all that rot."

"She's happy in Dublin, then?"

"Happy? Who knows when Lydia is happy? God knows what she wants. I don't beat her with a horsewhip, as some of her friends' husbands do; she has money, a nice house, grandchildren, servants—there's no pleasing women, Flaherty, you may take it from me." His lower lip stuck out in an ugly pout. Then he turned suddenly to Samuel and asked sharply, "How many children have you got now?"

"Still only three—Alice doesn't have children easily."

"You're lucky, Flaherty. We're fooled into marriage by our parents, God knows why. Like the fox that lost his tail, I suppose. They tie us up to some fool of a woman and then walk away and leave us to work our own way out. Perhaps it's revenge for what was done to them."

Repeating this conversation to Alice later, Samuel said, "I just couldn't bring myself to ask him to dinner, though that was the polite thing to do. And he's one of my oldest friends."

"He doesn't know what friendship is. I'm rather sorry for Lydia but it would be a pity to spoil two houses with them. Did you hear any news?"

"Nothing real. The rumors are crazy. They're not letting in any visitors, not even the wives. It's a strange situation. On the one hand the Castle people are so terrified that they guard the prisoners as if they were tigers, and at the same time they mock them as if their conspiracy were some kind of ridiculous joke. I did hear that they're likely to be taken to England."

"When?"

"No one seems to know but it will probably be at the end of all the trials. Alice, we can't do a single thing for him. I've tried everything. They mean to crush them this time for good and all."

"That can't be done." Anger flew through her so that she snapped at him as if poor Samuel were the enemy. "While the grass grows in Ireland, the fight for freedom will never stop. Samuel, I can't imagine Morgan in jail, taking orders, insults, rotten food. Samuel, will they torture him? What will they do to him?" Now she was in a panic, walking up and down the drawing room, hugging her arms to herself as she always did when she was afraid, her piled-up hair beginning to trail down the sides of her face. Samuel came and took her in his arms and quieted her, stroking her hair back in a way that infuriated her, but she would not have dreamed of letting him see it.

He said uncertainly, "I think Morgan will be good at this. After all, he has had plenty of hardship all his life."

"Do you think that will help?"

"It should, with intelligence added. Morgan has sense."

"Morgan is softhearted."

"He's a man."

That brought her up short—the suggestion that Samuel could know more about Morgan than she did herself. She stifled the quick answer that came and then despised herself for her dishonesty. But what use was honesty now? Samuel was a man, too, probably sensing something of her love for Morgan but happy with her all the same. It was she who was miserable, rightly punished as she knew she should be for her terrible sin of long ago, which had followed her everywhere she went. Other women had secrets like hers, surely, things in their past that they wanted to put away and forget, and could be rid of because their circumstances changed. But everywhere Alice went, there was Morgan dogging her footsteps.

Honesty? She was the most dishonest, wicked woman ever born. How well she knew that she wanted Morgan by her always, urged him to come again every time he left her, counted the days until he would come back, lived for days of bliss on each of his visits to her house, imagined him in her bed, at her table, with her children! God should strike her. Why had He not? Many a good, innocent woman was taken, while she lived in the lap of luxury, with healthy children and good Samuel beside her. She could have sent Morgan away long ago, appealing to his religious sense, which she knew was strong, but she preferred the misery of his visits to the misery of never seeing him again.

Yet she knew she was not altogether to blame and now she began to make the old excuses for herself, that she had married Samuel against her will, while she was in love with Morgan, that Morgan was Samuel's friend too and must inevitably be invited to the house sometimes. She could not discuss her torment with the priest in Confession. Instead she accused herself of being impatient with her children, lacking in submission to her husband, discontented and lazy—all the things she was not but that the priest expected of her, that made him nod with understanding and urge her to do better for the love of God and accept the lot of her station in life as a woman, obeying her husband even if he were demanding beyond reason. Samuel! She almost chuckled at the idea, his goodness was so patent, his concern for her always coming first, even his lovemaking so unselfish, while she was absorbed in herself and her own feelings, intent only on another man.

One evening in early spring, when he came back from Galway she whirled around, saying, "Morgan will never come back!"

"Alice, we must go to work at once. There's talk already of trying to get them an amnesty."

"On what grounds? You said they're determined to break them."

"The sentences were savage, and it looks bad that no one knows where the prisoners are. Public opinion in England may be useful, they think—"

"Who thinks?"

"Isaac Butt, for one. We can bring it all out into the open, the terrible provocation that drove the Fenians to conspire— the land especially, and the behavior of the landlords. Butt says he has a dossier of facts that will horrify the British public—villages knocked and the people driven up the mountains so that they couldn't vote against the landlord in elections, evictions from wretched land and hovels for nonpayment of a rent that a good Warwickshire farmer wouldn't expect to pay. He gave me details of some of them, and I could have capped any of his stories with more from the west. His are all proven. He wants to stress that the Irish don't benefit a thing by union with a great empire. Irish landlords are already known in England for their greed and heartlessness. He has formed an association to provide speakers in England as well as in Ireland and he wants me to join."

"What did you say?"

"Of course I'll join. What did you expect? He says my accent and looks will be very useful."

"Is it dangerous? Will anyone think you're a Fenian too?"

Samuel said bitterly, "Not while I look like this. I looked in the glass the other day and thought I'm getting more and more like an Englishman, more and more like my mother, I suppose. My father looked more Irish as he grew older, those bushy eyebrows and loose joints and heavy shoulders. He would have looked more at home in the Fenians."

"Surely you didn't want to be a Fenian?"

"Probably not but it would have been a great compliment to have been asked. I might have accepted, indeed, as one more way of annoying my gentlemanly neighbors. Mr. Butt says that most of his supporters will be Protestant conservatives and he'll need some Catholics. He's going all out for a home parliament, repeal of the Act of Union, the things that Daniel O'Connell wanted."

"Does he think we'll get those things by negotiation?"

"Mr. Butt says the only way now is the legal way."

"He may be right. Lawyers must believe in the law, but the law is slow. How many poor people will die while they're working it out? This means we must stay in Dublin," she added after a moment's thought.

"Yes," Samuel said in surprise. "Of course we must spend part of the year in Dublin always. Aren't you settled here? I think it suits you rather well and the children are better off in every way."

"Perhaps, but Anna is learning to be a snob. She talks of nothing but balls and parties and being presented at the Castle and new gowns. You'd think she had never seen poverty in her life. She wants us to have a ball here but I told her we would not, not while there are people starving, and as for being presented at the Castle, that will certainly never happen."

"You mustn't be hard on her," Samuel said mildly. "These are natural things for a young girl. She probably wants to forget some of the ugly sights she has seen. Perhaps you shouldn't let her have as many gowns and balls as she wants so that she'll become surfeited with them and want stronger meat. She's not fundamentally silly."

"Then why does she talk in that affected way with her friends? I came on her with Mimi D'Arcy the other day and she seemed to be listening entranced to all Mimi's foolish ideas of what she'd like to have, and the things that Belle Stratton's papa says she can have when she's eighteen—her own carriage, and a finishing school in Lausanne, and Belle's papa says she shouldn't wear pearls with her fair skin, emeralds are better. It was disgusting."

"But Anna was not speaking in this way?"

"No, but I longed to hear her tell Mimi that Papa Stratton is an unprincipled ass, as she knows right well, or at least to think it, but she was looking impressed and agreeing with Mimi that gowns should be frilled now to look the least bit fashionable. It was enough to keep Mimi chattering."

"Anna is shy, afraid to give offense, that's all," Samuel said. "She's best let alone."

"But she doesn't want to learn any better. The way she orders Jane around makes me mad. Sprigg, she calls her; she won't call her Jane, as I do. She says it's not proper. And Jane will leave me at a second's notice to attend to Anna. I've seen her let Jane go as far as the door twice and call her back each time to do some tiny thing for her—hand her a glass or pick a hair off her shoulders. And she's only fourteen!"

"She's probably teaching herself how to use a maid," Samuel said with sudden insight. "Does Jane mind?"

"She loves it. She was trained into it, poor soul. Oh, Samuel, I find it a penance to have a daughter who wants to be served like that!"

"Well, you know how impossible it is for a lady to dress without a maid, hook herself up, brush her hair. You had to learn, don't you remember? You have to use Jane yourself. Come now, don't look so angry. Let's go and visit them."

The children's sitting room was on the second floor, at the end of the corridor where their bedrooms were. It was a sunny room with windows opening on to the side and back of the house. On this bright evening the lamps were not yet lit on the big table in the middle of the room and the girls were holding their sewing toward the daylight, watched closely by the governess, Miss Conroy. Thomas was not yet home from school but was expected in a week for the Easter holidays.

Samuel drew up a chair to the table, as he always did, and said genially, "Well, children, how goes the work?"

"Mine is dreadful, Papa. I don't see the use of all this embroidery. I wish I could do something more amusing, or at least more interesting."

Julia dropped the piece of grayish linen on which she had been outlining a basket of spiky flowers and placed her two fists on top of it.

Miss Conroy said, "Julia, that's not a proper greeting for Papa. Stand up and behave like a lady!"

Julia came running around the table to kiss his cheek, and he took her on his knee with a strong feeling that his own behavior was not meeting with the approval of the governess either.

Anna had laid down her sewing neatly and had come to his other side, saying, "Every lady must know how to sew." She kissed his cheek demurely and sat on the chair beside his.

"And what would you consider an amusing occupation, Miss?" he asked Julia, studying her face closely while she answered.

In spite of Sprigg's best efforts, her black curly hair would not lie smooth but kept releasing little spirals that fell at either side of her round, rosy cheeks. Her eyelashes curled upward and her large blue eyes, as blue as Alice's, had a permanent look of concentration and intelligence that many people found unnatural and unattractive in a child of ten.

"I like the work we do in the mornings—history and geography and French—only I want to learn Latin and Greek and mathematics as well. Papa, do you know where Honduras is?"

"I'm not quite sure."

"Well I am! It's in Central America, and you should know all about it because you import timber—"

"Julia! What happens to impertinent little girls?"

Julia glanced furiously at Miss Conroy and turned back to Samuel, saying hurriedly, if with some condescension, "No one can know everything and perhaps you don't buy South American timber. I'd like to go up the Amazon in a canoe."

"Would you like that too, Anna?" Samuel asked, still holding Julia tightly but turning gravely to look at Anna.

She answered scornfully, "And be eaten by crocodiles? No, thanks."

"Crocodiles are only wicked if they're provoked," Julia said confidently. "I'd like to learn about politics and economics and all those things that Thomas talks about. When is he coming?"

"Saturday. And you'd better get on with your sewing because you won't be able to go up the Amazon for ages. What about you, Anna? Which subjects do you like best?"

She answered quickly and precisely, as if she had rehearsed it many times, "Drawing and needlework and French."

"Anna is a very good girl," Miss Conroy put in, her voice full of admiration. "I tell Julia she should try to imitate her. Such an older sister gives a very good example."

Standing by the window, deliberately out of the scene, Alice saw Julia's contemptuous expression before she turned quickly to nuzzle Samuel's shoulder.

He said, "Yes, Julia, do try to imitate Anna in these things. You can learn as many of the others that you want as well, later on. We'll talk about it again. There's plenty of time."

"Could I have Mr. Veale for Greek and Latin every day, as Thomas did? Please, Papa!"

She turned her big, blue, melting eyes on him with deliberately seductive effect, and covering his amusement at her tactics, he said seriously, "Thomas said Mr. Veale was very cross and used to shout at him. How would you like that?"

"He wouldn't shout at a girl," Julia said uncertainly. "Besides, I'd work so hard that he'd have nothing to shout about.

I know a little Latin already, that Thomas taught me." She raised her voice a tone or two to recite;

> " 'Amo, amas, I loved a lass,
>   And she was tall and slender;
>   Amas, amat, she knocked me flat,
>   And hammered my knob on the fender!' "

"Julia! What will Papa think?"

Miss Conroy looked really distressed but she relaxed at the sound of Samuel's delighted laughter. Anna also smiled indulgently when he turned to include her, putting out his hand to take hers. She responded gratefully, obviously overwhelmed by Julia's exuberance. Her pale smooth hair and fine, pointed face, her translucent skin and gray eyes, were all in sharp contrast to Julia's full-blooded coloring, yet she was not delicate, no more than Samuel was. Alice had noticed that he always treated Anna gently, never seizing her roughly, rumpling her hair or slapping her playfully as he did with Julia. Though she was sometimes impatient at this respectful treatment of a mere child, still she had to accept Samuel's consistency as proof that he had his reasons. Little by little she deferred to him in all of Anna's affairs and the gap of understanding between herself and her older daughter became daily wider.

43

Mr. Veale did come, and Julia started lessons with him in Samuel's study, which was often free while he was away in Galway. He laughed at Miss Conroy's complaints of the tutor's violence and unsuitability until one morning in June when she led him protesting to the door, opening it a crack so that they could listen.

Mr. Veale was snarling, "It's the gerund, you stupid fool, not the gerundive. By God, if you were a boy I'd have you across my knee for that!"

To which Julia's voice answered smartly, "By God, sir, if you want me to know the difference you should take the trouble to tell me!"

That was the end of Mr. Veale. Julia wept and howled and had to be shaken into submission by Alice, and then given sweets and promised that she would be sent to boarding school in Roehampton in the autumn. Alice missed her but had to admit that the whole household relaxed when she was gone. Anna especially seemed to flower now, occupied with sewing and embroidery and crocheting, painting delicate, uninteresting landscapes, trimming bonnets, arranging flowers and practicing at the piano and at her singing. Miss Conroy said she was the most satisfactory pupil she had ever had and that by the time she was sixteen she would be fit for any society. She became prettier every day, and the softly frilled and flowered dresses of the present fashion suited her. She wore her grandmother's jewelry with ease, her delicacy drawing attention to the fine carving of a minuscule Diana with her bow on a heavy gold-rimmed cameo, or to a circle of tiny pearls enclosing an emerald. Her hair was always neat, her hands quiet, her gray eyes calm and rather solemn. Samuel was proud of her, especially when she sat demurely at a dinner party, speaking when she was spoken to, listening with careful politeness to conversations that were above her head and later entertaining the company with one or two songs at the piano. These were usually Moore's melodies, whose accompaniments were simple enough for her to play for herself. She accompanied Samuel, too, and Alice always wanted him to sing "Barbara Allen," which Anna allowed was respectable. She considered the ballad of Lazarus and Dives too *farouche* for a Dublin drawing room.

These entertainments were only for Dublin. Twice a year, for three months of the summer and a month at Christmas, the household moved to Moycullen. For weeks before the summer journey of 1868, preparations went ahead, trunks were filled with castoff clothes for the neighbors, as Alice persisted in calling them, and Miss Conroy and Jane Sprigg joined in plans to overcome the worst of the misfortunes inevitable to their leaving civilization, packing card games, draughts, wool for knitting and rug making, and promising each other that there would be picnics and outings to Galway which would help to while away the time. Anna wept quietly and had long, low-voiced conversations each afternoon with Mimi D'Arcy and Belle Stratton and Rosa Middleton, who were her bosom friends. The D'Arcys had a house at Woodstock, only a few miles from Moycullen, and would come quite often, yet Anna and Mimi behaved as if they were parting from each other for years.

"You'd think Anna was emigrating to America," Alice said impatiently to Samuel after she had tried to intervene in one of these conversations. "The best families *never* go down the country, she says, though they all have estates. It's so vulgar there, not a bit elegant, and the house servants are all spoiled by idleness, and there are no balls. Anna suggested that we should go to Bath instead. Lord God, Samuel, where did we get her?"

"Don't say 'Lord God,'" Samuel said automatically, and sighed. "I think she must be very much like my mother. She'll probably marry a landlord who will take her to Bath."

"Your mother didn't," Alice pointed out, remembering Ellen's admiration for that perfect lady isolated in Moycullen. "And besides, every day there are fewer landlords fit to marry. With all this talk of reform there will be fewer still in times to come. Perhaps we should take her to Bath. She'll never find a husband to her liking in Ireland."

"Time enough, time enough," Samuel said. "There is no question of going to Bath or anywhere else. As it is, we don't spend enough time in Moycullen. I sometimes wonder if I shouldn't have stayed there altogether. Having a house in Dublin looks like running away."

"Everyone knows you didn't run away! And besides, you go to Galway every other week."

"I might never have left Moycullen if Fennell hadn't been murdered, though not much happens that I don't hear about. Father Ned keeps me informed of anything I miss."

"I'll be glad to see him," Alice said warmly. "How is he?"

"Always better in summer, of course, but very thin and worn. He spent the winter on horseback as usual, getting one wetting after another, climbing mountainsides on sick calls. He says someone is dying in every house. The people say he appears like a miracle at every deathbed in the parish. I want you to see the new cottages, Alice, and the gardens. You won't know them, they're so improved. Mr. Henry has been showing me his work at Kylemore. I think he pays wages into every cottage on his estate but it's hopeless, like trying to stop a tidal wave. A miracle of loaves and fishes is the only answer."

"How are the potatoes looking?"

Samuel said grimly, "They always look well at this time of the year. July is the month for the blast. We'll be there for it."

The journey to Galway was a delight to Alice, though she was irritated at Anna's obvious enjoyment of the special attention the family received at the stations both in Dublin and Galway. Julia was more manageable now, under the influence of the Roehampton nuns, and had actually learned in two years not to make sarcastic remarks, not to use rough language and to sit quietly like a lady. She could not control her lively eyes, however, and her thoughts were all too clear to those who

301

knew her well. Thomas made sure to sit with her, though he had promised Alice that he would not talk politics on the way to Galway.

Alice had taken him aside the evening before and warned him. "You know Anna hates it. She was terribly distressed at Uncle Morgan's arrest. Since then she bursts into tears if anyone mentions the troubles. The Rising last year was a nightmare to us all. You were away and didn't see it, but when Papa came home with news every evening, poor Anna rushed out of the room and wouldn't listen to any of it. Julia is different—she's tougher clay."

An unsympathetic look in Thomas' eye brought her to a stop and she waited for his reply.

"Anna may have been distressed," he said contemptuously, "but I heard her telling Belle that Uncle Morgan is no relation of ours, only a sort of servant from Moycullen whom Papa takes a special interest in."

"A servant!" Alice flushed with anger.

"That's what she said. Belle questioned her pretty closely and I could see she suspected Anna of hedging. Anna would have said anything to head her off. But, of course, it's true that he's no relation."

Alice gazed at him, suspecting that he was not telling her all of that conversation. It was easy to imagine Anna's fear that Belle would hint or even say that Alice kept strange company and was perhaps no better than a servant herself. This would be the way to torment Anna and Belle had a liking for tormenting her friends. A tall, slender beauty, she liked the company of younger girls whom she could impress with descriptions of activities that were still beyond their experience. Her father owned an estate in County Waterford which he never visited except at election time. He was there now, buttering up the tenants and the local clergy to make sure of his usual place on the Conservative benches after the election in the spring.

Thomas said, "It's funny to hear Anna and Belle talking. They have no interest in anything except dresses and balls. I won't marry a girl like that, you may be sure."

"That's good news, at least," Alice said tartly. "Now remember what I said about the train journey. It's bad enough to be cooped up together for hours without having arguments and quarrels as well."

"All right, Mama, I'll be good." Thomas was standing on his toes to show that he could look down on her. "I'll sit with Papa and we'll both be quiet."

It was a tedious journey. In the hot, dusty afternoon they got out at the station in Galway and found the two carriages from Moycullen waiting, as well as a variety of traps for the luggage and the big flat spring dray for the cases of claret.

At the back of the line Alice saw Mike Sherwin's trap and in a moment he was in the midst of them, slapping Thomas on the back, shaking hands with the girls and with Samuel and Alice, screwing his eyes in a delighted grin as he said eagerly, "I couldn't wait to see ye. 'Tis good to have ye back and a long summer before us for talk and chat. There's great doings in the country with the election and they say Mr. Moore is going for Mayo after all, a decent man, and Mr. Henry, too. They'll be wanting you for speechifying, Mr. Samuel, to get the right sort in and down the Orangemen. I was up north last month and nothing was bothering them there but would the new Government let them have the Orange processions and burn out the Catholics—"

"All right, all right," Samuel said. "Let's get the family home and we can settle down for a long talk in the evening. Has Paddy arrived?"

"He's waiting at the house. He's not sick but he does get tired. He has some news of Morgan Connolly."

"What news?"

"Where is Morgan?"

"In Dartmoor. He's waiting to tell you all about it. Morgan is well enough, ma'am, and bearing up." Suddenly Mike seemed to fall back to his true size and age, stooped, shrunken, bald, flabby, dispirited. "Let ye all come back to the house now and it will be like old times, when the Flahertys were kings in the land."

He turned back to his tiny trap, which was drawn by a strange bony beast that might have been a mule or a donkey. After Samuel, Alice and Miss Conroy had climbed into the first carriage, Anna said, with her foot on the step, "Papa, couldn't we have an elegant carriage here, like the one in Dublin, done in brocade? It's so much prettier."

Samuel said seriously, "Leather is more practical for the country. Did you hear what Mike said just now?"

"I don't listen to Mike, he's so dirty," Anna said, but her eyes were full of tears through which he could see her terror. He placed her carefully beside him and, taking her hand in his, held her close all the way to Moycullen.

At the lodge, the gates were standing open and the whole family was grouped at the door to wave as they went through. Julia and Thomas, in the second carriage, waved back and

Thomas said as they trotted up the avenue, "Joe Murphy told me there's a reception ready for us. Anna will be a study—I bet she tries to sweep into the house. Just watch!"

On the gravel a crowd of perhaps seventy people was gathered, and as the carriages drove in they could hear the sound of fiddles playing a jig. The evening sun was still warm and the heavy chestnut trees in full leaf were decorated with their tall white candles. The lighter-green leaves of the beeches shone as they can do only in early summer, juicy and clean, drooping slightly on their delicate branches. Alice noticed at once that the geraniums in the urns at either side of the steps were in healthy flower, the steps were brushed and clean and the great brass door handles were shining, proof that the household was working well. There was only a moment in which to take this in before Joe Murphy, the new coachman, sprang to the ground and the carriage door was opened. The music stopped.

"Paddy!"

He was standing with Master Fahy on the steps. He came tottering toward her but Fahy remained where he was, silently watching. He took her hand in both of his and held it so tightly that the rings pressed agonizingly into her flesh. She did not flinch but looked him up and down anxiously, noting his hollowed cheeks and unhealthy skull-like forehead and the new stoop of his shoulders.

"It's good to see you, Paddy."

"Good for me, too, ma'am. I'll be talking to you later on in the evening but now they want a song and a dance before ye go into the house."

"I'd rather talk to you first."

"It's more fitting this way. There's too many people about."

The fiddles started again, two of them, played by two expressionless brothers named Cody, from Moycullen village, who never looked directly at each other but indicated a change of tune by a nudge of the shoulder or an infinitesimal turn of the head or jerk of the foot. As they played, they edged gradually aside until they were standing apart from the crowd. Paddy took Alice's arm and led her forward, while Samuel found Kate, who was giggling in the background, and called out, "Come along, then! We'll have a set before we go in!"

At once three eights formed and the dance began, Thomas and Julia together among them. Anna clung to Miss Conroy, shaking her head miserably at the one shy young man who approached her blushing and who then went to hide himself at the back of the crowd. The gravel flew and the old men and women who were not dancing tapped their feet and grinned delightedly, sometimes making a stamping step or two to prove their participation.

At last everyone stopped, panting, and Paddy said loudly, "A song now! Who has wind for a song?"

Voices said "Leahy is here! Go on, Leahy! A song from Leahy! Give us 'The Rising of the Moon,' Leahy!"

Still standing with Paddy, as all the partners were together, Alice saw Leahy shoulder his way out of the crowd. He was not from Moycullen at all but from the desolate Maam Valley, twenty miles away. He was a handsome black-haired giant of a man with lively blue eyes and a baritone voice of great intensity and passion. A song in English was a concession to this household, since Leahy was mostly renowned for singing love songs in Irish. His speaking voice was sweet and had a vibrant quality that stayed in the memory.

He said, "I'll sing 'The Rising of the Moon' if Mr. Flaherty will sing afterward. I don't often hear a good singer."

"I certainly will," Samuel said.

Silence fell on the company. An evening blackbird whistled suddenly in a chestnut tree while Leahy composed himself seriously and began:

> "'O then tell me, Sean O'Farrell, tell me why you hurry
>   so?'"
> "Hush, mo bhuachaill, hush and listen," and his cheeks
>   were all aglow,
> "I bear orders from the Captain, get you ready quick and
>   soon,
>   For the pikes must be together by the rising of the
>   moon!'"

Samuel and Ailce looked at each other in bewilderment and could see that neither had heard this song before. The tune was familiar—the tune of "The Wearing of the Green," full of pathos in spite of the warlike sentiments of the early verses. The end was sad enough to fit the tune:

> "'Well they fought for poor old Ireland and full bitter was
>   their fate,
>   Yet what glorious pride and sorrow fill the name of ninety-
>   eight.
>   Yet, thank God, e'en still are beating hearts in manhood's
>   burning noon
>   Who would follow in their footsteps at the rising of the
>   moon!'"

305

By the time he had finished, several of the old women were sobbing and keening gently.

Stunned, Samuel said after a moment's pause, "That's a fine song, Leahy. I've never heard it before."

"It's a fairly new song, your Honor, a good song. Leo Casey wrote it a while ago, they say, but we only have it lately. Now we'll have one from yourself, one of Mr. Davis' songs."

Samuel lifted his angular chin and looked around at the people. One of the Cody brothers played a few notes of "The West's Awake" and stopped. Alice glanced across at Anna, who was holding her ground with Miss Conroy.

Samuel's eyes rested on her, too, and then he said coolly, "No, not that. I was never a fighting man."

Leahy said softly, "There's many a way of fighting, Mr. Flaherty."

"Then I'll sing another of Mr. Davis' songs."

He took a step forward, faced his audience and began to sing, as unself-consciously as he would do on any evening in his own drawing room.

> " 'Our mountain streams were rushing, Annie dear;
> The autumn woods were blushing, Annie dear;
> But brighter was your blushing
> When first your murmurs hushing
> I told my love outgushing, Annie dear.' "

"Good man, yourself!" said Leahy and other voices said in Irish, "God leave you your gift! Long life to you, Flaherty!"

His voice had kept its pitch and flexibility. Alice had heard him sing this song once before and she was prepared for the tragic verses about the burning of the cottage by the yeomen and the final lament of the husband over his dead wife.

> " 'Far better by you lying
> Than live an exile sighing, Annie dear!' "

Leahy said quietly, "Thank you for that song, Mr. Flaherty, and it's true that you're a fighting man."

"I'll never be a fighter," Samuel said, taking Alice's arm, looking around for the rest of the family, drawing them together at the foot of the steps. Then Master Fahy took possession of them with the air of a prime minister who has waited tolerantly while the people cheer the king, and led them into the house.

44

Though Samuel had warned her, Alice was shocked at the change in Father Kenny when he came after dinner the same evening.

"You're as thin as Paddy, without being in jail at all! What have you been doing?"

"Taking outdoor exercise."

Apart from his parish work he had spent months riding about the whole of Connemara and into Mayo, organizing for the coming elections. His eyes flashed and sparkled with excitement as he talked, sitting huddled in the armchair by the empty fireplace, warmed by a long ray of sunlight.

"An election now is a blessing, otherwise we'll have more risings, more fighting, more bloodshed. The people are desperate—they've reached the point where they have nothing to lose. That's what they all tell me—'Sure, things can't be any worse than they are'—and I can see them measuring me as if I were a traitor when I advise them to be moderate."

"Mike Sherwin has told me already that I'm expected to help," Samuel said.

"Yes. They want you to go to Carnacon to see Mr. Moore and persuade him to stand for election. He's very short-tempered, they say; no one wants to face up to him."

"Another landlord is expendable?"

"That's roughly it. We can't hope for more than one seat for the Liberals but there must be no mistake about that one."

"When do they want me to go?"

"The sooner, the better. If he agrees, we can have a formal meeting to choose the candidate. This time it seems the clergy and the bishops are going to be on the right side for once in their lives."

"And Cardinal Cullen?" Master Fahy asked.

"On the wrong side as usual. He's against the amnesty movement, which will be a main issue, but he can't very well be against disestablishment of the Protestant Church, and that's going to be tied in so close that no one will be able to tell them apart. It's a pure pleasure to watch him wriggling. He can't repudiate Archbishop MacHale but everything the Archbishop says gripes our Cardinal to the depths of his Roman guts."

He broke off as Thomas came into the room. They were sitting in the dining room, as they always did in Moycullen in summer to be near the garden. The children had disappeared after dinner, Thomas and Julia to the kitchen and the yard and Anna upstairs with Miss Conroy to unpack her clothes.

Thomas said excitedly, "Papa, Paddy has been talking to us about Uncle Morgan. May we bring him in?"

"Of course, at once! We're waiting for him."

Samuel sprang up and was at the door to receive Paddy and seat him at the table. Before Paddy could begin, the door was edged gently open and they saw that Mike Sherwin was there.

"Come in, Mike—you're just in time. Now, Paddy, tell us as much as you feel able to. I got the message that you were coming, that was all. How long have you been here?"

"Ten days. The horses are all different, Mr. Flaherty, except your own gray and that old article that draws the manure—he'll go on forever."

"And no one has any respect for him," said Fahy. "That's always the way."

"I left a message that you're not to work," Samuel said sharply.

"He hasn't been working," Thomas said, "just looking at the horses and giving orders. Paddy, tell about Uncle Morgan."

"He's in Dartmoor, or at least that's where he was when I left it. I worked with him in the laundry, a few of us together. First I was outside in the fresh air, and that was kind of healthy, though it's a cold bleak place. But afterward they brought us in to work in the washhouse. We were glad to be warm, after the frost and snow outside in the wintertime, but the steam was nearly worse, and handling the dirty clothes." He stopped and looked uneasily at Thomas, saying "It's hard to tell it."

"Go on, go on," Thomas said. "Tell them everything."

"When he first came, he was put pulling a cart, like a horse," Paddy said, "and after that he was set at stone breaking. It wasn't too bad for me because I wasn't important but they made sure Morgan and a few others had the worst of everything. There was a shed there, a little place, half the size of this room, and all the bones of the meat used to be taken there to be broken up into powder for manure. But first they were dried and rotted out under the sun so that the stink of them was enough to knock you down. Morgan was at that work all summer— Oh, ma'am, don't cry! It was after that we were in the washhouse. Other prisoners could ask for a change of work or to walk with a man they liked during the exercise time on

Sunday or have a visitor, but Morgan was never allowed anything. Special orders from the Home Secretary, the Governor said, for him and a few others. If he asks for anything, they put him in the punishment cells on bread and water, three days or ten days, according to the mood of the Governor. When I came away he had just been moved to the cells where they keep the mad prisoners—"

"Was Morgan mad?"

"No more than myself, sir, but they were hoping for it, I suppose, God help them. They're a strange class of people, the ones you find working in a prison, and it's a strange life altogether. You get kind of used to it. Would you believe me, I was delighted to see Morgan when he arrived in Dartmoor, the way you'd be glad to see a friend in any free place? We were hardly ever able to talk, and when we did we usually paid dear for it. He was there a while before I saw him, and I used to be always looking out for him afterward to see how he was doing."

"Did you talk with him before you left?"

"I got a chance on one of the last days, I don't know how or why. It was a miracle, for we were always watched. I didn't know then that I'd be going so soon. I was just called up one day and told I was to be released, and I was never allowed back to the prison again."

"Your term wasn't up."

"No. I got seven years, as you know, beginning in '64, so I had two and a half long years to go."

"And Morgan still has more than seven years unless we get him out before that. Will you come with me, Paddy, and speak at election meetings and tell what you've been telling us? I've promised to go down to Mayo and see Mr. Moore and ask him to go for election, and you know the whole summer will be taken up with meetings while the weather lasts."

"And you can tell about the chains, and how the ordinary prisoners were so sorry for the Fenians they gave them their bread and were punished for it, and how only the Fenians couldn't have parcels or see their friends," Thomas said eagerly.

Paddy reached out and took Thomas' hand, saying, "Of course I'll do it, though I'm no good for talk."

"You'll learn fast enough," Father Kenny said. "Only don't exaggerate; tell the exact truth."

"What else would I do?" Paddy asked in wonder.

"If you ask that, you'll never make a politician."

'There's fierce excitement all over the country," Mike Sherwin said quietly. "Big parish meetings everywhere and talk of Mr. Gladstone getting in with a government. They say he'll do a lot for Ireland if he gets in."

"He has good intentions, perhaps," Father Kenny said, "but getting the land from the Irish landlords will be like trying to take a bone from a dog. There's enough of themselves and their friends in the House of Lords to wreck any attempts to improve things here. And remember, we're not supposed to mention the possibility of repeal of the Act of Union lest we frighten off halfhearted friends of our own. Can you go to Ballinrobe tomorrow?"

"Yes, I think so. What do you say, Alice?"

"The sooner, the better, as Father Ned says."

After the carriage had left early next morning, Alice walked about the house in a state of tingling excitement, as if she had actually seen Morgan in his prison. She realized now that he had slipped back in her memory, losing a little of his mobility, so that she saw him now only in attitudes or pictures. There was a thrill in finding evidence that he was alive, though she could not believe she would not have known if he were dead.

Kate had talked a long time to Paddy and said to Alice, "Paddy thinks that Morgan will do a while longer. He's got his second wind. Being always thin was a good thing, Paddy says, though I used to be trying to fatten him up whenever he came here, and Morgan is tough from being on the sea, too. But many a fine man is going under. They wish them dead, though they were afraid to condemn them to death." Kate revealed her age in small moans and prayers in Irish between sentences when she was agitated. She was able for very little work but Alice had placed a basketwork armchair for her in the kitchen so that she could supervise the cooking and the dairy work, which she loved particularly. She gave an unexpected chuckle now, saying, "You'll never believe what Paddy told me—that he thinks it was James Fahy got him out of jail!"

"James! What makes him think so?"

"The Governor of the jail said something about an order coming from the Home Secretary, and something about a person in the—the—I don't know what he called it—to do with gold—"

"The Treasury."

"That's it. James is in there, it seems, and he's powerful. He was always crafty with people." She used the word dispassionately, meaning that he was tactful. "Maybe you could ask the Master to ask James to do a thing for Morgan. There's none of

310

us like to talk to him about James; he gets so cross you'd think he'd burst himself."

Alice almost ran out of the coach house, stumbling up the ladder until her eyes were on a level with Fahy's door.

"Master, Master! Are you there?"

He opened the door at once and stepped out onto the landing, closing the door behind him as he always did so that she could not see into the room.

He looked down at her with such surprise that she was brought to her senses and said weakly. "Can you come into the house and talk to me?"

"Bad news?"

"No. Please come."

She turned at once and went down, hearing him follow her cautiously on the creaking ladder. She waited for him in the dining room, saying as he came in, "Paddy told Kate that he thinks James had a hand in getting him out of jail!"

Fahy turned away, making sure that she could not see his face, keeping silent for a full minute. She had seen the narrowing of his eyes and the rigid line of his jaw at the sound of James's name, but the quickly produced sentence had been effective. He put up both hands and smoothed his hair, giving a twitch to the tail, now very thin, to lift it over his collar.

At last he said, "Did James go to see Paddy in jail?"

"I don't think so."

"Afraid, I suppose."

"Master, how can you say that? You haven't seen James for several years. It must have taken courage to get the Home Office to move for Paddy—"

"Courage? He should be doing it every day."

"If he did, he probably wouldn't be in the Treasury long," Alice said tartly. She was the only person who talked to him plainly, being the only one he had never taught. He glared at her and gave a growl of fury, his bushy white eyebrows drawn down. "James's usefulness will be in his position. That's why I called you, to ask you to tell him that Morgan is in Dartmoor."

"Do you think he doesn't know?"

This set her back but she said, "Perhaps he has been trying and failing, then, but I want you to write and ask him—tell him—"

"Write to him? I will not! It's his business to write to me. He owes me an apology—ten apologies!"

Even Alice dared not remind him that it was he who had done the loudest shouting on the terrible occasion of James's last visit, telling James that he was a renegade, a Judas, a traitor, a timeserver, a hack, finishing the tirade by snarling, "You were trained to be a doctor, to do something for humanity. You went to the university for years at the expense of your patron."

"Please don't mention that," Samuel had interrupted. "James is welcome to his education, whatever he does with it."

The look of gratitude that James had given him was too much for the Master. They were in the dining room after dinner and the row had blown up unexpectedly from a question of Alice's about the nature of James's work. He had boasted a little, perhaps, about the great men he rubbed shoulders with and the special interest of Lord Granville that had put him on the road to success, saying that he admired the way that English gentlemen helped people in whom they were interested and ensured their careers. From mild argument they had gone on to insults and at last James, white-faced, had rushed out of the room and had not spoken to his father again in spite of Samuel's appeals that they should make it up before James departed for London the next day. Fahy, indeed, had disappeared into his room and had not been seen until the day after James had left, and no one had ever been able to discuss the incident with him again. Kate had made one attempt to soften him, but though he would not be uncivil to her, he had stalked away so angrily that she had never tried it again.

Now Alice said tentatively, "It sounds as if James has changed—I think he just sees his work as an interesting job. If he had sold out, why would he bother with Paddy?" Fahy snorted but looked uneasy. "He has a good heart. He would probably like to hear from you in any case."

"Have you been in touch with him?"

"No. I wish I had been. After all, why should he not take patronage from Lord Granville, when he took it from Mr. Flaherty? He was used to patronage and being helped along."

"You think that was it?"

"What else can it be? He found that he didn't like being a doctor, so why should he continue if he had a chance of doing something more to his liking?"

"He didn't have to take a job running the Empire."

"I don't suppose it began that way."

"And he didn't have to put on an English accent."

"It's no worse than Samuel's."

"Samuel's is natural. James would be a laughingstock in his own country."

"But he doesn't live in his own country and he must speak to be understood. It's like having a good French accent—"

"I've got on very well all my life without a good French accent."

Alice remembered Morgan's account of his first attempts to speak French, using Fahy's ideas of pronunciation, and the howls of derision from the other students which had nearly silenced him for good. She considered offering to write to James herself but hardened her nerve to say firmly, "It would be a Christian thing for you to write and make it up with James, with the excuse that you want him to help Morgan—"

"I don't need an excuse to write to my own son!" Fahy thundered at her, walking off across the room to stand gazing out of the window, outlined crookedly against the glass, knobby knee breeches, out-turned toes, drooped shoulders and the absurd pigtail, yet the effect was more pathetic than ridiculous. She pretended to be angry, too, so that when he turned at last he would have to make the effort to be especially polite to her. It worked now as it always had. "I shouldn't speak to a lady like that—I forget myself when I think of James." But now he said the name without revulsion, sighing afterward resignedly. "He has intelligence. I suppose I should be glad he has enterprise, too, though it would please me better if he were working for his own country."

"What could he work at here? As a landlord's agent?"

"Samuel would have given him work at the mill."

"Perhaps he felt he had taken enough from Samuel." That was a dangerous line and she hurried on. "He needs to be away for a while—I don't believe he will ever forget Ireland. His helping Paddy proves it. Oh, Master, please write to him and ask him about Morgan! Perhaps he doesn't know where he is. You know they've kept it secret for fear of attempts at rescue. If James knew, and could help, and you never asked him—"

Now she could no longer hold back her tears, the last blow to Fahy's defenses. He hurried out of the room, saying sharply as he went, "I'll do it, now, at once, this moment."

Then she was left alone, in the grip of a dreadful sense of helplessness, as if she were leaping after her own mind, trying to hold it back, to prevent some desperate happening that had already begun. In a few minutes she was recalled by the sound of footsteps in the hall, the children coming to look for her. She escaped through the French window into the garden and thence to the paddock, taking refuge in the little corner stable.

She knew that love for Morgan was the one thing that could disturb her in this exact way, and she could feel only secret delight in the knowledge that the tornado could still fly through her and lift her into another world where her ordinary life became meaningless and the whole world was cut away. Then, as sanity returned to her, she hated her own madness and the division in her mind that made it possible for her to share herself between Morgan and Samuel, in the full knowledge that each of them wished her fully for his own. She was weak, mean, a whore, ungrateful to Samuel, unbalanced. She hurled insults at herself until she blushed with shame at her own wickedness and was at last able to go back to the house in a fit condition to be seen.

45

Samuel and Mr. Moore approved of each other at once and Moore quickly agreed to stand for election. His manner in private was the same as in public: he clipped off his words as if he were making a speech in Parliament and composed his cadences carefully. Samuel found this a barrier at first but gradually he got used to it and enjoyed Moore's irony, whose course was not always obvious at once. Sunday after Sunday throughout the month of August they campaigned together, always in the same pattern. First there was Mass in a country church, during which the priest announced that there would be a meeting outside afterward. An improvised platform, consisting of barrels with a few planks across them, was erected at the church gate, and as their turns came to speak, Moore and Samuel and the other speakers were hoisted onto it by excited men of all ages, who then pressed close below them, looking up into their faces eagerly, cheering throughout the speeches and often finishing by carrying them off on their shoulders to the parish priest's house for dinner. In spite of his age Moore seemed to thrive on it all, and from being rather uncertain at first, Samuel found himself growing in power as the weeks went on. Paddy proved a real find, his earnestness carrying great conviction. At the first meeting, in Ballycastle, he spoke in Irish, telling of the conditions in the prisons where the Fenians were held:

"If I were a man like other men, I would have died of hunger and thirst and hardship and cold, of blows and kicks and the lack of rest and sleep. But I was a Fenian and I thought of my country, of Owen Roe and Hugh O'Neill and Michael Dwyer and Wolfe Tone, and those thoughts fed me and warmed me and gave me drink when I was thirsty, as they do now to all the Irishmen that are suffering in English jails. Most of all was the comfort of knowing that my people would never forget me, that they would work for my release, that they will elect only those they can trust to demand that all the Fenians be set free, and that peace and justice will come to my country at the end of all. For this we suffer, for this we go willingly to prison, for this we endure cold and hardship and starvation, so that our children will own the land of their fathers and live without fear under their own roof."

Father Kenny called out in English, "Now raise a cheer for the prisoners! God save Ireland!"

This was answered by yells of enthusiasm that were redoubled when Father Kenny climbed onto the platform to speak, his gaunt body outlined against the blue sky like a dead tree.

"Only last winter, three young men were hanged in the city of Manchester for a crime that everyone knows they did not commit. Their last cry on the gallows was 'God save Ireland!' and that is the cry of every man here. God will save Ireland, but first we must make the way clear, with courage to demand our rights, the first rights of a man to a roof and enough food to keep him alive. We must have the kind of courage that Paddy here has described, courage that looks like cowardice at times because it comes so slow. But it comes sure, and it's the kind of courage that we ask now of every man at this meeting. What will your landlord do for you? Less than he would do for a cow or a pig on his farm. Animals must be treated with care or they will die. If you die, your landlord rejoices because he has got your holding of land without the trouble of paying your passage to America. But we have two landlords with us today to prove to you that landlords don't always behave like landlords, that they can care for the people and work for them and speak up for them in the foreign parliament until the day comes when we get a parliament of our own once again. Mr. Moore is a good landlord, and Mr. Flaherty is a good landlord. If Mr. Moore gets to Parliament he will find a friend of Ireland there in Mr. Gladstone, a man who has said in public that the Irish grievances must be very real to make men fight so hard and so long. 'Let us remove the grievances of Ireland,' he said, 'and instead of

315

hearing in every corner of Europe the most painful commentaries on the policy of England toward Ireland, we may be able to look our fellow Europeans in the face.' "

Cheers and shouts greeted this and Samuel was astonished to see that such ragged, hungry, wild-looking men could take hold of an idea so remote from their everyday lives. What was Europe to them? A line in a ballad, perhaps.

"The French are on the say—
They'll be here without delay,
And the Orange will decay
Says the Sean Bhean Bhocht."

Samuel knew that he had in general a good reputation as a landlord, though he heard execrations of the whole seed and breed at every meeting. At Ballintubber a few weeks later, as he climbed down from his barrel after making an impassioned speech in favor of Moore and Gladstone, a voice called out, "To hell with all the landlords! We'll never have peace till they're all under the sod!"

At once a wild roar went up, and an answering roar from Moore's supporters.

"Back to the wall!" Father Kenny shouted in Samuel's ear, at the same time forcing him by a hand on his shoulder toward the low wall that surrounded the chapel grounds.

Here they were on a little eminence and could see over the heads of the nearest part of the crowd to the rising ground beyond, where a ferocious fistfight had started up. Samuel saw the constables move in from the line they had taken up a short distance away, drawing their batons and whacking at heads as they came. Knots of struggling men seemed to flow through the crowd and there were shouts of:

"Down with the landlords!"

"Up the rebels!"

"Up the Fenians!"

Stones began to fly through the air and Samuel could see the parish priest, Father Murphy, attempting to climb onto the barrel again to address the crowd. Only those nearest to him could hear him yell as he was helped up by some of the men:

"Order, order down there! What way is this to behave? We brought you two decent landlords that will work for you. In God's name who will you send to Parliament? It has to be a man of education, a man that can talk up for the people—"

A voice called out, "Rack-renters!"

"Flaherty never rack-rented in his life!" Murphy yelled.

Now the people nearest to him were listening and gradually the scuffles eased off as all the heads were turned toward the barrel again. "Flaherty is the man that will stand up to the likes of Lord Lucan—"

The name aroused howls of fury from all sides.

"Know your friends, then!"

A light, high voice shouted, "Soap-the-Rope!"

This seemed to be about to cause another bout of fighting but again Murphy managed to be heard.

"Mr. Moore has proved he's no Soap-the-Rope. There's many a man I can see down there before me that had as bad a grandfather as Soap-the-Rope. Mr. Moore never had a man hanged in his life. Is his grandfather going to be held against him now, though he's spent his life in working for Ireland? Don't you know your own Archbishop MacHale is supporting him, the very man that brought your fathers out against Soap-the-Rope twenty years ago?"

"Up MacHale!"

"Up the Archbishop!"

"Go home and think it over. Ask yourselves one question: Do you want a man in Parliament that will take the Protestant leeches off your backs, the bloodsuckers that grab your taxes to keep up a church you don't believe in? Seven hundred thousand Protestants taking taxes off four and a half million Catholics. Do you want a man that will put a stop to that?"

"Yes! Yes!"

"That man is Mr. Moore, and I'll say one thing more, that any man that finds it in his heart to vote the wrong way can be sure of eternal damnation in the fires of hell and never need hope for the sight of God!"

He leaped down from the barrel. Samuel heard the loud groans of terror that his last promise had evoked and felt the shock of closeness to the primitive run through him. He could scarcely look Father Murphy in the face when he came elbowing his way to them, shoving the people roughly aside as if they were sheep. He was a short bull-necked man, red-faced, heavy-jowled, wild-haired, whose whole appearance was redeemed by a pair of perfectly innocent deep-blue eyes that would have been worth a fortune to a girl.

He slewed his eyes sideways at Samuel and said, "You needn't give me that look, Mr. Flaherty, sir, for it was the truth I told. They know well from their conscience where they must vote, and they know that all sleeveens go to hell. I'm only telling them what they know already." A thought struck him and he turned suddenly and plunged back through the crowd, calling out, "Wait! Wait! I have more to say! Let me up on that barrel again till I tell ye more!"

"Esprit d'escalier," said Father Kenny into Samuel's ear. "He's a terror."

Father Murphy was being heaved up onto the barrel, panting, clutching wildly, waving his arms to steady himself. He turned his chin up to the sky and gave a sort of crow that silenced every voice and brought back the few people who had begun to wander off home.

"Stop! Stop and listen! What I want to say is a very short sentence, and not my own. A few years ago, when O'Donovan Rossa and John O'Leary and Thomas Luby and James O'Connor and Morgan Connolly and many another good Irishman were all condemned to waste their lives in jail, the Most Reverend Bishop of Kerry, Moriarty, made a statement." He brought out the name and designation with scathing contempt. "The Most Reverend gentleman said, as you'll all remember, that hell is not hot enough or eternity long enough to punish those Irishmen for their attempt to free their native land from the yoke of foreign domination. I say to you today, and you can go home to your houses, those of you that have the like, and think it over: that I'm no Reverend Bishop, but I know that hell is not hot enough or eternity long enough or the devil's forks sharp enough to prod the living life out of every man that is here today and that goes to the poll and casts his vote for any man but Mr. Moore. Let ye remember that on the day of judgment when ye'll ask me to put in a word for ye. I won't do it—I'll let ye rot in hell for evermore!"

And he seemed to slide down off the barrel.

"That will finish them," he said with satisfaction as he came back through the thinning crowd to where Samuel and Mr. Moore and Father Kenny were waiting with Paddy and the local organizer, Michael Jordan, who was chuckling with joy.

"You cleared away their last doubts, Father Murphy," Jordan said. "The only trouble is that half of those poor devils haven't a vote at all. God help them—a man with a valuation of twelve pounds on his land in Mayo would be like a king."

"They can bring pressure," Father Murphy said.

"That's a polite word," Mr. Moore said sourly. "At this moment my life is being threatened by a person calling himself Rory. He writes me letters. He's not very clear about his grievances against me though he does mention that he wants my land for himself. Does this happen to you, Flaherty?"

"I don't get letters, but my father was shot after threats of that kind."

318

"Of course. I remember it well. Beastly business. I'd like to meet this Rory and argue it out but he's not likely to come close enough for that. They never do. We'll all abdicate in the end, of course, but not yet, as Saint Augustine said."

They followed the two priests, who were walking slowly toward the presbytery. Paddy and Michael Jordan came with them, chattering eagerly in Irish.

Moore said, "I've worn my heart out over Ireland. Sometimes I think there's a new spirit coming, a new breed that will be able to do something for themselves. I hear there will be an English candidate for Galway—the Recorder of Liverpool, no less. Have you heard this?"

"Surely not! I've heard the names of Morris and Blennerhassett. Morris is from Spiddal, I think, and the other is a Kerryman."

"My spies tell me that the Cardinal has other plans. Aspinall is his name—you'll hear it. He's a Catholic."

"I can't believe it! Besides, they're all Catholics."

"They're not all in the Cardinal's pocket—some want the Fenians released. Remember this conversation when it happens." With a quick glance at Samuel he said, "Morgan Connolly came to see me a few years ago. He mentioned that he was a friend of yours."

"We've just had news of him. Paddy, my groom, who spoke at the meeting, was with him in Dartmoor."

"A fine type, if he ever gets out. Those fellows are the hope of the country. He's the first peasant I've ever seen who was able to lift himself into a different station."

Samuel with his habit of restraint was able to suppress a flash of anger at this description of Morgan. He said mildly, "Connolly is an educated man now, however he may have begun."

Moore nodded in understanding, saying, "I see, I see. To tell the truth, Flaherty, I was rather surprised to find you mixed up in this kind of thing. I know how it happens. I had sworn I'd have no more to do with politics but I find myself unable to keep out either. A famine every year or two, dead and dying neighbors all around us—what can we do? Did you ever think of emigrating to England? It's the easy way out."

"And live on rack rents collected by an agent? I couldn't do it. Besides I have the mill to think of."

"Yes, you have the mill and I have my horse breeding. That makes a world of difference. Some of the landlords in my neighborhood are nearly as badly off as their own tenants, trying to live on two or three hundred pounds a year, making new bargains all the time with the tenants to squeeze a few more shillings out of them, their houses falling down around their ears. It's the same around Moycullen, I suppose. The only hope is to get back a native parliament, repeal the Act of Union, and that will be my first effort if I get elected. You could help us, Flaherty. You're a good speaker, and the people seem to tolerate you. Have you any connection with the Fenians, the I.R.B.—any of that lot?"

"I'm not a fighting man."

"I thought not. Neither am I, at least not officially." Then, in a different tone, less casually, "But at a council meeting lately it was suggested that you would be useful. Your wife knows the country from another angle, I hear, useful too. At least it could be. May I tell them you'll help if you're called on?"

"I'll help as I'm doing now but I've never been a fighting man."

Though he had answered automatically, the conversation worried Samuel. A council meeting? What council was that? He could see that he was arousing violence by taking part in this election, pointing to the sufferings of the tenants in Mayo, escorting Paddy, who could give chapter and verse for so many injustices and cruelties to the Fenian prisoners. What effect could this have but to madden the people further and drive them to excesses that he was sure would only react on themselves sooner or later? Surely their best chance was with gentlemen like Moore and himself, who could speak for them in Parliament and elsewhere. But the people he had seen at these meetings were not prepared to wait.

Throughout dinner at the presbytery he sat silent and miserable, watching the others and wondering how they could be so clear-sighted and single-minded about such a complex problem. Paddy was not naturally a fighting man but he was simple and dedicated. The same was true of Father Murphy, gobbling his boiled bacon and beef and cabbage and potatoes with the appetite of a healthy young pig, uninhibited by qualms about the curses with which he had just been threatening his parishioners. Master Fahy would say of him: "Irks care the crop-full bird?" Father Ned Kenny, thin, sophisticated, educated, was not a fighting man either, but he was impelled by savage indignation. The same was true of Moore. Jordan had a desperate look, like a man trying to hold back flood waters with his bare hands. Where did he, Samuel, come in, with his scruples and his hairsplitting?

He felt himself begin to shake, so that he had to hold his

hands together on his knees. Realization had come to him like this once before, when he knew that he must ask Alice to marry him, the best decision he ever made in his life, though he had paid dearly for taking her from Morgan. He wished that she were here now, but even as he conjured her up in his mind he realized that he knew what she would say—that the time had come to join Mr. Moore, now that he had received a direct invitation. It was this knowledge that was making him sweat and shake, fear of what would happen to himself and to his family. Mental courage is no match for physical fear—he had never felt like this on the hunting field, at point-to-point races, riding or driving alone into Galway. A prickling sensation at the back of his head seemed a premonition of disaster, ridiculous at this point, since he had declared his sympathies already at many meetings like the one they had just left.

It was after five o'clock when Moore said, "Flaherty and I are going on to Partry tonight. Father Lavelle is expecting us."

"It's a long drive." Father Murphy's eyes sparkled with anticipation for them. "But you'll get good whiskey at the end of it."

Moore laughed, the first time Samuel had heard him do so.

"We'll be pickled by the time this election is over. If you're staying with the Reverend Mr. Murphy, Father Kenny, have a thought for your liver. Can you come in my carriage, Flaherty?"

"Yes. I'd like your company. Paddy can take my trap."

"An open trap?" Moore looked mildly shocked. "Do you think it safe enough?"

"So far, yes."

"It's faster, of course, but less comfortable. You're young and strong."

He turned away as if the exchange had been unimportant but Samuel knew it was a warning. In the carriage he and Moore were able to have a long, uninterrupted talk, by the end of which Samuel had not a single doubt left as to the right course for him to follow.

"Don't blame yourself," Moore said wearily. "I well remember the hell I went through in making my own decision. It always comes down to the same thing in the end: can one stand by and leave the Government of the country to a collection of timeserving entrepreneurs, whose strongest feeling is hatred for the very land they walk on, or must one take action against them simply because one sees what they are? I left them to it for a long time, and then I realized that to take no action is as

321

much of a crime against the people as joining the ascendancy highwaymen. That was Swift's word, though he was referring to Protestant bishops. I've forgotten the context but I remember the remark very well, that when a bishop is appointed to an Irish see, he is invariably set upon by highwaymen as he crosses Hounslow Heath on his way to Ireland, and these gentlemen rob him of his robes and credentials and successfully impersonate him in Ireland when he arrives."

"I've heard Master Fahy quote it."

From Partry next morning, Samuel and Paddy set out in the trap, arranging to meet Moore again at next Sunday's Mass in Ballinrobe.

46

It was a glorious morning of dry, crisp air with a far-off suggestion of frost to give it bite. Samuel felt healthy and well, taking an actual pleasure in the tautness of his muscles. His courage had come back and his new decision filled him with a sense of physical strength and direction, matched by the perfect rhythm of the horse's feet on the gravelly road, trotting at the exact pace that Paddy had always favored. Paddy was a lord of creation, holding the reins deceptively loose, his eyes narrowed happily against the sunlight. Samuel felt very close to him now, sensing that they were sharing a desperately important experience.

He asked suddenly, "How old are you, Paddy?"

"Eight years older than yourself, sir, sixty-one. The mother always told me that, otherwise I wouldn't know it."

"And how do you remember my age?"

"Everyone knows you were born the year of the big battle, and that was in '15. I do be working it out sometimes. That's the kind of thing that runs through your head in prison, old times and old faces and friends long dead. Some of the things were not welcome, things I'd be glad to forget. I remember my father saying the same happened to him when he was in his last sickness."

"Then you knew my mother."

He had never spoken of her to any of the servants before. Paddy did not pause in his reply but said easily, as if they had often discussed her, "I do well remember her, a lovely lady, the image of yourself. She had your jaw, and your way of talking, too, though that might be only the accent. She was a gentle, delicate lady, not a bit like your father, God rest him." It was a plain statement, not an insult. "I was at the house the day she arrived and I remember how delighted she was with the place. It was a day like this, bright and clear, and we were all outside the door waiting for her, myself too, though I was only four years old, I suppose, but I can see it still. His Honor had got a new carriage all lined with embroidered stuff and he had two fine grays that lived for years and years after."

"I remember them."

"And they drove up to the lodge, and one of the boys came running across the lawn to tell us they were there, and we were all ready and waiting to raise a cheer. The first to get down out of the carriage was Ellen, that was lady's maid, and my aunt that was always a bit simple said out loud: 'She's no chicken.' My mother was mortified and told her to shut her gob, and then down stepped the lovely lady herself, in her new silk clothes, and Ellen carried her purse and basket for her, and his Honor, your father, Mr. George, looked so lively. That's what I remember about him, and why wouldn't he be lively, and he only just over the forty years of age at the time."

"Do you remember all that, just as you told me?"

"Every bit of it. Mr. George took your mother's hand and led her toward the house, and she stopped on the steps and said, 'It's a beautiful place,' and something else, I suppose, but that's all I remember. The people were glad he was married, I knew that much, thinking it would be better for everyone with a lady around the demesne, but then she died, poor soul, and it was very quiet for a long time."

Even Paddy did not care to speak of the episode of Mary. Samuel was silent for a while, seeing the picture that he had called up. Everyone on the estate must have been there. Kate, for instance, could well have been one of those cheering servants and might have spoken of it, but perhaps they had all felt that his mother's arrival was a sad occasion in retrospect since she had lived only four years at Moycullen. For the first time he felt a closeness almost amounting to identity with his father, living with him that warm moment of optimism that had dried up so soon, understanding something more of the mixed courage and cowardice that had composed his relationship with Mary.

Soon he and Alice would make their annual visit to Mary, who was almost blind, though she was not yet seventy, and who spent hours every day since Thomas' death in praying for him and for her own eventual salvation. On their last visit she had held Samuel's hand all the time they were in the house, using the excuse that she could not see him properly and had to rely on feeling, and he had been aware of a current that crossed between them, giving life to her. Many years ago he had been converted from his certainty that his father had wronged her. Indeed, he had come to the conclusion that George had been Mary's benefactor, and once he had recognized this, the confusion about his own moral standards had given him many uneasy hours. What if man were not intended by nature to be monogamous? Would this not mean that there was parsimony in refusing to share one's body and soul with more than one person, carefully chosen for one's own gratification in the first place? Moral theologians with their rigid rules would shriek at this view of charity, condemn him as a libertine, a monster, a freak, a danger to the whole social structure of the world, but Samuel felt he could justify his theory to some extent by observing the labyrinthine complications of Alice, who had been created with so much capacity for love that she could achieve the impossible in loving Samuel no less because she loved Morgan too. Before he had worked it out in words, Samuel had found that he knew this and it had kept his jealousy of Morgan within manageable bounds. All the same, there was a deep, dark spot in his mind that rejoiced when Morgan was taken away to prison, out of Alice's reach.

This spot of hatred lay on his conscience. Samuel was secure in the knowledge that she loved him the better of the two. He had never once thought of her as being unfaithful to him, not even in Paris when he feared that she had been in Morgan's bed. His respect and love for Morgan seemed to draw off jealousy, though this in turn seemed monstrous. How could it be so? He hated to share the woman he loved, yet Morgan was immune from hatred. Ireland makes oddities, he concluded ironically at last, especially in the country. Dublin society was more stable, farther from the horrors of beggary and starvation that stung the mind here every moment of the day. Probably this was the real cause of the situation between himself and Morgan—all life was so grim that a private quarrel seemed an indecency. Yet all around him people were falling in love and marrying as if the country were at peace. Better not to think too deeply; probably the true situation could not be justified on any grounds, moral or philosophical.

Paddy seemed happy in the silence, pursing his mouth like a man tasting something sweet, as if he had always planned to tell Samuel about the scene he had witnessed and had been aware in advance of the effect he would create. For Samuel, it was as if he had realized for the first time that he had not come out of nothing, but was the real son of a young man and woman, George and Sylvia, who had chosen to give him life. A great vista seemed to open before him, making his future full of possibilities and explorations hitherto out of the question. It was yet another new beginning, like his decision to help the Fenians, and the beginning that came to him that morning seventeen years ago when he rode home from the wedding in Cappagh and saw the seal sunning himself on the rocks in the dawn.

Then, rounding a long curve on the way into Clonbur village, suddenly a ragged man with a rifle in his hands, pointed toward them, leaped onto the stone wall beside the road. Paddy pulled up the horse so sharply that it slipped on the gravelly road, its hooves splaying dangerously, while he shouted in Irish, "Get off that wall, you fool! This is Flaherty of Moycullen!"

The man took careful aim and fired, then dropped behind the wall. Samuel felt a sharp pain in his chest and put up his two hands as if to ward off the bullet that had already entered his body. Paddy was sobbing with fury, helping him to sit up, taking away his hands to look at the blood already spurting from the wound, pressing his own hands with all his might against Samuel's chest as if he could stop the flow. Then, as quietly as if he were falling asleep, Samuel fainted.

In a daze, hours later, he saw Alice. She was quite close, holding his face between her hands as gently as a bee walking on the petals of a flower. Her eyes were glazed with tears, her lovely dark hair untidy, so that he wanted to smooth it for her, but his own hands would not move. He had to speak slowly, hearing his voice come in a whisper, not positively, as he wanted it to do.

"Alice, my dear, sweet Alice, Morgan will come—Morgan will look after you—and the children—my little Anna is not clever—love Morgan—she should love—and Thomas—you'll tell them—Julia—"

"Yes, yes, Samuel, I know. Don't talk. It will be all right. Just lie quietly."

But he knew it would not be all right because she could not hold back her tears, and he wanted to tell her a very important thing, slowly, to be whispered.

"Alice, we had good times. I loved you always. I'll be with you. Whose house is this?"

Then Samuel died, with no curiosity about the answer to his question, but with great sadness and a sense of loss.

47

Alice could not believe that Samuel was dead. She sat beside him for hours, calling to him softly, holding his cold hands, stroking his face, laying her head down on the bed by his chest to listen for his heartbeat, rolling upward then to look at his colorless face, which was no longer the face of Samuel, while tears and sobs shuddered through her tired body. It could not have happened, she knew that Samuel could not die, though everyone else in the whole world might have to, sooner or later. It was all wrong for Samuel—he was to be there always, to be with her, to keep her from the foolishness and stupidity that she would fall into without him. If she stayed with him long enough, he would revive, open his eyes, look at her again, tell her what to do, tell her what had happened to him, why that man had shot him even after Paddy had said it was Flaherty of Moycullen. Paddy had told her this in the first moment he saw her and it was this that had convinced her that Samuel would be all right. He would recover—the doctor said he was very strong and the bullet had been taken out. He would be ill for a long time and then he would be well and she would sit with him as long as he wanted, talking to him as they always did so comfortably together, no matter what misfortune or trouble was on them from outside. A good man, good right through his whole being, a man to respect and love. How could she bear it all without him?

The priest was pulling at her sleeve now, telling her to behave like a Christian, to accept the will of God. He sounded shocked. What did he know about love? Half of herself was lying there and he was telling her to walk away and abandon it, to let the women of the village come and wash Samuel—*wash* him!—for the funeral. He said his sister had made tea and wanted Alice to come down to the parlor and drink it before it got cold. She cared nothing for tea, hot or cold—that God of his had taken Samuel, and she would not tolerate it.

Now the priest had her by the shoulders and was lifting her up, saying, "Mrs. Flaherty, your husband wouldn't have liked you to behave like this. Come downstairs and be good. It will pass off; you'll feel better later on when you've had time to get used to the idea—"

The poor man's babblings were pitiful but they were the

first inroads made on her, forcing her to realize that she was causing him pain and embarrassment. She let herself be lifted into a standing position and be led to the door, but there she turned back to look at Samuel and found that she could not stand upright but had to sink down onto the floor, leaning against the wall and whining like a small dog in distress, both for herself and for the trouble she was giving to everyone. Samuel would not have liked it, but Samuel was dead, and there was no one now to care what she did, no one ever again but her small, miserable self. She tried to turn and look at him again but found that she could not bear it and covered her eyes with her two hands.

Then some woman came and said, "If you can stand up I'll help you to walk to another room and you can lie down on the bed."

She stood up but all beds were evil to her now since this one where Samuel lay had betrayed her. In the future she would sleep on the floor, or outside in the fields where Samuel would never be a memory, where she would not look to see him as she must always look at home. But she would keep this plan for herself: no use in talking to anyone, telling anyone what was in her mind for Samuel, just another man whom no one cared about, no one thought valuable, only the one woman who knew every little turn and move of his mind, who could predict nearly everything he would say in every situation, who had watched him and studied him for seventeen years—for much longer, ever since she was an infant and he had brought her her first dolls. That was the same Samuel—it was not to be believed, impossible for anyone to understand what it was like to see him dead. She closed her mouth firmly, to make sure she would not betray herself about the dolls, and walked from the room.

"Good, good," said the woman at her elbow encouragingly, the priest's sister, a kindly person who had had a lot to put up with in the last days. Alice was aware that the priest was giving a long sigh of pure relief behind her. There was no need to promise anything, better not to say she would be all right now, just go with them and drink that tea and try to talk to them about ordinary things, though nothing would ever again be ordinary in this world for her. "We had good times. I loved you always. I'll be with you." She said the words over and over to herself, stamping them into her brain clearly and sharply so that they would stay forever, knowing she would need them and that if she were not careful the voice would fade and she would be left alone. In this way she would be able to keep him always, ignore the advice to try to forget him. The priest had said it already—he was a professional comforter. She had heard it said so often.

The funeral next morning was a torment that had to be endured. Paddy drove her back to Moycullen himself, trusting no one else to look after her, though he was not supposed to be strong enough to drive the big carriage with two horses that had come for her. The coffin was driven down to Recess and put on the train, to be taken off at Moycullen. Thomas sat in the carriage with her, holding her hand silently all the way. He had come over to Clonbur on the first day and she knew he was somewhere in the priest's house but everyone said he was too young to be allowed to stay with his father.

As they came near Moycullen, they passed crowds of people walking along, all drawing off to the side of the road out of the way of the carriage, and on the huge lawn of the house there were so many that it looked like a race meeting. Families were sitting together, in circles and in little groups, resting on the warm, cropped grass after their walk. She knew a great many of them, mountainy people from Recess and Maam, and from as far away as Carraroe, by the sea, where Samuel was known for his charity and kindness. There were some Cappagh people there, the Cooneys and the Hernons and the Conneeleys. Most extraordinary of all was a detachment of well-drilled men, all carrying pitchforks over their shoulders like pikes, all dressed in white jackets of bawneen tweed, all with battered black Spanish hats, marching in formation behind the coffin when it was brought to the house. Before they set out for the church Alice asked Father Kenny about them.

"They're the Mayo Fenians," he said. "They know he had promised help to the Fenians on the day before he was shot— Mr. Moore told them that."

Here was something unexpected that she had to come to terms with at once. She went out to speak to the men, welcoming them to the house, thanking them for coming to the funeral. Their captain was a tall, loose-jointed man with heavy ginger-colored eyebrows and the soft hazel eyes of a fox.

"We are all sorry for your trouble, ma'am, and we want to pay our respects to Mr. Flaherty. It was a sorry day for Mayo that we lost him in the way we did."

"It was a mistake, surely."

"It was that, and no use saying more about it. He was a good man and a good landlord. If they were all like him, we could rest at home in our beds."

"He wanted to help the people—he thought always about the people—"

"God help you, ma'am, why wouldn't you cry after him? In a little while, we'll come back and talk to you, and maybe you can do an odd thing that he would have liked."

The clear hazel eyes seemed to bore into hers and to have read the answer to that oblique invitation.

She said, "Yes, I'll do whatever I can but give me a little time."

Then the procession started out, headed by Father Kenny, who looked so thin that it was a wonder he was able to put one foot in front of the other. Then came the coffin on a cart drawn by two of the big farm horses, led by Paddy and the new groom, one at either shaft, as if they were going to a fair, then Alice walking, and Thomas, who still held Alice's hand so that she would not cry, and Anna and Julia with Miss Conroy between them, all three in hurriedly made black dresses, and Master Fahy, and James, who had appeared the night before without warning, then the house servants, and Alice's brother Dan from Cappagh, and streams and streams of other people, some that no one knew at all. The Martins' carriage was there, and the Bateses' and the D'Arcys' too, but their owners were safe in Harrogate or in Bath. Some Protestant landlords from Mayo and Galway who had come with their carriages had left them at Moycullen House and walked with the procession to the graveyard from the church, though they had not come in for Mass first. Mr. Moore was there, looking gloomily and angrily at the crowds of country people as if he blamed them individually for Samuel's death.

At the graveyard the crowd thinned into a line to get through the narrow gate, then fanned out again until the people were standing on every hump and hillock of the old graves in a great circle around the family vault, which stood almost in the center of the graveyard like a little stone house. The grille was open and a space had been opened in the floor at one side to receive Samuel, the earth piled carefully on the flagstones and the two gravediggers standing aside with their shovels ready to heap it all on top of him. Alice watched in a daze, knowing that nothing was expected of her now but to keep quiet and dignified if she could. She was too tired, in any case, so there was no fear that she would disgrace herself again. The priest from Clonbur kept an uneasy eye on her when Father Kenny began the prayers for the dead, all about not letting Samuel stay forever in the fires of hell, as if any reasonable God would even consider such a thing. Then the hazel-eyed man made a speech, suddenly facing the crowd from the top of a flat tombstone, speaking in Irish.

"Flaherty of Moycullen is not going into the grave without a word of thanks from his own people. He was generous and kind to every man that came to his door. He was a good friend and a good landlord. He was a quiet man, but when he saw the need for it, he was in the gap of danger like a hero. May his memory live in the minds and hearts of the people of all Connacht. May God watch over his wife and children and forgive the fool that took their protector from them."

He stepped down from the tombstone. At once an old woman from Maam Valley began to keen, throwing herself on the ground and beating her breast with her closed fist.

Alice felt her control slip as the primitive sound drilled into her brain, and turning sharply she said to James, "Can we go now?"

"In a moment. It wouldn't look well to go at once. How long can you stand it?"

With a surge of gratitude she said, "About two minutes, then."

Little James had dignity, his head held high and his dapper clothes fitting perfectly, a new, firm look of authority in his eyes. He stood close beside his father so that the resemblance between them was suddenly apparent, one a miniature version of the other. Tensed like soldiers listening to the Last Post, they waited while the woman wailed through cadences as old as the ground on which she knelt, until James said, taking Alice's arm, "Now we can walk home."

The keening followed them for a long time, fainter and fainter, like the song of a lark fading into a clear blue sky on a summer day.

At the house a vast meal had been prepared early in the morning so that Kate would not miss the funeral. Everyone had to be given a glass of punch and Alice soon found herself moving among them as if it were a party, chatting to them for a few minutes each, listening to praises of Samuel and thanking them for coming. She saw that some of the more timid had gone away—the landlords, Blake of the mill's countinghouse, several Galway businessmen and members of the County Club who liked to visit at the officers' mess in Renmore Barracks. The air was clearer without them. More than once she found herself planning to tell Samuel who had come and who had stayed, catching herself on the point of hysteria not a moment too soon. At last they began to go, and she was on the steps with the wrong person beside her to see them off—James again, assuming the part of host so naturally that the guests turned to him and shook hands after they had finished with Alice. Her brother Dan was one of the last.

"Can't you stay a little longer?"

"There's the cattle—five cows to milk and the boys don't be able for it all yet."

"How is Agnes?"

"She's well enough at times but then she gets the fever and it weakens her. She can hardly work at all."

Agnes will die—everyone will die, just like Samuel—madly coursing through Alice's mind were faces of all the people she had known who had died young and pretty like Agnes, or had been shot down like Samuel.

Dan was saying desperately, "Alice, love, I shouldn't have told you that. Agnes is well enough."

But it was easy to see that this was not true.

Alice asked, "Does the doctor come?"

"He does, very often, a good decent man. He said the new rooms are fine, and the best chance that she'll get well, and to keep the whole house warm and dry and not to let her work. We're doing that, and she's eating well, thanks to Samuel, God rest him, so we hope it will pass off. The boys do everything for her, so she tells them she doesn't feel the need of a daughter around the house."

"I'll come to Cappagh soon and see her. And Mother?"

"She is well." Dan looked distressed. "It was in her mind to come to the funeral but she couldn't bear it when the time came near, and Agnes told her you wouldn't take it ill."

"Of course not."

"I'm thinking that not being able to see the people looking at her—that was what kept her away, knowing she couldn't look them in the face. But she was planning to come, for your sake."

"What difference does it make? She loved Samuel—"

"I'll stay, if you want, Alice."

"No. It's better to go. Has Tom been to the mill yet?"

"Yes, last week. He's to start in the countinghouse on the first day of October. Samuel had it all fixed, God rest him. I'll see you in Cappagh next week, for sure."

"Yes, next week." But next week was a ridiculous idea. There would be no next week.

Julia had been sent upstairs with Miss Conroy and Anna but she was always disobedient and now there she was at Alice's elbow, saying, "Mama, that's enough. Come upstairs. No one will mind. James is here to talk to everyone, and the Master. Come along with me, now, this moment. Here, I'll take your arm. No need to look back. They all know you've had enough. Hold on to the banister. Lift your skirt. That's fine. Thomas and Anna are in your room and there's a nice fire."

Silently Alice let herself be led into the bedroom and seated on the chaise longue in front of the fire, as if she were ill. Anna's face was white, with huge uncertain eyes looking Alice over as if she might have changed in the last few hours. They were all watching her, to know how they should act, what they were to do next. Did they think she knew? In this room to which they had brought her as the center of their own lives, the presence of Samuel was everywhere. With horror she remembered him as he lay in his coffin, now deep under the ground in that cold, mean vault where all the Flahertys were lying in wait for him, for her, for all her children. No use trying to pretend to be alive while the rain would seep through to Samuel, washing away all peace from her mind, washing in a gravelly mixture of resentment and hatred and fear.

Thomas said restlessly, "The people are so religious, one doesn't know what to say to them. Everyone said that Papa is in heaven because he was so good. They're so sure of it all. How did you answer them?"

She made no reply though she knew they were watching her more closely now. After a few minutes' silence Anna announced in a high, unnatural tone, "Sprigg is leaving, she says, because Papa was a Fenian."

That made Alice sit up.

"When did she tell you?"

"Last night, when she was helping me to go to bed."

"The night before the funeral! She said that!"

"Yes."

No wonder poor Anna was in such a state of fright, tears pouring down her cheeks now, her shoulders shaking so that Julia took her on her lap on the floor and petted her, as if she were the older one, until Anna became quieter.

Thomas stood up, saying, "I'm going down to talk to James. There will be arrangements to be made about lots of things."

"Wait! You can't—"

But Julia looked up from Anna's hair, where her face was pressed down softly, saying, "Let him go, Mama. He and James can very well take charge."

Alice leaned back, soothed by Julia's hand on her knee, her mind repeating Samuel's words again and again.

"We had good times. I loved you always. I'll be with you. Alice, my dear, sweet Alice—"

And he had spoken of Morgan, though she couldn't remember that part so well. Samuel would live just as long as she was able to keep the pain alive, fierce and terrible as the sting of a wasp. She must never weep because that was said to be a relief, but now at the idea of it, suddenly she could hold off no longer and she put her head down on her open hands and wept bitterly as she had not done since she was a child, knowing at last that she would never, never, never see Samuel again.

48

James drove to Cappagh with Alice when she went, as she had promised, to see her mother and Agnes. No longer afraid of horses, he wanted to take the gig as being faster and because the weather was dry and clear, but Paddy would not allow it.

"A lady can't go in an open conveyance a week after her husband's funeral," he said, but there was no sourness in him, and besides, James no longer cared what the servants thought of him.

He simply added this information to his almost perfect store of knowledge about the gentry and asked, "Which carriage would you recommend, then?"

"The barouche would be good. You could have the hood down on quiet parts of the road, or maybe all the way, and you'd have the benefit of the fresh air."

"Then we'd have to have a driver."

"I'll come with you myself. I'm well able for a drive now and no one will touch her as long as I'm on the box."

"You think they might—"

"How do I know? The lunatic that killed Mr. Samuel could kill his own father and not know the difference. The sergeant was up yesterday to say they've arrested a young fellow and they want me to identify him. 'If he's young,' I said, 'he's the wrong man.' But he didn't take much notice of me, only said I'm to go into Galway on Friday anyway. Half threatening me, he was, knowing well I'd be afraid to be landed back in jail if they take a fancy to the idea. I'll have to go, anyway."

"They won't land you back in jail. I'll go with you to Galway on Friday."

"God bless you, Mr. James. I'll be glad of it, for to tell you the truth I'm shaking at the thought that they might get their crooks on me again. I should go to America, I suppose, but now with his Honor dead, I should better stay here and do a thing for Miss Alice."

"Perhaps you could go later, if you see things more settled here."

"God knows I don't want to go at all unless I'm driven to it, though they say it's a fine country, but I think you need your youth and health for it and I'm not in good condition at this present moment."

At the memory of Dartmoor his face had turned white and he had begun to shake and stutter so that James had to lay a hand on his shoulder and say, "Look, Paddy, I had a promise that you won't be rearrested. I had it from the Home Secretary himself. Now please don't make yourself ill."

"I can't but think of the others—Morgan drawing the cart—"

"Morgan will be out soon."

Paddy stared in amazement.

"How do you know?"

"I just know," James said uncomfortably. "I don't like to speak of it. My father wrote to me about him. If I talk about it, I may not be able to do much more. I have some influence."

Fortunately Paddy took the hint and went back more calmly to arranging that the barouche would be ready at nine in the morning.

It continued fine and the trees were still green on the roadside except for the big blotches of orange where the chestnuts were. The air was warm, a warm wind blowing Alice's veil so that she had to hold it with one long-fingered hand under her chin. The woman from Jay's Mourning House who had come a few days ago had made her an elegant black silk dress and had trimmed a widow's bonnet in black with streamers. James was overwhelmed at the pathos of it: her dark-blue eyes seemed larger and more brilliant than ever and her face more delicately pink and white. She was thirty-six now, only three years older than himself, still the most kindly, generous, good and honorable lady he had ever known. Beside her, the London society ladies were cheap, with their gossip, and their conventional gestures to express all kinds of bitchy views, and their satirical, tinny laughter. James often had an idea that they were laughing at him, and since the terrible episode of Lavinia he had never attempted to marry one of them. He did, however, enjoy seducing them from time to time, going through a series of preliminary tricks with more or less success, depending on the lady, and calculating with amusement at what point she would either succumb to him or give him to understand that he was wasting his time. He had noted that they never spurned him outright or called on their husbands to defend their honor. Instead, one and all seemed to have a real affection for him which he found delightful.

Of course he did not want Alice to know about this side of his life and there was no reason why she should ever find out. She was clearly glad to be with him today, looking more relaxed than she had done since the funeral.

After Woodstock, she leaned back against the cushions and said, "It's been so good to have you here this week, James. You've done so much for me. Sprigg was all ready to make a scene and upset the other house servants. Kate told me she had started already, telling them that they should all leave now before the house would be burned down and more murders committed. She said that if Samuel had been a real gentleman he would have left Moycullen long ago and gone to live in England. That didn't go down so well with them but they were beginning to get uneasy. It's all too much—"

"I can stay until you feel better," James said impetuously. "I'm due a long holiday if I want it."

"And those policemen who come around asking questions about Samuel, what he said to me before he died, scraping over the whole thing again and again, telling me they're going to hang someone for it, as if that should please me—"

"Alice, please don't think about it."

He took her hand, turning it over in his as if he were examining it for blemishes while he tried to think of words to comfort her.

She sat up straighter and said, "I'm sorry, James. I really must learn not to do that to you." She smiled deliberately and he felt a strong urge to take her in his arms there and then, in the open carriage, within sight of anyone who might be passing by.

He said, "We never expected reasonable behavior from the police." He lifted his chin in a way that he had found was impressive. "I had a talk with the inspector yesterday and told him in short order not to bother you with any more of that."

"Oh, James, how wonderful!"

Could he risk it now? He pressed her hand instead and noted that she returned the pressure warmly. With a London lady he could have placed a hand on her knee, but with Alice, only a week after Samuel's death, this would not do.

Experience was without a doubt a great teacher—one could learn what *not* to do, as well as what to do, and use it all in a good cause. His aspirations were pure enough; he respected Alice and was determined only to use his devices to arouse her interest in him at a later stage. She was so innocent, she might not even understand their significance, or if she did, she would be shocked. His mind racing ahead, he began to imagine how she would be in bed. Certainly a completely new experience for him, quite unlike the blasé ladies he was accustomed to. Slowly he straightened himself up to reduce the burning that had begun in him at this idea. A carriage drive often had this effect on him and women were aware of so much, he had found. His head must rule his heart at all costs, this time above all others. He would ruin his chances if, for instance, he were to pat her bottom—one of his most effective starters, impossible in a carriage, of course. The thought worked like a cold shower.

Alice was saying, "It's good to see you on such good terms with your father again, James. It has taken years off his age."

"Yes, I behaved abominably to him. It was shameful of me not to have written to him after that blowup. He wrote to me about Morgan Connolly in the end—"

He felt her hand go limp. Staring straight ahead she said, "I asked him to do that. Have you had any success?"

"I think so—I hope so. It's not easy. I have to go very carefully."

Now her mood had changed again and she was breathing quickly, withdrawing her hand from his, saying, "If we had Morgan here, he would organize the people better than anyone else could ever do. He knows everyone and they all know him. The poor people respect him. We could go all over Mayo and Galway and hold meetings and tell the people to fight back, not to let their houses be knocked down around them, to fight the bailiffs when they come to evict them, to hold on to the food and eat it themselves instead of handing it over to the landlords. Tell me, James, how soon do you think you'll be able to get him out? But of course he won't be in fit condition to do anything for a while afterward. They're always sick for a long time when they come out of jail."

During this excited speech James had felt all his wish for her leak away like a bucket of water spilled on sand. A lady? She was a fighting peasant, for all her fine clothes and clear accent and well-kept hands. Speeches! Meetings! If he were married to her, his whole life, built up over the years, would crumble away to nothing. How could he produce her in London? Then, shame at this wild succession of cowardly thoughts coursed through his mind. What was he himself? A renegade Irishman, pretending to be a gentleman, a figure of fun who had been fooled once by a scheming woman and had since lived immorally with the wives of his colleagues, tolerated for the passing amusement he afforded them, never taken seriously, thrown some patronage from time to time as one might throw a bone to a yard dog that has been let in by mistake. He was a coward, and this was like having a wooden leg, a disability that could neither be overcome nor ignored. What kind of a halfman was he? How right his father had been in his contempt for him! How Samuel must have despised him, too, Samuel who had even had the courage to associate himself with the Fenians. And here he was, little Jamesy Fahy, thinking lewd thoughts about Samuel's widow a week after his death, planning to have her and her house and the mill and the life of a country gentleman, scheming to get all this for himself, out of greed and selfishness and lust and general moral filthiness. As the barouche passed through Bushy Park and along by Dangan, approaching Galway town, he lashed himself with every form of insult that occurred to him. Alice was silent now, fortunately. Morgan would be released, indeed, and she need never know of his own wickedness. He thanked God that he had not revealed himself still more. With any luck, her depressed condition made her less aware, so that she would have seen only kindly interest in his attitude to her.

So it seemed to be. Leaving the town on their left, they drove straight out toward the sea and along the sandy road toward Cappagh where the wind blew more freely, carrying a strong tang of rotting seaweed. The tide was in, and as the horse walked up the hill toward Loch an tSáile they saw that the little sea lake was full and there was a seal sitting on a rock sunning himself.

Alice half turned to James, saying, "Samuel told me how he saw a seal there when he was going home from my brother Dan's wedding, in that same place."

Above the road, the miserable hovels stood shoulder to shoulder, with ragged people standing at their doors to watch the barouche pass. James had never been to Cappagh before and was shocked at the poverty of the land; the rocky fields with their crazy tillage of potatoes and cabbages seemed to climb around and over the ridges. An occasional field of barley or rye, still uncut, made a darker patch in the green. Stone walls were everywhere, running like hares up and down and across the fields. The cabins were a uniform filthy gray and the people moved with the slowness of death.

He asked Alice meekly, "Should I take off my hat?"

"No," she said with a little gasp. "Samuel always wore a top hat when he came in the gig."

"Yes, yes, I remember."

Samuel setting out for Cappagh, supervising the gig being filled with bread and bottles and jars and sacks, as much as it could hold, with his alert, satisfied look, darting from side to side while the horse shifted its hooves uneasily; Samuel coming back from Cappagh in the evening, slow and tired, with the empty gig, throwing the reins to Paddy, walking heavily into the house with his hat in his hand, as heavily as he walked after a day's hunting; Samuel pausing to look up at the window of the Fahys' room over the coach house, waving to little James, who was always there to wave down to him; Samuel taking him to the County Club, to the university, to the tailor in Galway for the suits that he had to give away in London later, they looked so bucolic. James felt tears fill his eyes and he put up his two hands, the fingers pressing the moisture away in what he hoped looked like a gesture of mere tiredness. Samuel! Oh, Samuel! What was the world without him? Who was left to commend him, to think well of him? Why should he bother any more with that comedy existence in London, among those cynical people who were always more than a match for him? They had to acknowledge that he was very well advanced at thirty-three years old, an Irishman, too, a man who might become so powerful that those who had slighted him might live to regret it, but all that was sour now. All he had ever wanted was to be respected by Samuel and now Samuel was dead and no one cared a hang about James Fahy. Except his father, of course, but he was a special case. In alarm James realized that he could not stop the flow of weeping.

Alice called out to Paddy, a hand on James's arm, "Walk the horse for a while, Paddy. We don't want to arrive just yet." Then she was gazing at James, saying, "Poor James. Coming here with me is too hard for you. All this is too much—I shouldn't have allowed it."

"No, no." He muffled the words in his handkerchief, mopping his eyes quite openly now. "It's just that I began to think of Samuel as he was long ago, coming here—"

Even Alice despised him now—otherwise how could she have said that she should have protected him? She had not

338

meant it as an insult, obviously, but that is what it was all the same.

Then into his mind crept a memory of one of his London ladies who had said as he left her after a rather successful though brief affair, "Never make little of yourself, James. You're quite a man, in your own way. Be yourself—it's always best."

She was lying back in her own bed, her husband being on a trip to Vienna, the green brocade padding of the headboard giving a greenish tinge to her bronze hair, which was lying loose all over the pillow. James in his shirt walked from the dressing table and looked down at her and was suddenly seized with a desire to take her again, once more, before leaving her for good. She had looked almost frightened but awfully impressed at his capability, and had said as he drew back from her, in the sleepy voice that had been her first attraction for him, "I'm sorry it's got to end. Jerry will be home and nothing like this can happen while he's in England."

"When? When is he coming?"

That tinkling laugh, and she said, "Don't push it too far—never push too far. Tomorrow, in fact, but it's the end in any case. I did enjoy you, James, dear."

Though he was worn out, he stroked her all over as she loved him to do, as a reward for the best piece of advice he had ever had in his life. Never make little of yourself. He had almost done it, just now. And then, for no reason that he could ever properly comprehend, the solution to his problems came to him ready-made. Anna! Pale, beautiful Anna, a perfect lady, young, inexperienced, longing to get away to London as she had already confided to him, in appearance so like Amy and Lavinia that it was uncanny, sure to give him all the joys in bed that he had expected of those sweet little virgins, full of respect for his age and experience and wisdom, with smooth, unused flesh very different from Alice's, with the blood of Samuel, whose mother was English, to ensure that she would be able for the tinklers of London, though he would have to make sure that she was prepared in some way for one of them telling her of his exploits.

Alice was saying, "That's better, James. Perhaps we could go on now."

The barouche turned aside and began to climb a hilly road from which the dust had long been washed away so that the wheels sang on the naked stones and the whole equipage shivered and shook, while James and Alice were thrown together and apart. Up and up they went, the sky seeming to grow clearer with every moment, so that at last when James turned to look downhill he saw the immense panorama of Galway Bay spread out below them, the high blue hills of Clare and the three dark-blue humps that were the Aran Islands. It was the top of the world, a beauty he had hardly thought could exist in Ireland, compensating for the closeness of the wretched people, the slinking dogs and the squalling children, and the shambling, unkempt men and women who lurked in every doorway. Not all stood still. Seeing the barouche coming, some ran forward with their hands out, falling back again in shame when they recognized Alice in her black clothes. She kept her head down, he noticed, as she had done at the funeral, and he could not guess at her attitude to these people who had once been her neighbors.

At last the barouche pulled up at the door of a much larger, neater cottage than the rest. The area around it had been paved with flagstones and was cleanly swept. Through the open door he could see right into the kitchen, where there was a dresser full of shining plates and jugs, and a scrubbed table, and a turf fire blazing. An old woman walked swiftly out to meet them. Paddy shouted to the horses to halt, leaped down from the box and ran around to open the door. Alice sprang down and ran into her mother's arms.

49

James waited several days before inviting Anna to take a walk with him. He had been unmanned by the sight of Alice and her mother so freely and almost childishly lamenting Samuel, Mary's blindness adding an extra poignancy to the scene. In their grief they had not forgotten him but had insisted that he come into the cottage and sit by the fire, though he wanted to remain outside with Paddy. A young woman, evidently Alice's sister-in-law, whom they called Agnes, made tea for them all and added a liberal shot of whiskey to each cup. Alice asked anxiously about Agnes' health.

"I'm not too bad lately," she said, "but I couldn't go to Moycullen for the funeral."

"Of course not!" Alice said indignantly. "You must do as the doctor says, rest a lot and eat well. Dan looks fine."

That must be the brother who was at the funeral. Agnes

was a small, pretty woman, who looked quite elegant in the traditional wide, heavy flannel skirt, which he noticed was clean and good, unlike the clothes of most of the neighboring women that he had seen. He cursed his new powers of observation, or his newly awakened conscience, or whatever damned inconvenient thing it was that now made it difficult for him to avoid seeing the wretchedness of all the people around him. Out on the edge of the world, they were no one's responsibility, abandoned by everyone except people of heroic vision like Morgan and Samuel and Alice. James felt himself shrink like a snail at the thought of what Morgan was enduring at this very moment. Because of his position he had been allowed to speak to him alone for half an hour in Dartmoor, and had heard details of prisoners who had gone mad and others who were permanently disabled or broken in their health because of the brutal conditions of their imprisonment.

On the day that James saw him, Morgan himself had a bruise on the side of his face from a blow and smiled sourly at James's exclamations of horror, saying, "That's part of a new attempt to break me down. It seems I look like surviving my sentence."

"What do you mean?"

"There's no great secret about it. All the long-term Fenian prisoners get the worst treatment. An ordinary prisoner is treated fairly if he keeps the rules but we are persecuted every day. We asked for it so we can't complain, but it would have been more decent to hang us all. How is Alice?"

"I haven't seen her. I haven't been to Ireland for two years."

He saw Morgan's eyes blaze with contempt. James said, his head down and his voice coming in a low mumble, quite unlike his usual bell-clear statements, "My father wrote about you. I'm trying to do something. It's not always easy but there may be a way. I don't want to raise your hopes—"

"Thank you, James. Don't risk your neck."

James looked up quickly but it had not been said ironically. Morgan was smiling, his old easy smile, superior to James in age and wisdom and experience as he had always been, unaware or uninterested in the social differences between them. James doubted now for the first time whether these differences existed and he was overcome by a wave of misery such as he had not experienced since leaving Ireland for London thirteen years ago. He would never go back there again, to be made little of, to feel the disdainful glances on him from every angle—from the rich because he was not rich and from the poor because he was not poor. In England, when you threw in your lot with the Establishment, at least you knew what to expect. Or did you? He squirmed at the memory of half-suspected gibes that had caused him only a second's uneasiness at the time.

He finished the interview with Morgan by saying, "There's a movement to get an amnesty for all the Fenians who were sentenced in '65. I'm interesting myself in that." Then on a sudden impulse he said, "For God's sake keep your heart up, Morgan. We're not forgetting you."

Then he fled out of the prison, whose hellish atmosphere had worn down his nerves to a point where he feared to lose control of himself altogether. And he had not been able to keep to his resolution of staying out of Ireland: Samuel's death had made it necessary to return, only a month later.

Walking with Anna, down toward the lake, he felt for the first time freed from the confusion caused by his visit to Morgan and his subsequent return to Moycullen. For one thing, Anna was a small girl, at least an inch shorter than James, and he found that he liked this, though he had usually gone after large women in recent years. Anna put on no demure airs with him. After all, he had always been a part of her life, almost as much so as Samuel, when she was an infant and later while he was a student at the university. On his last visit home, two years ago, she had greeted him with real affection, as if she had looked forward very much to his coming. She had sat beside him and had asked him questions about London, what the elegant ladies wore, about their carriages and servants and especially about the wonderful balls and parties that took weeks to prepare, and about the Queen. After the first day, she had always waited until they were alone to ask about the Queen, since Alice had reproved her sharply for it, saying, "What is that Queen to us? Why are you so interested in her?"

Anna had replied falteringly, "I don't know—all the stories are about kings and queens—I think it's very exciting. James can see her sometimes when she goes out driving—her horses —and her clothes. Oh, I don't know why, but it all sounds so grand and fine, compared with the way we live here."

Fortunately dinner had been announced just then and Anna had escaped Alice's cold eye, keeping her head bent during the whole of the meal.

Later she had confided to James, "I hate all this talk of elections and evictions and rent and tenants and famines. Why can't people just be happy? Our tenants are well treated and Papa builds them cottages and gives them work, but Mama will go and see to other people's tenants who aren't her business at all, and the other landlords don't like it. She can't reform the whole world. And a lady can do very little, though a man may be able to make some changes. Oh, James, I wish we could stay in Dublin all the year round! But Papa has to come here and I suppose it wouldn't do."

James had not encouraged her in her discontent, as Alice and Samuel would have been displeased, but he knew exactly how Anna felt since it was a reflection of his own ideas when he was young.

Now he remembered many such conversations as they walked under the brilliant autumn trees, crackling the dry fallen leaves underfoot and feeling a sense of light airiness from the afternoon sun pouring through the half-bare branches. Sometimes they heard a faint rustle as an animal moved stealthily out of their path. The lake below them was a dark opaque blue, ruffled with the first cold wind of autumn. James took Anna's arm and felt her tremble.

On an impulse he said, "Anna, I love you. Do you think— could you—will you marry me?"

She looked up at him without speaking, her gray eyes full of alarm.

He stopped and turned her gently around to face him, saying, "I had meant to ask Alice first but I couldn't wait. Besides, it will help if you can give me your answer. Do you think I'm too old for you? I'm nearly thirty-four, that's not old." That sounded foolish and he went quickly on, "We could have a nice life together. It's lonely for me in London." Most of those women dare not speak of their association with him. Angela might have to be threatened but a single warning should do it. She was goodhearted enough, in her own way. "I'd look after you well, Anna." He intended to, indeed, and it sounded clearly in his voice. "May I speak to Alice this evening?"

"Yes, James."

She bent her head so that her smooth pale hair was near his face, smelling like summer heather. Suddenly and unexpectedly he felt himself flooded with happiness. In a few minutes, everything in the world had changed. He need no longer hold his face in that painful, twisted expression which was his main protection, intended to express cynicism and detachment. The muscles of his mouth relaxed, allowing it to form a smile free of ulterior motive. His whole body began to glow, not just with desire for Anna, though that was part of it, but with good will toward the whole human race. This was an end as well as a beginning. He might even begin to go to church again. He would drop all those loose women—fortunately there was no one on the tapis at this exact moment—and he would devote himself to making Anna happy. Samuel's daughter! His good fortune was beyond any natural explanation. Samuel! He had always treated Anna with respect, a lead and an example to James.

He lifted her hand in his and kissed it gently, saying, "Well, let's continue our walk."

After dinner he said to Alice, "May I speak to you for a few minutes?"

"Yes, James, of course. We'll go into the study."

It was just as it had always been for Samuel, the red-leather-topped desk tidy and polished, a good fire of turf and logs, even Samuel's sheep dog Lupo lying on the hearthrug, twisting his head expectantly toward the door as they came in. The firelight shone warmly on Samuel's bookcases, glass-fronted Spanish mahogany, for examples of which James had toured the furniture shops of London in vain. Two great flowered wing-backed armchairs stood one at either side of the fire. James stood uncertainly in the middle of the room, not wanting to sit in Samuel's chair, but the carved leather-covered chair at the desk would be worse.

Alice walked across to the fire and sat down, saying, "Come here, James. It's no use putting off living. Samuel wouldn't have liked it." But he saw tears in her eyes at the mention of Samuel's name, and how she stroked the arms of the chair in which he had always sat. He guessed that she had taken this one from delicacy, seeing that he did not want to sit in it.

"I know how you loved Samuel, James," she said after a moment, using the word unashamedly, as he could never have done. "I saw it the first day I came to Moycullen, and I admired you for it." She gave a long, shuddering sigh. "I'd like you always to feel at home here. That's what he wanted for you, as he often told me. He said you are a child of the house." She smiled, and he felt at a loss to answer, recognizing the old-fashioned phrase as typical of Samuel. "I hope you can stay a little longer. You are a great comfort to all of us."

She had spoken so warmly that he could not begin at once but had to walk around the room before sitting down, aware that she was watching him with pity.

He jerked his chin up to steady himself and said, "Alice, it's very soon to speak of it but I see no real need to put it off. Anna and I—I want to ask you—" Oh, God! There was a vision of Mrs. Taylor, like a cold, wet ghost, before him. "I want to ask Anna to be my wife!"

344

Alice's look of amzement lasted only a split second. Then she said, "Have you spoken to her?"

"I shouldn't have, without your leave, but this afternoon I did mention it and she seemed pleased."

"She's only sixteen. She spends her time in the schoolroom with Miss Conroy. James, she's not a woman yet."

"That doesn't matter—plenty of girls marry at sixteen." His confidence was coming back. "It's not as if we didn't know each other. I know she's an heiress but I have plenty to offer her. I'm afraid to be slow in asking because very soon other men will begin to put in for her and I might lose her."

He could see that bolt going home. From living in Dublin society Alice must often have seen the traffic in pretty young heiresses.

She was looking uneasy now, saying, "Of course you're right, James. Oh, what will I do without Samuel?"

She sounded so desperate that he became his London self, sitting up confidently.

"I'll always advise you as best I can, Alice. In this case I think I know what's right for Anna. She's gentle and shy, and it would be bad for her to be tossed into the marriage market. Some girls thrive on it, and she would do her best, but it wouldn't suit her at all. She hasn't the stamina for it. I'll look after her well and I think she'll be happy with me."

"She's not happy here. Perhaps she would do better in London."

She seemed to be talking to herself, looking distraught and miserable, so that he took her hand in his and said, "Please don't worry about it, Alice. It's a good solution for Anna. For me it's a miracle. Please say I may go to her now and tell her you agree."

"Yes, James, yes. Do arrange it all. It's for the best, as you say, and you will really be a child of the house then." She smiled, pressed his hand and stood up wearily, saying, "Wait here. I'll send her to you."

A few minutes later, there was Anna in the room. She was wearing one of her new black evening dresses, which had the effect of making her seem even smaller than she was, like a tiny mourning shepherdess in china, so delicate that he dared not believe she was really his. Those big, dashing women were all wrong for him.

He went to her and took her hands, saying, "Anna, your mother has agreed that we can be married. Oh, I'm so happy!"

And it was really true: here was a woman to whom he could

345

confide all his most intimate thoughts and ambitions, who would give him unquestioning love and sympathy, who would never expect him to be a scholar or to cut a dash, who had known him as a poor boy living on patronage and had seen him rise to heights of which she had no experience. She would have to ask him many things and it would be his pleasure to tell her. And she would help him. He would no longer find himself suddenly ignorant of some basic tenet of society, afraid that he could never belong no matter how long he lived in it. From now on, when he returned home there would be this delightful little creature to comfort him and love him as no one had ever done in all his life. He was quite sure of this; his father's feelings for him were a mixture of impatience and pride and instinctive interest, no more. How easily Alice had used the word "love." He would have to learn to do it. Each time he thought of it he could feel his heart melt a little, like the boy whose heart had turned to ice in "The Snow Queen."

He practiced it now. "Anna, I love you."

And he took her in his arms, very gently, and kissed her mouth and eyes and hair and neck, never letting her feel his energetic wish to have her in bed now, at once, without waiting for the marriage ceremony. She would have been shocked at this, he was sure. He led her over to the fire and they sat together for a long time on the hearthrug, pushing Lupo out of the way, her head on his shoulder, while he talked to her of London and the house that they would have there.

"It will take me a long time to learn all the things I'll need to know," she said anxiously.

"Not at all! I'll get you a housekeeper who will look after everything. I'm quite good at supervising, after all my years as a bachelor. I'll help you, all the time."

"Dear James! I won't be afraid of anything so long as you're with me."

50

At first Alice blamed herself for agreeing so quickly to Anna's marriage to James but very soon she began to believe that it was all for the best. It was true that if Anna waited, she might make what was called a brilliant match, since she was elegant and pretty and would be noticed by all the Dublin parents who were watching out for heiresses for their sons, but as James had said, that kind of marriage would not suit Anna.

Alice had noticed that some of the young ladies were not finding husbands at all, since so many of the estates in the country were bankrupt and could not give even the most modest dowry. The annual season at the Castle was a pitiful spectacle, with a frantic background of teas and receptions for the marriageable girls whose fortunes were known to the last penny. It would have been more decent to parade them at the Royal Dublin Society's show and let the men bid for them. As the weeks went on, the anxious thoughts of all the women, mothers and daughters, began to show on their faces, while the laughter became shrill and undignified. Old battle-axes who had nothing to lose delighted in assessing the failures of the girls and spreading gossip and scandal, ascribing motives and ambitions, making witty remarks that could never be answered, until Alice had found it impossible to be in their company for more than a few minutes at a time without losing her temper. Anna would avoid all this, all the humiliations, jealousies and tears that the other girls suffered. Her triumph would be that she was going to live in London, splendid, remote London, where James was a great man and where she would have a choice of parties every night for the rest of her life. This would cancel out any suggestion that she was marrying beneath her.

James said that he would extend his holiday, and in the following days, memories of her own youth stung Alice painfully every time she looked at her daughter. Her adoration of James was complete; when he brought her little presents and flowers from Galway and took her arm to escort her for walks, Alice imagined that she saw a reflection of how she must have looked herself when Samuel had taken charge of her. Yet that adoration had not been love as she knew love for Morgan. Locked up close inside her was awareness that she had lost not one but two husbands. Morgan's imprisonment, as final as death, had cut as deeply into her heart as Samuel's death did later. She was aware of a creeping sourness filling her whole being, visions and images of death haunting her day and night until she thought she must be going mad. The empty space beside her made her detest her bed, so that she sat up for hours at night, until there was no more turf for the fire and Eileen, her new maid, was drooping with fatigue when at last she went to her room. Her dreams were filled with pictures of Samuel and Morgan, either or both under the cold earth of Moycullen graveyard, either or both in the cold damp horror of Dartmoor prison, their bodies rotting, beyond her reach, beyond her help, so that she wept and wept for both of them and had no comfort from it.

Love was a trap: she would never love anyone again. But James had said that Morgan might come home and she had even answered that he would be useful in the organization, able to urge the people to stand up for their human rights and refuse to die or emigrate at the landlord's orders. She didn't believe he would come. Morgan and Samuel were both dead. Soon she would be dead herself, with luck in a few years. Then there would be no more of this pain, tearing at her day and night so that she could have screamed with agony.

A week after the conversation with James, she went out to Master Fahy's room meaning to sit with him for an hour. She didn't wait for an invitation to enter the room but just walked in the moment Fahy opened the door, saying, "Let me stay for a while—not for long."

He pulled out a kitchen chair for her from the deal table where his papers were spread out. He was obviously writing something but she had no interest in it. He sat on the bed, courteously upright, and talked of everyday things, the farm, the tenants, the servants, the accounts, until she began to relax and at last was able to say, "Master, I hope you are pleased about James and Anna."

"Yes," he said dryly. "It's an honor for my family."

"We'll have the wedding soon. There's no point in waiting and winter is coming on. They'll have to find a house in London. James says they can live in his rooms for a few weeks. Should I go to London and see about it all?"

"No. You're not fit for it. James will look after everything."

"Is that proper?"

"Proper enough. You don't have to answer to anyone for what you do."

"That's true. Only to do what Samuel would have wanted. What would he have thought of this, Master?"

"Probably that Anna is too young to be married. But in the circumstances it's all right. She looks very happy." He sighed heavily and stretched out his bony legs, like a bird's legs in their black stockings. "Don't fret about them, Alice. They'll do well enough. Did you know that Jerome Burke is thinking of coming back?"

"Surely he can't! The house is in ruins."

"He talks of rebuilding it. James met him in the County Club in Galway. It seems Lydia is dying. She's had a cough for a long time, the same as the children had, and now she hardly gets out of bed at all."

"Jerome should be with her."

"He never was a hero."

"But why should he think of coming back to Galway? I'd have thought he'd consider himself well out of it."

"He's been buying big estates that are selling cheap. Being a lawyer he's in the way of knowing when they come on the market. He has one at Headford and one near Tuam now, and of course he never was able to sell his own, though he tried long enough."

"And the tenants? What is he doing about them?"

"I haven't heard so far, but I wouldn't expect a great deal from Jerome. Perhaps he'll leave them alone if they can pay the rent."

"Perhaps!"

"You know well that everyone is raising the rents again this year."

"I'll go to see Jerome."

"You did that once before and it was no use."

"You don't think he has changed?"

"No. He's weak, and weak people are far more dangerous than wicked ones." And he intoned in the voice he always used for quotations, "What destroys people is not wickedness but triviality."

"Triviality is a kind of wickedness," Alice said sharply. "I wouldn't let him off so easily. After the wedding, we'll have to make a few plans."

"What sort of plans?"

"I thought of it at Samuel's funeral when that young man spoke to me, the ginger-haired man from Mayo."

"His name is Morrissey."

"Is it? He spoke well at the graveside. He has courage. He knew the police were watching him and that people are being arrested every day and kept in jail for months together without trial, and still he got up and said his say. Why haven't I been doing something for the people?"

"But you have—you know it well. Besides, a lady can't do much—"

"Since when was I a lady?" Alice asked tartly. "From now on, I'm going to be independent of that drawback, at least."

"And what about Samuel?"

"Who would have thought that Samuel would promise to help the Fenians, or go to election meetings and make speeches? Samuel had seen that he would have to change."

"Samuel hated violence."

"Don't look so uneasy. I'm not going to be violent. Master, the people must be taught not to starve quietly and not to walk out of their houses at the landlord's orders and see their roofs thrown down."

"God help them, what can they do? The police and the Army are always there to make sure they make no stand."

"Surely it would be better to die fighting."

"So you are talking of fighting. That would be a fight! A handful of men armed with pitchforks and shovels and slanes against a detachment of British troops armed with the latest weapons—what kind of a fight is that?"

"They can put up barricades. They can call out the whole countryside to attack the soldiers from the rear. They can refuse to leave the houses. They can eat the food that they give to the landlords now, instead of trying to live on rotten potatoes."

"That's a full-scale war."

"Call it what you like, it's a better way to die than in a cellar in New York or in an English prison."

"James is going to try to get Morgan released at once. He's going to London especially to see about it in two or three days' time."

Alice asked after a moment's pause, "When did he tell you this?"

"This morning. He has already got machinery in motion, he says." Fahy snorted. "An abominable expression. James no longer speaks the King's English, always this London jargon. He seems to have powerful friends."

"He's generous and good," Alice said warmly and saw Fahy smile with pleasure.

"James says that the British Government no longer takes the Fenians seriously. They can see that the movement was riddled with spies. Even the generals gave information, hurried to give it, to get money for it."

"That's the best reason for having no more conspiracies. And if they're not taking it seriously, I wonder why they're still sentencing men to death for high treason. If Mr. Gladstone gets in, things should be better—but it's hard to care what happens to anyone now. Why did they shoot Samuel, Master? Why should anyone want to do such a thing? I'll never understand, if I live to be a hundred."

"It's the climate of the times. He was a landlord, that's all. Paddy says they'll never arrest the man who did it—he's gone to Australia. He was driven to desperation, his wife and children all dead, and his house gone, razed to the ground by Lord Sligo's agent."

"God help him."

"The devil go with him, I say. With that load of misfortune on him, he should have thought of the sorrow of others."

"He was half crazy, I suppose. It's not right to put a curse on him."

"I'm only afraid my curse won't work," Fahy said in a hard tone. "There's a devil got into this country that will take a long time to get out again. The people don't know right from wrong anymore, and no wonder. All their lives they've seen injustice upheld by the law while the poor and innocent are trodden underfoot, and they know in their heart and soul that that's how it will be forever."

"If Mr. Gladstone gets in—"

"He may be a decent man, but don't forget that a politician is always a politician. In any case, he'll be surrounded by those who will do everything they can to prevent him from giving away as much as a shilling that might go into the pockets of the landlords. I don't understand it very well, being out of the stream of things here, but I can see clearly that Ireland will get free of England when cows fly."

"I'm not thinking of that—only how to keep the people alive. I used to be sorry for the people before when someone would die in a house, but I never really knew what it was like until now. Master, Samuel was a rock, a hill, a high wall. He should have been always here." She felt herself blush with shame for such foolish talk and still she went on. "It would be a great thing for me if I could die now too."

He was looking at her kindly, not as he usually looked at fools. He gave a noisy sigh and said, "You're a young woman still. When my wife died, God rest her, I knew I was finished, a bit of a laughingstock with an infant to rear at my age, and then I thought I'd just go on from day to day, living each bit of my life until the end would come as a relief. It's not like that at all. Every day there's something interesting, something to make me curious about the future, to make me want to live until tomorrow at least."

He pulled a foul handkerchief out of his pocket and blew his nose, turning sideways to look at her afterward, saying, "You have a strength and courage. You'll make no mistakes.

351

Soon Morgan will be home, if what James says is true, and he'll help you out. He's a fine man, Morgan."

Could he possibly know of her love for Morgan? Could he possibly have seen it in her eyes when Morgan came, or heard it in her voice when she spoke of him? She felt panic at this, for of course if Fahy had seen it, so had Samuel, perhaps even her children, perhaps Father Kenny, or the servants, or anyone who came to the house. Perhaps it was public property and she had never known it. But what could she do? There was a disease of love that could not be removed by any means. It would be easier to cut off a finger than to be rid of it: there it was, and so far as she knew, there it would be as long as she lived. No matter how she tried to kill it, no matter how long she waited for it to die of its own accord, there it had stayed all through her life with Samuel. Did he know about it now, wherever he was? Could he see into her mind, as some people said that dead people could do? What if his spirit were hovering near her now, aware that she was beginning to glow with the thought of Morgan's return, with a monstrous longing for him, aware that she was a mean-spirited, ungrateful woman who had never been worthy of his love?

She felt a heavy pounding in her ears, like waves on a stony shore, dragging her down into blackness as she slid off the chair to the floor.

51

Alice was ill for several weeks with exhaustion and nervous strain. Michael Conroy, the new young doctor from Oughterard, said she must stay in bed for at least a month, but from the day when James came back from London with hopeful news of Morgan, she began to recover. She was bitterly ashamed of her weakness, answering almost brusquely when callers asked about her health. Mimi D'Arcy and her mother came over from Woodstock at three o'clock one afternoon in answer to an invitation that Anna had sent by Paddy early in the morning. Alice saw the carriage drive up the avenue. She was lying by the window on the sofa in the upstairs drawing room, with a view over the lake, but by the time they came in she was upright in her usual chair, a piece of embroidery gripped in her hands, looking up with a steady, social smile.

Mrs. D'Arcy said, "Alice, my dear, we've been so worried

about you. Mimi said you were ill in bed and might not see us at all."

"Nonsense. It was just a passing thing. Of course I'm not staying in bed."

"I thought you might be *enceinte*."

Mrs. D'Arcy was a little elegant woman with glittering, curious eyes and a perfect English accent, acquired somewhere between her English boarding school and her Dublin home. She leaned forward in her chair and lowered her voice so that the young people should not hear.

"Are you sure you're not—"

Her disappointment was comical when Alice said, "Quite sure. It was the first thing the doctor thought of."

Reluctantly Mrs. D'Arcy let go of the lovely, tragic idea.

"I wanted to tell you we're so happy about Anna."

Alice looked at her sharply but saw that there was no gibe intended. Not so long ago, James would not have been thought such a catch, but now Mrs. D'Arcy's eyes were narrowed with envy and she was saying fretfully, "I don't know what I'm going to do about Mimi and Pauline and Jane. Three daughters, and scarcely an eligible man in the country nowadays. If one of them were to marry, it would be easier for the others." She chewed her lower lip anxiously, not bothering to keep on her best behavior just for Alice. "Perhaps we'll go to London for a while, but Irish girls are not popular in London just now."

"Mimi is hardly sixteen," Alice said. "It's better not to make her anxious. And she's so pretty. I'm sure you needn't worry."

"Pretty faces are plentiful," Mrs. D'Arcy said sourly. "Her best asset is her uncle's money. She's the only one of them who will have anything, and even that is quite a drawback in some ways. The officers from Renmore seem to know all about it. My maid told me that Mimi is the fifth best catch in their circle. Fifth best! How horrid!"

"It certainly is. If I were you, I'd keep those gentlemen out of the house."

"No doubt you would, but one can't be quite so independent with three daughters to get married. Now you won't have to take Anna to the Castle, though it would be fun to take her as a bride or an engaged girl."

"They'll be married quite soon. We see no need to wait. James must go back to London."

"London! Mimi was so envious when she heard that Anna would be living in London. It's every girl's dream. And James is such a man of the world." She stared at him coldly, where he sat looking almost boyish beside Anna, chatting with the group of young people as one of themselves. "I dread the Castle season. Those tea parties, and the tantrums every night after the balls, and all the new clothes, which may be quite wasted—my bill at Moon's would frighten you—and Mr. D'Arcy says things are getting tighter and the tenants won't pay. Oh, Alice, I'm so worried lest the younger girls may have to be governesses and ruin all their chances, unless Mimi marries well and has them to stay with her, and perhaps her husband won't allow that." She brooded, wrinkling her pretty forehead, and then said in a rush, "You're so lucky, Alice, to have the mill, and now to have Anna so easily off your hands."

Alice could almost have laughed at this description of her situation, with Samuel so lately murdered. But Mrs. D'Arcy seemed really unhappy, with the hunted look that Alice associated with the poor women who came to the back door looking for food. D'Arcy was a dull man, no use for comfort in hard times. James would never be like that with Anna.

There was every excuse for having a quiet wedding, which was just as well because it was hard to know who should be invited. Some of the Protestant gentry had decided that Samuel's death proved he was mixed up in the Fenian conspiracy, and they had withdrawn to a safe distance. They were impressed, however, when word got around that the Henrys were coming from Kylemore, and the later answers to the invitations were warmer even when they refused. Alice would have pitched them all to the devil but Anna was looking anxious, knowing that Belle Stratton and the D'Arcys would be watching beady-eyed to see how things turned out for her. Mr. Stratton had said that Samuel was "almost an Orangeman," a compliment from him, and this was why Belle was being allowed to come, staying with the D'Arcys at Woodstock.

"I heard Mimi and Belle discussing it," Julia said contemptuously. "They never seem to think I matter. Perhaps they think I'm playing with my dolls."

"What did they say?"

"That Papa would have passed as a good Protestant, according to Mr. Stratton. And Anna was listening, saying nothing. She looked furious but when she said nothing, I couldn't speak."

"Anna has good manners."

"What use are good manners? It was not mannerly of Belle and Mimi to talk like that in front of us. When Anna goes to London, I'll never have anything to do with those girls again. They won't want to have anything to do with me either, so that will be easy."

"Which one of them was talking? Both, or only Belle?"

"Belle, I suppose. Mimi is not quite as bad."

"Why don't you go to work on Mimi then? She's not too old to learn."

"No. But she'll think I'm too young to teach her. Besides, she should know how to behave by now."

But Alice noticed that Julia was especially attentive to Mimi during the wedding. Knowing Julia, she was not afraid that Mimi would be the stronger of the two but she was surprised all the same to see how often they had their heads together, and Mimi seemed to have lost the anxious, peaky look that had begun to make her look so like her mother.

After they came back from the church, the whole thing suddenly looked too much like the funeral, even to the crowds of country people on the dry lawn grass. Autumn was long that year, with slowly fading colors instead of the usual bare sweep of leaves cleared off for good and all by a hearty storm in September. Now, though it was the end of October, most of the trees were still green, an unnatural state of things that made people uneasy. Alice heard several of the old women quote a prophecy that when summer took the place of winter, a great disaster was about to fall on Ireland. When they spoke like this, they adopted a heavy, slow way of speaking that she found unbearable. How could they ever improve their condition while they took such trouble to depress everyone around them with this kind of talk? It was their only power, and they had to use it. The potato crop was bad again and a hungry, terrified look was on everyone's face. Still they sang and danced in the coach house and in the barn, while the gentry were having their celebration in the drawing room. Anna looked very young and helpless, but intensely happy, happier than Alice had ever seen her. James seemed very much in love, arranging her Limerick lace veil, which had belonged to Samuel's grandmother, at every opportunity. He was precise in his movements, yet he did not look ridiculous, and the country people made admiring remarks about him in Irish, loudly and freely.

"A fine sight is James. A great sport."

"He's like a king would be, and fit indeed to marry the daughter of Flaherty of Moycullen."

"Flaherty of Moycullen was a gentle, good man that would put his hand in his pocket for every person in need. It's not every day you meet a gentleman that you could trust with your life. A decent man, and a good Irishman in his own way, and a fine singer."

"James is as neat as a bird and as clever as a fox. He'll get on in life, you may be sure. And he's a good man to help the poor, they say, and the men in prison."

"I heard a new song last week," said a young man named Jordan from Moycullen, who had come to help Murphy with the horses for the day. He stood out in front of the rest, without being asked, and began to sing the song in Irish. He was soon surrounded by a chuckling group who joined in the chorus.

> " *The prison oakum, the prison oakum,*
> *That's what's in store for the Fenians of Ireland!'* "

They saw Alice standing by and made room for her to move closer and listen to one or two verses.

> " *There is a fine garden in the prison,*
> *Full of cabbage and potatoes and all kinds of vegetables;*
> *So long as you're there, you'll never be short of food,*
> *And you'll never be idle with the prison oakum to your*
> *hand.*

> " *You can practice every trade known to man in the prison,*
> *Weaving and carpentry and the making of boots,*
> *And all around you there are strong walls and a good roof*
> *To keep out the wind and the storm and the rain.'* "

Now they knew the chorus well and all joined in.

> " *The prison oakum, the prison oakum,*
> *That's what's in store for the Fenians of Ireland!'* "

"That's enough of that—now we'll have a love song! A love song for the wedding!"

Jordan smiled obligingly and asked, "What would you like?"

" 'My Cause of Sorrow'!"

He paused with half-closed eyes, creating a different mood deliberately, and sang the song, very softly, in Irish.

> " *One night before the feast of Brigid, I was at a wake near*
> *Mullaghmore,*
> *When I fell in love with a sea-white maiden, whose youth*
> *and beauty have destroyed my soul.*

*The leech of Fionn will never cure me, I never more will
    have peace nor rest;
My heart within me is in a thousand pieces till my hand
    goes proudly to her soft, white breast.*

*" 'It's my cause of sorrow that I can't go courting to the lonely
    valley where my darling stays.
There is buttery cream there and honeyed rushes, and the
    cows are milked in the autumn days.
The calves are pretty there, the fish are plenty, and the
    swan sails out on the quiet wave,
And if I were wiser I'd have gained my fortune, and leave
    to stretch by my own white love.' "*

"He's a good singer, indeed," said a man beside Alice conversationally. "If we didn't have the songs to keep our hearts up, we'd be gone with the wandering long ago."

Then she saw Morrissey watching her from the coach-house doorway. She felt fear rise in her throat, though his look was kindly. She edged around to him, passing through the group of men who were now asking Jordan to sing "The Rising of the Moon." That song hurt her because of the day she had heard it with Samuel in the early summer before this new nightmare began.

*" 'There beside the singing river that dark mass of men was
    seen.
And above their shining weapons hung their own beloved
    green.' "*

The songs in Irish were easier to listen to because that would always be her real language. She was glad when Morrissey spoke to her in Irish.

"A weding puts an end to the sorrows of a funeral. I'm glad to see your daughter married, a fine girl, God bless her." He looked her over in a detached way and then said, "I've heard you were not well. That's no wonder. You have a better look on you now."

"You're wondering if I'm too weak to be of any use to you." Morrissey looked down at his boots.

"It's true, we get callous. I was thinking of the help you said you'd give us. It's work a woman can do when the men are in jail if she's tough and strong."

"Don't you know well that I'm one of yourselves."

"Perhaps you were once, but not now, and perhaps that will be a good thing for us. They'll be slow to arrest a lady."

"Arrest! What are you thinking of?"

"What you said to Master Fahy a while back, that it's time the people stopped letting themselves be evicted without a fight, that they should put up barricades and attack the soldiers from the rear—"

"Master Fahy told you all that?"

"Of course. It was a good saying. The people will need a leader."

"That's a man's work."

"Yes, but there will be work for the women, too, and you and others like you will be able to do it."

"I'll be there."

"We'll be beaten," Morissey said, dropping into English. "They won't stand for it, but it's the fight that matters, to make the move in the right direction. The Castle will send more and more soldiers. The only way we get anything in Ireland is by fighting."

"How can you say that when it never works? I want it to work this time."

"So do I, God knows, but we're up against a bad crowd, ma'am. They're hopping mad now that they see a break in their own ranks. There's a fine crowd of Protestants in the Amnesty Association, following Mr. Butt and their own common decency. Amnesty is a nice quiet idea; they won't like it so well when it gets ugly. Your own class will turn against you."

"Only the ones I don't care about." She jerked her chin upward. "My husband's class never loved me. I'm fine and independent."

"Morgan Connolly will be home soon, the Master says."

"Did he say that? I know James is trying."

"It's the same thing. James gets what he wants. If Morgan is in any kind of good condition when he comes, he'll be the man to lead Mayo."

"But if he does anything, they'll put him back in jail again. He must be quiet for a while, at least, if he comes."

She stopped speaking but her voice went on in her heart: My dearest Morgan, my love, my darling, why must this danger always hang over us? Why can we never be together day after day in peace, until we no longer need to look up at each other, until we each know what the other is doing, until we're a part of each other as God surely meant us to be? Is this the punishment for my sin, and your sin, in Aran long ago? If it is, then that is an unjust God, punishing out of all proportion to our crime.

She turned away, lowering her head, and felt Morrissey grasp her shoulder, recalling her to reality, saying, "There will be time to think of that when he comes. It's true, he will be in danger; but that's nothing new for Morgan. He'll want to be in the fight, if there is one. He's a man, after all."

That was what Samuel had said once, she remembered sadly. Then it occurred to her for the first time that Morgan might be so changed and hardened by prison that he would care no more for her. It seemed impossible, yet she could not be sure. "He's a man," she repeated to herself, prepared to be excluded from a mystery that only the men understood and would not explain to her.

Morrissey was looking at her compassionately, saying, "You're old friends, you and Morgan. Of course you'll be wanting him to be safe now. We'll think of what to do later on, when we have him at home. Times are changing—perhaps I'm too hopeless. It's good to have all those Protestants working with us. Perhaps they'll get to work on the landlords and things will be better."

He left her then and she did not see him again, though she looked for him in the crowd that soon collected at the front of the house to watch the young pair climb into the carriage.

Murphy had put in two grays, well matched in color and style, and Alice had sent the carriage to Galway to have the inside upholstered in brocade, remembering Anna's complaint on the day that they had come back to Moycullen in June. Her gray traveling dress matched the gray of the horses and she had touches of pink here and there though she should still have been in deep mourning. Both she and James had difficulty in climbing into the carriage. Thomas helped Anna but Alice saw him draw back from James, as if in fear of hurting his feelings by calling attention to his small size. Thomas was quite delicate sometimes.

Murphy flourished his whip and the grays trotted off down the avenue, followed as far as the gate by a cheering crowd. Alice stood on the steps of the house, pain for her daughter closing in on her like a clamp, until she felt Julia's hand slip into hers and heard Julia say softly, "Anna will be all right with James. She hates Moycullen and Dublin and Ireland in general. She can't find any good thing to say about life here. For people like that, London is better."

"And what about you?"

"I won't leave Ireland—unless I fall in love with someone from another country."

"Time enough to think of that."

The carriage was out of sight now, hidden by the trees of the wood beyond the avenue. She turned wearily back into the house, still holding Julia's hand, seeing Thomas come back across the gravel with Charlie Shaw and one of the Blake girls, Letitia, who was the same age as he or a little younger, perhaps twelve or thirteen. She was looking very excited, having run with Thomas after the carriage, laughing and panting for breath between the two boys, the long curls hanging at either side of her face damp with sweat. In the drawing room Fahy was trying to entertain the uneasy group by the fireplace while they waited for their carriages to come around from the stables.

"Some claret, just a small glass for the road, that's what you need. Come, let me get it for you, Mrs. Blake, just a small glass."

"Thank you, yes," she said coldly, turning away, and Alice saw him cringe with insult as he went to the sideboard where the decanters stood ready.

Why did she tolerate these people, why not sweep them out of her house now, this very moment, drive them down the steps into their carriages and run upstairs to her room to weep and weep for Samuel and Anna, both gone forever. She drew a long breath of distress and pressed her hands against her cheeks, as if she were holding her mouth from saying these things that must never be said.

Silently, Father Kenny was putting a glass of claret into her hand, indicating with a lifted eyebrow that they could move away from the group by the fireplace and stand by the window at the far end of the room.

"Weddings are always like this," he said in a low voice. "Weddings and funerals. You should be happy today."

"She's only sixteen. What will become of her? How could I have allowed it?"

"She wanted it and you had no business to stop it. James will look after her very well."

"That's what Julia said. But to be married at sixteen—"

"You were not so much older yourself."

"It's true, I suppose. Samuel would have been pleased with James. He didn't want her to marry into the gentry. But what I'm really afraid of is the whole of life, hers and mine and the other children's. How can anything turn out well in a world like this one? Everywhere poor people are turned out of their homes to make money for the rich, or for people who have become savage because they see that they won't be rich much longer. And the poor people are not much better. They have legalized killing and the torture of animals and revenge. They have a cold look on their faces, even the best of them. They want to fight, not to have peace. When the time comes to have peace, they won't know what to do with it. Fighting will have become a habit of mind with them and with their children. In Belfast and Derry, the children are out in the streets throwing stones at the Orangemen, and the Orangemen are stoning the Catholics and burning their houses in the name of Christianity. It's a way of life with them. Ireland is a 'most distressful country,' indeed. But not all the people want to fight. Those who don't are getting a crafty look, as if they'll never again be able to tell the truth, or even to tell truth from lies when they see it. They're all in debt and all afraid of what's in store for them."

Father Kenny was sipping his claret, nodding slowly but saying nothing.

Alice went on. "If the men come home from jail, they'll be furious when they see the condition of the people. I've just given a promise to help stop evictions," she finished abruptly, watching his face.

He thought that over for a moment, pursing his mouth in a new and unbecoming gesture that made his face look even more skull-like. Then he said, "You could be very useful. You're speaking of Jerome Burke."

"What do you mean? Jerome Burke?"

"Hadn't you heard? He's replanning the home farm, putting the Callaghans and the Donahues and the O'Rourkes out. They say they won't go. How can they? I thought they must have appealed to you."

"They did not, but they should have. This is the last straw. I'd heard that Jerome was back and going to live in Moycullen again. I might have known how he'd go about it. When is the eviction to happen?"

"The process server has come. Notice is served for Friday."

"All Souls' Day—how could they?"

"One day is as good as another to them."

"I wonder why Morrissey didn't tell me."

"This is a Galway affair. Morrissey is only for Mayo."

"Is the organization so good?"

"Not good enough, but 'twill serve. That party on Friday won't be very like a wedding."

"Why does everyone talk to me as if I were a pampered

lady?" Alice demanded furiously. "You'd think there was some secret about where I came from. I never give it a thought nowadays."

"Probably that's why everyone else has forgotten it too. Samuel was partly responsible. It's a good thing; I'd advise you to hold on to your position if you're going to begin to interfere in evictions and things of that sort."

"For my safety?"

"Perhaps. I know Samuel didn't want you to be anything more than the lady of the manor, handing out soup and kindness at the back door. That is the proper role for a lady. And you have your children to think of, and this house."

"I can only ask myself what I would be doing if I still lived in Cappagh. Would I stand by while my neighbors were turned out of their houses? I don't think so, not at my age. But the children—"

"Well?" he said gently, when she had paused for too long.

"If I stand by and do nothing, what are they to think of me? They'll think I'm a hypocrite. I'm always telling them what Christ said, feed the hungry, comfort the afflicted."

"You may bring misfortune on them."

"I can't help it. I'll go to Galway tomorrow and talk to Jerome. Perhaps he could be persuaded to put it off. What do you think?"

"He should be given another chance. Can you stand it?"

"He can't eat me."

"And you needn't go to Galway. He comes to the house quite early every morning to supervise the repairs. I've talked with him myself."

"You didn't tell me." In Samuel's lifetime she would have been told. "Did you appeal to him?"

"We measured each other and he knew what I wanted and dared me to say it. I didn't give him the satisfaction of refusing me."

"Then why do you think he might listen to me?"

"I don't, but I think it's worth a try. Look, your guests are beginning to go."

52

The next morning at nine o'clock, Alice had Paddy drive her to Jerome Burke's house. The weather had changed to a dull, blustery sky, with drops of rain on the wind. Flashes of silver showed in the clouds, the color of a herring. In Cappagh today the sea would be gray and dangerous-looking, continually changing direction, seeming to rear itself up to meet the dancing clouds. They went in the gig, Samuel's old gig, newly painted by Paddy, who found the days long.

Alice wore her smartest outfit, a new black skirt and jacket with velvet trimmings, and a velvet-trimmed mantle, which she knew suited her, so that Jerome would see at a glance that she intended to keep up her position.

She had not been to Burke's house for several years, though Samuel always walked over there when they came to Moycullen, giving her an account of the condition of the house and the park when he came back. She was not surprised therefore to find that the avenue was thick with weeds and grass, the semicircle of gravel before the door roughened by the hooves of cows and the beech hedge surrounding it gone ragged and spiky. Patches of green still showed among the brown leaves that would remain all winter long, an insult to their summer beauty. Both she and Samuel had disliked beech hedges for this reason but had left the one by the front lawn at Moycullen House because it was tradition.

The front door stood open, solid and strong, though its white paint was badly stained by the weather. She sprang down almost before the horse halted and said to Paddy, "Walk him in the avenue for a while, not too near the house. I don't know how long this will take."

She rubbed her cheeks hard with her knuckles to bring up the color, and whirling around to go toward the door, she saw that Jerome was standing there, watching her. He was dressed for riding, swinging from heel to toe, looking healthier and thinner than when she had seen him last. When was that? In Dublin, long before the trials, at someone's dinner party, sitting all evening with a discontented scowl, like a badly brought-up child, answering shortly, so that even the host—yes, it was D'Arcy's house—had been driven to say, "What's the matter, Burke? Sickening for something? Cat got your tongue?"

Jerome's smile had been forced and unnatural, she remembered, seeing in her mind's eye even the brocade wing chair in which he had been lounging. His expression had changed now, softened into an uncertainty that was more pleasant.

He came down the steps with his hands out, saying, "Mrs. Flaherty! I'm so glad to see you at last. I had meant to call and talk about Samuel and find out how you're doing."

He led her into the house, holding her hand too long in his, turning to look at her directly instead of avoiding her eye in his old shifty way. She liked to hear him speak so warmly of Samuel.

"He was a fine man, a man of principle, an example to the rest of us." This was promising, and she felt some remorse at not having asked him to the wedding. Her excuse had been Lydia's illness, a poor excuse it looked now.

She began to make apologies. "If I had known you were coming out here so often, I'd have asked you to come to the wedding yesterday——"

"It's my fault," he interrupted. "I should have called on you but I was weak with myself. I kept putting it off. Samuel was one of my oldest friends, from childhood."

She felt herself soften still more. Poor old Jerome! He had his troubles, too, as bad as her own and worse, since he had never had the satisfaction of happy companionship with that whining Lydia, even when she was healthy. She walked into the drawing room with him, surprised to find that a carpet and a little furniture had been put in——just a sofa, a table and three big chairs, but it was enough to give the room some of its old character.

"You've been busy," she said, looking around. "Soon you'll be able to come back to live here. I've been told you're planning it."

"Yes, but there are so many things to be done. Even the roof is leaking. I was lucky that the cattle didn't break in and make a stable of the whole place."

"Samuel told me that he did some repairs——he got our men to put back the yard gate once when it fell after a storm."

Jerome wore his more familiar scowl again while he spoke of the damage to the house, and she remembered the other scene, in this very room, when he had advised her to count her blessings and keep out of men's affairs. That was about the evictions in Creevagh, when his life had been threatened by the Whiteboys. After it she had never wanted to see Jerome again, but Samuel's way was different, and she had consented to speak to him if they met, for decency's sake. Besides, old George's death had wiped out her anger and she had not seen Jerome for a long time afterward. It seemed incredible that he had learned nothing from that night, when his hayrick was burned and his house might have followed it.

In a rush she said, "I've come to ask you to leave the tenants on the land a while longer. I've heard there's an eviction notice for Friday. The people have no place to go."

He walked away from her toward the grimy window so that

she could not see his face. Once she had cringed with fear of him but that was long ago.

She went on quickly, "You haven't been here much in the last few years and you don't know the tenants as well as I do. Things haven't improved at all. They live on the edge of starvation all the time, not just when the potatoes are bad. There isn't a single thing in the houses because there is never money to replace broken things and old things. The Callaghans hadn't even a pot until I sent them one last year, and I have to bring material for clothes, and old blankets to them all. And cups and plates, of course, because those get broken most often."

"What is the use of leaving them there?" he asked softly. "They'll be no better off next year or the year after that."

"If they had decent farms they would work. I've heard that there are places in Cork and Tipperary and Waterford where the land is good and where the people make a decent living. Here they can only live if they get help and if the rents are kept low. All they have is their houses—"

"Hovels."

"We can build them better ones," she said eagerly. "That has been done in some places. Everything will have to change in Ireland soon. You could be a model landlord—everyone would notice your good example. There are plans to be had for model villages. Mr. Henry has done wonders—Mr. Guinness, too, I've heard—"

"Have you heard what the Fenians say about those landlords?"

Taken aback, she said, "No. The Fenians are finished, surely."

"That's dishonest of you, Mrs. Flaherty." The joking tone took some of the harm out of this. "You know they are not finished. The Fenians will be with us forever, by the look of things, and they don't like good landlords. They say a bad landlord is a better advertisement for the cause."

"It's not true! They're not so perverse."

"Aren't they? I wouldn't know. It's a fight to the death, and the sooner the death comes, the sooner we'll have peace. I've been hearing it all my life, until I'm sick of it. A clean cut now and the country will very soon become more comfortable for everyone—that's the only possible way to look at it."

"But you can't talk of clean cuts when there are people, real people, concerned."

This was exasperating, since Jerome knew as well as she did how much the people suffered. It was a waste of time to argue with a man who scarcely listened to her, who had heard it all before, as he admitted. Surely there were arguments that would reach him if only she had the wit or the skill to think of them. It was damnable being a woman, never to have been in the places where the men go to talk and argue, never to have learned what it is that touches them. She could see that it was no use trying to soften his heart.

She drew a long, forced breath through her teeth. She must not lose her temper; she hadn't done that for years because Samuel had taught her that it hadn't even a good dramatic effect. A lady who remained a lady was ten times as powerful, Samuel said.

"I say, you look wonderful when you're furious," Jerome said, "with your eyes flashing and your chin stuck out."

Startled by his remark, she turned toward him and saw that he was really looking at her admiringly. Perhaps she lifted an eyebrow in a way that suggested an invitation, for a moment later he had seized her around the waist and was forcing rough, hot kisses on her lips, clutching at her left shoulder with one hand while the other explored her breast expertly, leading her step by step toward the sofa. To her amazement she felt herself melt with physical longing for him, while she gathered her fists together and pushed him away with all her might.

He let go of her waist, though he was much stronger than she was, and still holding her by the shoulder, he said, "That was not very subtle, but after all, why should it be? You and I would make a good team, Alice. May I call you Alice now?" He laughed softly. The new soft tone of his voice was one of the most disturbing things about him, hardest to understand. "You obviously need a protector."

"What about Lydia?"

His grip tightened.

"Lydia is dying. It's a matter of weeks now." In spite of herself she pitied him for the desolate tone of this. "That's all behind me now. Soon I'll have to begin everything again, as if Lydia had never existed. Why should we pretend? I don't mind that you don't come from my class, since Samuel didn't mind. That's good enough for me, though I thought it strange at the time. This country is falling to pieces; it's a time to make a fortune."

She let all that pass, really taken by his pleading tone and anxious, unhappy expression. She drew back her head from him, to see him more clearly, while he still held her shoulders so that his round doggy face with its tightly trimmed beard and sideburns and curving eyebrows, and his pathetic dog's eyes, were very near her.

"What about the children?"

"Children marry or die. I never cared for them. Some people seem to enjoy children but I never could, I don't know why. Alice, I want you. Don't you like that? You're in the same boat as myself, only worse for being a woman. I'll look after you."

"I doubt if we'd agree—there are so many things we don't agree about."

"They would all disappear once we're together. You're going to need help in bringing up your own children, especially the boy. A boy needs a man to control him."

She said desperately, gasping for breath, "I think that's one of the things we wouldn't agree about. I'm sorry, Mr. Burke. There's no point in going on with this. I've told you what brought me here this morning. We'd better keep to that."

She began to wriggle out of his grasp, seeing him consider kissing her again and change his mind, as clearly as if he had said it.

He released her and stood with his hands hanging, saying, "We can come back to it. It's natural for you to be full of do-gooding ideas for the poor, since you know so much about them from the inside. I wouldn't mind a little of that. Mrs. Henry does it."

He was watching her all the time, his expression at odds with the reasonable words.

She moved away from him, smoothing her jacket with an effort not to laugh hysterically, saying unsteadily, "So you'll call off the evictions?"

"I haven't said that. You spoke of building model houses. That could be done later, for gardeners and caretakers, but not for the Callaghans and the Donahues and the O'Rourkes. Those people would have animals in the houses in no time. They'd make a manure heap outside the door."

"They could be told not to,"

"You think they'd listen?"

"They've listened to Mr. Henry."

"I doubt if they'd listen to me. I suppose Father Kenny sent you?"

She began to deny it and then stopped. Burke laughed.

"I thought so. You see, you need a protector. What a mission for a lady! Did you know that my cattle were maimed last week?"

"I heard something of it. I'm sorry."

"The people have become beasts. It's the best thing for them as well as for me to send them to America. Look here, I'll make one concession, for your sake. Those hovels have to go, there's no question about that. But I'll let those three families have three derelict cottages of mine in Ballinrobe until they can arrange their passages to America. O'Rourke's brother said he'd send the money but they say it hasn't come. That may be to fox me, for fear I'd take it from them for the rent, though it wouldn't go very far. Between them they owe me four hundred and twenty pounds odd."

"Is Christy O'Rourke sending the passage money for all three families?"

"It seems so, if he can raise it. Do you know him?"

"I remember him, a short red-haired man. He went to Boston in '55 or '56."

Morgan had told her that he worked with Martin Connolly as a builder's foreman but he had certainly not made a fortune.

She asked, "Would you think of paying their passage money yourself?"

"And be accused of exporting them? No, thanks. I've seen that happen too often. Besides, that would be throwing good money after bad—they owe me so much already, as I've just told you."

"How can they possibly owe four hundred pounds?"

"Each of them has a rent of forty pounds and it's more than three years since they paid." Jerome's eyes narrowed with temper. "We're not all in your happy position of being able to keep people in idleness. If I owned a flour mill or two, no doubt I'd be more generous."

"But you have your legal business in Dublin."

"You know nothing about it. I must say I find your loyalties very strange. Your husband and your father-in-law were both killed brutally by these precious people of yours. Does that mean nothing to you? What about Samuel? He was what's called a good landlord, built cottages, gave the people jobs on his farms and in the mill, never pressed for payments, and what did they do in the end? Shot him down like a fox. I tell you these people are mad!"

"What drove them mad? Oppression and poverty and contempt since the day they were born, contempt for their church and their country and their language and their whole way of life, and in the end, contempt for their poverty. God help us, what can they be but poor? How can they do anything for themselves? It takes them all their time to stay alive. It's a wonder to me that they have energy for anything else, or that they can produce fighting men at all. If ever we get a leader again, things will be different. The people will hold on to their land and their homes and refuse to give them up."

"That's sedition!"

"It's common sense. Can't you see it coming? Don't you remember Fennell? He wasn't afraid of anyone, and they killed him, as they may kill you if you go ahead with these evictions. They've already burned your hay and they would have been glad that time to have burned your house. They've maimed your cattle. What's left for them to do?"

"Are you concerned for me?"

"For you and for the people. These things bring misfortune on everyone."

"Are you rejecting my offer of the cottages in Ballinrobe, then?"

"It would be better than nothing. The people don't want to go to America. Putting them in Ballinrobe is only a reprieve."

"We're back where we started."

She brooded, glaring at him. Much good her efforts had done, indeed! She had only invited an assault and a declaration, both of which were most unwelcome, and had got nothing at all out of him. The cottages in Ballinrobe didn't count. If only Samuel were here, he might have been able to do better. Burke was watching her, keeping his distance now, smiling in that strange new way of his.

"Where are the workmen?" she asked suddenly. "It's very quiet. I'd heard you had a team of men here at the repairs."

"There's no one. I sent them away for the rest of the week."

"Because of the evictions, of course."

"Can't you think of anything else? Yes, it was because of the evictions. Alice, you can't spend your whole life at this kind of thing. You're trying to make changes that a whole army of determined men has failed to do. You're only young once. Soon you won't be young at all."

"I was never young!"

"That's no compliment to Samuel."

The mention of Samuel's name infuriated her.

"I never wanted to be young!" She pressed down her anger as if it were an escaping animal in a bag. "What good is it to be young when you see nothing but hunger and misery all around you, people dead and dying everywhere, cruel law backed up by foreign soldiers, soldiers who will come out from Galway on Friday to throw down houses that are more like rabbit burrows, at your orders, the orders of a fine gentleman.

A fine offer you made me, too—that you wouldn't hold it against me for not being lady born. Well, I can tell you I'd rather be born in a stable than be your kind of lady—or have anything to do with a man who would make an offer like that and his wife on her dying bed—"

She sobbed with rage and lost her breath, recovering it to see that he was advancing on her with crooked elbows and clawlike hands. A sharp thrill of fear ran through her, sending her starting back toward the door, which she had no hope of reaching before he had seized and gripped her, this time with fury in his doglike eyes, and his white teeth gritted as he snarled, "You whore of hell!"

Quietly, on the gravel outside, the wheels of the gig and the horse's hooves sounded, placidly walking: Paddy had come back to fetch her. Jerome threw her hands from him violently and turned away with a snort, leaving her free to wrench the door open and dart out into the hall, where she paused to smooth her rumpled hair with her hands and draw herself up into the posture of a lady before walking down the steps to climb into the gig.

53

By Friday the blustery wind had become a gale, carrying sleet almost horizontally, so that it crashed against the windows and flew into the hall when Alice opened the front door at six o'clock in the morning. The flame of the oil lamp shot up to the top of the globe, sending a dancing shadow out on the gravel. She shut the door quickly behind her, clutching her storm lantern against her in an attempt to hold down the ends of her shawl. It was intensely cold, with the bite of winter. No light whatever came from the sky but she could make out the position of the barouche by the dim light of its side lamps.

Paddy called out softly, "Is that you, ma'am?"

"Yes, yes, be quiet."

He held the door for her and she climbed in, placing her basket and the lantern on the floor at her feet, asking in a whisper, "Did anyone hear you come out?"

"No one followed me but someone always hears when you don't want them to."

He led the horse to the inner gate and out onto the avenue,

closed the gate and came again to the door to say, "We may be quiet but they'll be there in their numbers later on, now that they know you're coming."

"Do you think so?"

"Of course. What else would they do? Mr. Burke has that news, too, and there will be a strong force out from Galway, I'm told."

"You promised to keep back out of sight. You promised to stay with the horse."

"Don't upset yourself—I'll do that, ma'am, if I can at all. I know I must mind the horse. The wind is annoying him."

"What about Murphy?"

"No sign of him. I'm never sure what goes on in that man's head. Sometimes I think he's a spy. What is a Corkman doing in the cold wilds of Galway?"

"He needs a job."

"That's true but I'm never at my ease with him. He has this funny way of looking at you, kind of pitying, as if he knew what's in store for you."

She hated the suspicion about Murphy, who seemed a quiet, hard-working man, but everyone was suspicious these days. She said, "Perhaps he's really pitying you for what you went through in prison. A spy wouldn't give himself away so easily."

"True for you, ma'am. But I think he's the one that told Mr. Burke what's happening today, whether he meant any harm by it or not."

He shut her in carefully and she could hear him climb slowly up onto the box. His joints had stiffened since he had been in jail, from the cold, he said. He drove slowly at first, but when they were away from the house, he touched up the horse to a trot. At the road gates there was no delay, so he must have arranged that they were to be standing open. In spite of the closeness of Paddy, she was glad of the little ring of light around her lantern, a reasonable, steady, everyday thing, keeping off the ghosts that walk in the early morning. No matter how long she lived the life of a lady, she could never rid herself of the fears that had belonged to her childhood, fears shared by every man, woman and child in Cappagh and probably in all Connemara, of meeting evil spirits from another world, or ghosts of the dead, in dark and lonely night places. Now this fear was as strong as her fear of the police and the soldiers.

The drive was short. Soon she felt the roughness of a lane and the horse picking his way, rolling loose stones experimentally under his hooves. When they stopped, she waited until

Paddy came around and opened the door for her, leaning in to take the lantern to light the step and the muddy strip in front of Donahue's cottage. She had had the wit to wear boots, which kept out the squelch until she stood on the stone flag at the front door.

Paddy tapped softly and a voice inside said, "Paddy?"

"It's myself."

The door opened and they went into the kitchen, which was lit by the blaze of a turf fire only.

Michael Donahue was holding the door, saying, "The blessings of God on you, ma'am, and you're always welcome. I'm sorry for the smell—we sent away the animals last night but they've left their card behind them, though we scrubbed and washed."

"Never mind, Michael. It's a healthy smell."

It was overpowering and disgusting but she knew better than to disrespect the animals that had made it—the pig she had given herself, and one goat and its two kids, now safe from the bailiff. She went at once to old Mrs. Donahue, Michael's mother, who was sitting huddled on the hob beside the fire, a little bag of bones, clutching her tattered shawl around her shoulders, her head bent and a soft crooning sound of prayers in Irish coming from her incessantly, like the humming of bees.

She grasped Alice's hand swiftly, squeezing it repeatedly, saying in Irish, "God bless you, love, you that were always gentle and bighearted, but it's not right for you to be here, with a family at home depending on you. They might do you some harm when they come."

"Would you like to go to my house now, Mary?" Alice asked, in Irish, too. "I have the coach and horse here, and Paddy would drive you there at once, out of harm's way. I'll stay here with Michael."

"I won't stir, love," she said, rubbing Alice's hand against her cheek. "I came into this house with Séamus Michael and I a young, hearty girl, and I'm not leaving my house until the roof is thrown down on me. Did you know that they want me to go to America?" She gave a little cackle of laughter. "In old age, you'd hardly believe there's such a place at all. And I'd never last a sea journey. You have the right idea, girl. We'll stay where we are when they come and dare them to knock the house on top of us."

Alice turned away and whispered to Michael, "She's as well off here. It's all the same."

He showed her the preparations he had made, the planks she had sent from the sawmill, the tree trunk, the iron bars.

"No firearms, as you said, though a taste of their own medicine would do them a power of good."

"It would be their excuse to shoot you down if they as much as see a gun."

"It's hard to face guns without having one in your own hands to answer back with."

"This is going to be another kind of war, better than any guns. Are the O'Rourkes and the Callaghans ready? They'll have to fight their own battle."

"Yes, they're ready."

Michael's wife Sara came out of the inner room, with her two half-grown daughters, who kept close by the wall near their grandmother, looking terrified.

Sara was brisk and loud, almost hysterical. "You're welcome, Mrs. Flaherty, though we have nothing to give you, nothing but misfortune from now on."

Alice made her sit down and uncovered the things in the basket to show a loaf of bread, butter, a cake and a small bottle of whiskey.

Sara said instantly, "I'll give a drop to the mother, if you please, to keep the fright off her. Here, Barbara, Katie, let ye eat a bite while ye can."

"Where are the boys?" Alice asked, helping her with the food.

"Three of them went over to Oughterard last night to tell that we're holding out, and the others are out around the place. I'd rather have them outside than in."

The girls looked more cheerful when they had eaten but they stayed close by the fire and hardly spoke at all.

Ten o'clock was the time named for the eviction. Light came slowly, creeping through the tiny pane of glass, nine inches square, that was the only window, a dull, mean light that showed the true squalor of the little hovel. The ashes of the fire lost their glow, streaks of damp and smoke showed on the whitewashed walls, the filth left by the animals stank coldly, the old woman looked more than ever like a corpse, her yellow-white face scarcely moving though she continued to croon her prayers. Despair flew through Alice as she watched Sara gather the pitiful objects she valued into an old apron and tie them safely by the strings. There were two sepia-printed photographs of her two oldest children, a boy and a girl, in the usual stilted poses, sent from America a year after they arrived there, to prove that they were alive and well dressed. There was an English pottery jug with a picture of a farmer and a dog and some sheep, which Alice recognized as coming from the nursery of her own house, a gift of several years back. There was a pottery cat, too, which Barbara stroked gently as she handed it to her mother, an oleograph of the Holy Family in a tarnished gold frame, and the little red-globed votive lamp that went with it. There was the family knife and spoon, and two plates, totally covered with hair cracks, as well as three chipped mugs. Alice blamed herself for not having brought them more household things—ridiculous to think of that now. She had so many people to think of, all as poor as these.

Sara wrapped the breakable things in some rags and a skirt and, placing the bundle carefully under the window, went to sit close by her mother-in-law on the floor. Alice had the second hob, the place of honor, while Michael leaned against the rickety table. There were no chairs.

"I gave the stooleens to the Joyces," Sara said, still in a loud, unnatural tone. "They might as well have the good of them." She snorted. "Stooleens won't be much good to us from now on."

"Be quiet with that kind of talk," Michael said sharply, as one of the girls began to weep. "Can't you trust in God?"

About to reply, she gulped the words and buried her face in the old woman's lap.

Mrs. Donahue said, "Let her alone. Sure, her heart is broken, the poor girl." And she stroked the younger woman's hair gently.

Michael took some turf, the last sods from the little pile by the hob, and built up the fire with a series of expert, jerky movements, saying with mock cheerfulness, "We might as well have a bit of comfort and we waiting."

No one answered and presently he went back to stand by the table again.

Soon after nine o'clock they heard someone running. There was a brisk tap on the door and Paddy's voice called out, "Open up for a minute, quick!"

Michael threw back the door, revealing Paddy, suddenly looking younger and livelier, saying, "They're below at Woodstock. There's about sixty policemen and a whole pile of soldiers. They're going to call at Burke's on their way here for a battering-ram—"

"How do you know this?"

"No names, no pack drill," Paddy said. "They're all joking and laughing among themselves about the fight we're putting up. They said Mr. Burke will have a stirrup cup for them at the house, the same as for a fox hunt, God forgive them, and he's coming with them himself."

"No!"

"That's what I've heard, ma'am. You know well some of the landlords do like to be present. They're coming here first, as we heard, and going on to Callaghan's then and O'Rourke's last." He looked quickly around the room. "It will be a dirty business by the looks of things. Michael, wouldn't you take your mother to a place of safety?"

"She wants to stay. Last night I asked her to go over to Joyce's but she said she won't leave the house while Miss Alice is here."

"They won't want to harm the women," Paddy said. "Maybe it's better to leave them." He took Michael by the shoulder and turned him aside, lowering his voice almost to a whisper. "When you're in jail, keep your heart up. I hadn't chick nor child nor wife but I saw it was worse for the men with families. I'll give you a sign when they're at the crossing."

Then he threw his arms around Michael, embracing him warmly, and went trotting off down the muddy lane without looking back.

There was plenty to do now. Michael dragged the kitchen table into position behind the door, end on, and built a barricade to brace it with the planks and the tree trunk, making a continuous line to the back wall. He had made sockets to hold the iron bars in place behind the door but the wood of the door was so rotted that they would be no more than a token.

"When Paddy gives the sign, you'll shut the door," Alice said, "and you'll get your barricade in position immediately. Your mother and Sara and the girls must keep well back. You'll have to break the window to hear what's going on outside."

She stood by the open door to breathe the clean air, shivering with the cold of it but exhilarated by the thundering wind, as if she were by the sea at home. From her position on the doorstep she had a view downhill toward the lane and into the hilly fields around, and now she became aware that men and women were hurrying along as if they were on their way to Sunday Mass, chattering among themselves, gathering in little groups at a distance of fifty yards or so from the house in any place from which they had a view of it. The younger men carried pitchforks and slanes and the older ones blackthorn sticks. Michael Donahue's son Tadhg seemed to be leading a group of boys of his own age, about sixteen, who were jumping about like young calves, pretending to strike one another with their ashplants, shouting louder and louder the slogan that was in everyone's mouth these days: "God save Ireland!" Then she saw Tadhg stand out before them, gesturing them into formation until he had them closed into a tight square. She was amazed at how quickly they did this, as if they had been drilled to it.

Diverted by their antics, she had hardly noticed a new sound, the clatter of the approaching horsemen, until Paddy suddenly appeared at the top of the lane, waving his arms wildly above his head. She darted into the house.

"Here they come! Barricade the door—break the window."

She heard it crackle to pieces a minute later, while she stood outside, clutching her shawl around her to keep out the piercing cold. A flurry of big raindrops struck the house but the sky had cleared a little, leaving a few white patches among the sagging gray clouds.

"Michael, can you hear me?"

"Yes, yes, no trouble."

He was by the broken window.

"Don't come out no matter what they do—promise me. Everything depends on how tough we can be with them. No matter what they do,, remember."

"Very well."

As the horsemen approached, she noticed that the watching crowd became silent and still, and then she found herself huddling close against the house door, like a cornered cat. In front came the mounted constabulary in their hard hats, about sixty of them, as Paddy had said, all armed with carbines, led by Sergeant Mullins from Moycullen and the fat little bailiff from Galway. She recognized four of the Moycullen constables as well, Broe, Scully, Nolan and Riordan, all from the midlands. They were on foot, carrying the battering-ram between them. Behind the police came the soldiers, riding four abreast in perfect formation, their officer out in front on a splendid bay, with Jerome riding his black hunter beside him.

They strung out to turn into the lane, the police letting the soldiers pass so that they streamed all around the house until they had encircled it, with the crowd behind them. Jerome and the officer took up positions to one side, the officer calling out, "Bring up your men, Mullins!"

An Englishman, by his accent. The sergeant led his men forward, filling the lane from end to end, the horses twitching uneasily and tapping the ground with their hooves when they were halted. By this time, Alice was spread-eagled against the door, her hands flat on the wood, her head up and her shoulders back, as if she were facing death. Mullins and the bailiff dismounted and came forward, ignoring her.

Mullins called out, "Donahue! Open up in the name of the law!"

Michael's voice came from inside the house. "I will not! Get away to hell out of here!"

Mullins consulted with the bailiff, then went to speak to the officer, who seemed to have little patience with him. Still Alice said nothing, though she knew that Jerome was watching her. A scuffle had begun at the foot of the lane, horses shouldering one another aside, a man running, pushing his way through them, his hands on his hat to save it from being knocked off, and then Father Kenny burst out of the crowd of policemen and stood panting beside her. A gasp went up from the crowd but no one ventured to cheer. Kenny was laughing with excitement.

"Alice, what are you up to?"

"I told you the other day—"

"You didn't tell me this."

"I was afraid you'd try to stop me."

"Perhaps I would have. I'm staying, too. This is one way of doing it."

"Go away," she said earnestly in a low voice, turning so that the policemen could not hear. "They'll put you in jail. It's all right for me but they'll have no mercy on a man."

"Nonsense. Of course I'm staying with you. What else would I do?"

"Thank God for that! I was nearly frightened out of my wits."

54

Father Kenny turned and intoned in a voice long conditioned by the pulpit, "A fine day's work, Burke! I see you've come out with swords and clubs." He lowered his voice to a conversational tone. "Have sense, man, and call it off. Is this all the Christianity you have?"

The officer turned to Jerome to ask in a tone of wonder, "You an R.C.?"

"Of course not," Jerome said savagely. "I know my rights. I'm sick of this palavering. Get them out of there, quickly!"

"But the lady," Mullins said. "What about the lady?"

"She can stand out of the way if she knows what's good for her."

"What are your rights?" Alice called out, no longer a lady. "A good sound house, three meals a day, a warm coat on your back. Aren't these the rights of every man and woman ever born? The people inside that house know their rights, too, and they're not going to give up what they have so easily from now on. It will be a war, Mr. Burke, and I wouldn't like to be the man who started it!"

"Do you hear her threatening me? Can't you put a stop to it?" Burke said furiously to the officer.

"You can indeed," Alice said in the same loud voice. "You can knock me and the priest down, trample us with your horses, lay us out with your sabers and your guns, walk over our bodies and drag out the unfortunates who are within and knock their little house to the ground. But I'm telling you that if you do that, word of it will go from end to end of Ireland, into every other shack and hovel like this one, and you and your kind will have a hard time of it to live in Ireland from this day forward."

She felt Father Kenny's hand on her arm and turned to hear what he had to say.

"Good girl, Alice. Well said—but now we're for it."

Together they filled the door space as four constables came forward on a signal from Mullins. She heard the officer ask, "Who is she?"

"Widow of a landlord," Mullins said irritably. "Flaherty of Moycullen. Gone off her head—her husband was shot a few weeks ago, just before you came. Hurry up with that, you men!"

The officer was looking at her curiously, taking no part in what followed. That was for the police, who could only call for help if they were attacked.

The constables were swinging the ram between them. It was a short, thick tree trunk, very like the one that Michael had fixed in his barricade at the other side of the door. Two other men dismounted, throwing their reins to their companions, and the six took hold of the ropes, three at either side of the ram.

Mullins marched to the door, shouting, "Stand back! Out of the way! Donahue! Tell Mrs. Flaherty to stand out of the way!"

"Mrs. Flaherty knows her own mind!" Michael's voice came clearly from inside the house.

One of the soldiers tittered nervously and Mullins reacted to the sound with fury, screaming hysterically, "Out of the way, both of you, or it will be the worse for you!"

Barely waiting for a sign that they would not move, he signaled with a jerk of his head to his men. Four came sliding to the ground from their horses, running forward and seizing Alice and Father Kenny by the shoulders, dragging them from the door. Then, embarrassed at laying hands on a priest and a lady, they muttered together and finally took them to stand beside the mounted officer. Weakened by fear, Alice looked up blankly at Jerome. He jerked in temper at the horse's reins so that it side-stepped. He seemed about to speak but changed his mind, gazing with an air of desperate concentration at the men on the battering-ram.

They swung it gently back and forth, back and forth, in longer and longer sweeps, until it began to hammer at the flimsy door. Alice felt tears run down her cheeks, while a long wail went up from the crowd. Some of the men shook their tools threateningly but dropped them at once. The ashplants trailed from the hands of the boys. Still the dead, hollow sound went on, like the tapping of nails into a coffin, accompanied by cries from the women inside the cottage.

The men holding her arms loosened their grip, in awe at what was being done, and watching her chance she suddenly darted away from them and stood by the constables on the ram, calling out to them, "There's three brace of brave, strong men! On with the good work! You'll have it down in no time! It's not worth a curse. Break it up, throw it down! It's only worth forty pounds a year to Mr. Burke and a pound more for every flagstone and lick of paint that goes to decorate it. Did you know that, sir?" She swung around to the officer. "Did you wonder why they live in that pigsty? He watches like a hawk, and if they tidy it up, up goes the rent at once. They've proved they're rich. They've proved they can afford it—"

"Shut her up, can't you!" Jerome roared.

Her two captors sprang forward and seized her again, dragging her back to her former position raging and weeping hysterically.

Father Kenny said quietly, "That's enough, Alice. You can't do any more. That's enough for this time. My turn next."

The door was splintered and still the battering went on, knocking the barricade aside piece by piece. Six other men went to relieve the first lot, who went back to their horses, wiping their foreheads with their handkerchiefs, keeping their faces down from the crowd, which had now begun to jeer and scream like a collection of sea gulls at sowing time. They became quiet again when the last of the barricade was broken, and dropping the ram the men climbed over the debris and disappeared into the cottage. They came out a moment later with Michael Donahue a prisoner between them.

He called out to Alice before he was hustled down the lane, "God spare you, ma'am! Long life to you!"

More policemen entered the cottage and brought Sara and her two daughters out, lastly helping old Mary to stagger across the muddy patch of ground to where the rest of the family stood huddled together. They watched in silence while their possessions were pitched outside—the splintered table, the dresser and their one bed. Sara clutched the apron that she had filled earlier, her mouth twisted into a hard knot of pain.

"Let me go to them," Alice said sharply to the men who were holding her tightly now. "It's all over. Let me go!"

They slipped their hold and she went over to Sara and took her in her arms, rocking her to and fro. She heard Sara's dry, nervous voice low in her ear.

"Michael is gone with them but they didn't take the boys. The boys must be up there on the hill."

"Yes, yes, I saw them. They haven't been down by the house at all. They're quite safe. Don't say a word about them. Keep quiet now and you can come with me soon."

Still holding Sara against her, Alice watched while the battering-ram was taken around to the gable of the cottage, where the swinging began again.

Father Kenny began to call out, " 'Blessed are the poor in spirit, for theirs is the kingdom of Heaven. Blessed are they that mourn, for they shall be comforted. Blessed are they that hunger and thirst after justice, for they shall have their fill. Blessed are the meek, for they shall possess the land.' All you people up there, listen to me, and watch that wicked work that's going on here. When your time comes, you'll no longer lie down under this treatment! Your day will come, when you'll learn to fight, to fight hard and hold on to your houses and your land—"

"Stop him! God damn it, can't you stop him!" Jerome sent his horse plunging forward, his whip raised. Father Kenny looked up at him, braced for the blow, until Jerome's arm dropped and he turned the horse aside.

"Take him away!" the officer bawled out, and the policemen hustled Father Kenny quickly down the lane.

When the gable wall collapsed it dragged the roof with it, cracking the roof beam across like a broken bone. At once the wind caught the thatch, scattering it in flying wisps so that the whole area around was littered in no time. Defeated at last, Sara clung to Alice while the policemen carried the ram away from the house, now a heap of rubble, and started down the lane on their way to the second eviction. As the officer and Jerome jerked at their horses' reins to follow, old Mary Donahue sprang into their path, her head cocked sideways and her eyes half shut, intoning a curse in Irish.

"God's curse down on you, Burke; may you never lie quiet in bed; may your children wither and die; may your rooftree fall; may your seed and breed in every generation from this day forward bring forth a thief or a murderer of his own kind; may brother rise against brother in every generation; may you never see the face of God; may you live to see the ruin of your family; may you die roaring for the priest and him far away—"

Halting, watching her curiously, the officer asked, "Do you know what she's saying, Burke?"

Jerome muttered furiously, "Come along, for God's sake. Leave them to it."

He kicked at his horse's flanks so that it leaped forward, avoiding the old woman, who sank to the ground, covering her head with her shawl as the whole cavalcade passed her by. When they were all gone, Mary's two granddaughters ran forward and lifted her up, holding her between them, whispering to her and stroking her as they would do with a cat or a dog. Alice saw that the crowd was streaming off through the fields in the direction of Callaghan's cottage.

Slowly she followed Sara and Mary down the lane, now churned into thick mud by the hooves of the horses. The gusty wind carried cold rain that struck them from every angle. At the foot of the lane they paused, a miserable little procession. She looked around desperately for the barouche and then saw it turn the corner, followed by the trap driven by Johnny Doherty, the stableboy.

Silently she helped Sara and Mary into the barouche, putting Johnny in charge of the two girls. Numb with cold and shock, she found that every decision required an effort. What would she do with these people now? And the O'Rourkes and the Callaghans would certainly come to her for help later. They could be accommodated somehow in the stable yard, perhaps in the coach house or in the loft above the stables if some of the hay were moved. But there would be ticks on the hay. Inside the house would be best but there was simply not room for all the people. She began to count them as Paddy drove cautiously along: four here with her, at least five at O'Rourke's and five or six at Callaghan's—fourteen or fifteen people, counting the women only. There were young boys at Callaghan's as well, who would have to be with their mother. She would get all the hay out of the loft and the little room behind it, and they could all sleep up there unless the weather got colder. It was cold enough now but together they would probably be warm enough. Somewhere on ground level there would have to be a fire where they could sit. She knew from experience that some of the soldiers would come back to make sure that the cottage was not rebuilt and that there was no sign of the family in the neighborhood. Would this mean that Moycullen House would be raided? What would they do, how could they protect themselves, a houseful of women and old men? Where was God?

By the time they reached the house, rain was falling heavily, chilling the barouche and drenching the occupants of the trap so that they looked like a bunch of wet hens when they stood in the coach house. Old Kate was watching for them, waving from the kitchen doorway. The wind plunged into the yard, sending sheets of rain battering down from the black sky, drowning the cobbles so that they walked to the back door in inches of water. The kitchen glowed with warmth and smelled of soup. Kate put Mary Donahue close by the stove, in her own basket chair, muttering endearments to her as if she were a child, hurrying Maria and Jane, the kitchenmaids, to bring the pot to the table and begin to ladle the soup, throwing towels to the girls so that they could rub their faces and hair dry.

Seeing them all so well cared for, Alice went quietly through the kitchen and upstairs to her bedroom, untying her bonnet as she went. There was no sign of Fahy. She would have to consult with him—he always seemed to know what was happening everywhere—but first she must get dry clothes and something to drink and try to calm her mind. Her anger was taking too many directions at once—against Jerome for his inhuman treatment of the tenants, against the soldiers and police for their part in the eviction, against the men who had stood quietly on the hillsides while the house was pulled down. But what was the use of any of it? Jerome belonged to his tradition, the soldiers did as they were told, the people knew that if they intervened with their sticks and spades, they would be shot down like rabbits. It looked as if they would never fight again—soon there would be no one there to fight; they would all have gone to America. They lost their nerve at the sight of guns.

Eileen had undressed her and wrapped her in a blanket inside two minutes. She had a fine fire built up on the hearth. She was a Dublin girl, sent by the agency to replace Sprigg and far more to Alice's taste. She seemed to like Moycullen, a pleasant change from the usual grumbling Dublin servants who could never get back to the city quickly enough. Her only disadvantage was that she had never known Samuel, so that Alice could not ask her from time to time, "Do you remember how Mr. Flaherty used to like tea whenever he came in—an excuse to sit down and chat? Do you remember how he always sat in that chair, though it was too low for him? Do you remember how he liked flowers in this room? Do you remember—do you remember—"

Eileen remembered nothing but she was good to Alice and had taken on some of Samuel's functions in protecting her. While Alice was sipping her tea, she went to answer a tap at the door and said, "Miss Alice is not dressed yet and can't come down for a while. She'll go down when she's ready and no sooner." She came back to twitch angrily at the petticoats she had set to warm at the fire, saying, "The day is long—let him wait, whoever he is—think people can be at their beck and call every minute and hour of the day."

"Who is it?" Alice asked anxiously, worried that she was beginning to feel drowsy from the heat of the fire and the tea. "Have the Callaghans arrived already?"

"Someone wanting to see you but if he wants it bad enough he'll wait a while. Take your time there now. You'll have enough to do later." She stood behind Alice and massaged her shoulders with a powerful plunging movement of her thumbs and palms. "Nellie said she never saw him before. Maybe he's the traveler for wine that you said was coming. If that's it, he'll be glad to sit by the fire for a while."

"Is there a good fire in the dining room?"

"Yes, as good as here. I saw to it myself."

"Where is Miss Julia?"

"With Miss Conroy—she's all right. Master Thomas is there too."

So she let Eileen dress her slowly in the warm clothes, and brush her hair until it felt clean, and hook her into one of the horrible new black dresses that had come from Jay's.

"They make me look like a walking tombstone—all that drapery and the flounces. In the name of God, what are they supposed to do for a woman?"

They were meant to make her look pathetic, to dramatize her, and as she left her room she caught sight of herself in the long glass by the door, black hair, black dress, dead white face, enough to give the traveler for wine nightmares for a month.

Outside the dining-room door she paused and deliberately put on an expression of welcome, kindly, noncommittal, promising nothing. She opened the door and walked in, and there, standing gazing into the fire, was Morgan.

PART
SIX

55

They talked for days, meeting whenever they could take time from the unfortunate people in the yard, sometimes with Thomas and Julia and Fahy present, more often alone, rarely taking their eyes off each other, as if each were afraid that the other would disappear. When they were alone they usually used Irish, the language of their childhood.

"Morgan, you're so thin. I can see all the bones of your face and your hands are like a bird's claw. And you're pale—you must eat well and get back your health, but gradually. It's not good to eat much all at once. Kate says she's making special small dishes, and you're to have something between meals for a while. And your clothes are wretched—she has something of Samuel's for you—you won't mind wearing Samuel's clothes. He would have wanted that. What am I saying? Of course you're jealous of Samuel but it doesn't matter. Samuel was jealous of you, too, but he never talked about it. Why am I talking about it now? I never thought to speak of such things but now nothing matters, and I'm a bit mad. I can only think of your being here with me, my love, my darling. I loved Samuel but I wasn't in love with him. I wonder if he knew? He didn't expect much from life and perhaps he was satisfied with what he got, but it wasn't enough. Now I want to be honest again, and still we might be better not to talk so much."

"It's better to talk now. When we were young we were so confused, we understood nothing. We were primitive then."

"I understood, all right. Even now I'm sure I did right, though somehow you were wronged by what I did. I used to curse love, and think it was a disease, something to be cured, but I don't think that now. Every love has good in it, no matter how it breaks the law of God or man afterward. There is so little love in the world that anyone who has it should be glad. Coldness and indifference are the great sins. When you drew me and made love to me in Paris, it was a sin but it was justice, too, after what I had done to you. We won't talk about that yet, but later on when things are quieter we can discuss it."

"I'm not angry, Alice. I've had a lot of time to think about Paris and why I acted as I did. I was showing you that you were still mine, I was keeping my hold on you, and that was a sin because you belonged to Samuel. That's what it meant to me at the time. Then, in prison, I thought, no one belongs to anyone else, only to himself, and I was glad I had shown you beyond all doubt how much I loved you. You're right when you say that all love is good, and in the end we didn't injure Samuel because we both loved him. That was the most important thing, and yet anyone listening to us discussing it would say we are a pair of hypocrites. If Samuel knew about it, who knows what he felt? He must have been hurt, and still he must have known that we didn't want to hurt him. He loved us too, you more than me, of course, because you were his wife, but I know he loved me too. In prison, I had a lot of time to think about love and what it does in the world, and how it sometimes generates hatred, but that didn't happen with us. In prison, everything was brought down to a question of love. We were there for love of Ireland, and the men who were married and had children were broken down by love for them —it was no blessing then. I wish Father Ned were here so that we could talk about it to him. Did you confess to him?"

"No. After we got back from Paris I went to a deaf old priest in Galway and told him I was unfaithful to my husband, and he said like a nice old pussycat, 'How many times, my child?' And I had to tell him I couldn't remember. So he asked if it would happen again, and I said no, and that was that. But it felt all wrong to talk of you as a sin, because I wanted to bring you back again and again, remember you holding me in your arms, and your kisses, but I had to stop that because the old priest made me promise. It was important, he said, because my whole attitude to life would change if I wanted you to make love to me again, I'd begin to live a double life and that would affect my brain in the end. He said it all in this sleepy voice, as if he had often said it before, and perhaps he had. It didn't make me feel any better but it worked. What about you? Did you confess me as a sin?"

"Yes, in Millbank, when I thought I was going to go mad and then die. I wanted to tell how much I had injured you but the priest wasn't interested. He only wanted me to confess that I had sinned in belonging to an oath-bound society, but I had to tell him that love of country was a virtue, not a sin. Then he wouldn't give me absolution; so it was rather a comedy after all. In the end I left it all in the hands of God."

Morgan organized the evicted families in living quarters in the sheds and coach house in the yard, consulting with Thomas all the time, reminding him, 'When your turn comes to own all this land, you'll have to know how to look after the people.

You'll have to go back to school in a few days but this will be useful experience."

"How long will they stay here?"

"The shortest possible time. Most want to get to America at once, never to set foot on Irish soil again, which was Burke's idea, indeed. When the money comes for the O'Rourkes, they'll be off, and your mother is going to pay for the other families, even if O'Rourke's brother sends enough for all. Burke should do it, but he says they owe him so much that he doesn't see why he should throw good money after bad, and he's angry at having had to evict them by force."

"He wouldn't have done this while Papa was alive."

"Indeed he would, and did. He's been doing it all his life. He did it in Creevagh and in Ballinrobe. When he was living all the year in Dublin there was some peace from him, but if he comes back, he'll never stop until he has cleared the whole place out."

"What will he live on if he has no rents?"

"He's a lawyer, don't forget. Sheep and cattle are the new tenants on the land. Now we'll see what we can do about the harness room. The hearth there is big enough for everyone to sit around, and there's a crane that will take a twenty-gallon pot of potatoes."

The evicted people sat on straw on the floor, doing nothing, just watching Morgan and Thomas like children, waiting for them to arrange everything. Mrs. O'Rourke wept without ceasing until she looked like a tall, yellow-faced ghost. Though she had a two-year-old child, she looked about seventy years old. Her anxious, bitter face haunted Morgan's nights.

"You'd think she had been in Dartmoor for ten years," he said to Alice. "That's the look that was on the faces of the men there, as if they expected the sky to fall on them at any moment, as if they had never had a moment's pleasure in their lives."

"What was the worst thing?" Thomas asked.

And Alice said anxiously, "Can you talk about prison, Morgan? There's no need."

"I'll have to talk about it as long as I live, not to ease myself but so that people everywhere will know what it's like. Prison is a foretaste of death. Everything stops for you; you have no more need to think or act individually and after a while you don't want to. The world you knew has disappeared, as if you were underground; nothing moves except time, but every day is the same. Food and sleep are both hateful to you because they have become ugly; pain and cold represent the decay of your body, just as it will decay in the coffin. That's what it all is, really, a symbol of death, a threat of what will come and of the power they have over you." He had been talking in a half dream and only now noticed that Alice was weeping, holding Thomas' hand in a desperate clutch. "You're right, Alice, I shouldn't speak of it."

"No, no. Go on! It must be said."

"Every hour is like a day, every day is like a year. Faces of the other prisoners become like masks, horribly quiet, expressionless. Sometimes one of them goes mad and tries to kill himself, going about it badly, trying to eat broken glass or stab himself with a little file that wouldn't kill a bird, screaming with terror while he does it. These men are said to be malingering and acting, but if that were true, a professional actor would envy them. A clean coffin to oneself would be a better proposition than the filth all around you, the clothes, and the men who are not allowed to wash even when they're sick. Outside the air is clean but sharp as a gale in Galway Bay, all the year round blowing over you, piercing cold in winter and blistering hot in summer. There's a symbol in the work, too, pulling a cart like a horse, as man goes back into the earth and becomes part of creation again, perhaps giving strength from his body to a grazing horse. These were the things I thought of in prison, and they were what I was meant to think of. The warders and the Governor are twisted up in their minds because of the unnatural things they have to do. They're as miserable as the devils in hell; their only amusement is to torment the prisoners. They justify it on Christian principles, that man must repent of his sins and the recalcitrant must be brought to a realization of their guilt, though a great many of the ordinary prisoners are really insane. Some of the Fenians went mad and some died of hardship, men who would have worked hard all their lives in freedom and never have complained. Those of us who didn't go mad were not brave; we were afraid at every move we made that we'd be beaten and kicked, but it just wasn't in us to go mad, I don't know why. There was a real game of trying to drive O'Donovan Rossa mad but they'll never get the better of him. I wasn't brave; when my chance came to get out I took it like a shot. Now I'm afraid of what will happen to Father Ned. He's not the kind of man who does well in prison. Michael Donahue is safer. A thinking man is at a disadvantage. And still I may be wrong. Mr. O'Leary and Mr. Luby had a way of holding themselves in reserve, of not allowing themselves to suffer inside themselves, and Father Kenny will have his prayers."

"Did you pray in prison?" Julia asked without looking at Morgan, sitting on the hearthrug with her head on Alice's knee.

"Yes, I did pray, but in a comprehensive way. I went back to the beginning, to Christ on the Cross, but it didn't help to think of another person suffering. In the end I just said to God that I was in his hands and could do no more. I'm not sure if that's praying but it was the best I could do."

When they were alone he said to Alice, "Perhaps I shouldn't have talked so much, perhaps it was only self-indulgence, but whatever about that, it has cleared my head of some things I was afraid to see. I had never thought it out in that exact way before, and now that I understand it, the whole thing is easier to bear. I didn't mention the worst part of it, because of the children, and that was the fantasy world that I began to live in, and that I thought would drive me mad, as your old priest said it would do to you. Sometimes when I came in after a day outside in the blinding light, I used to see you quite clearly, standing in a corner of my cell. I never tried to touch you but I used to talk to you, just as I'm doing now, this unnatural way, explaining how I felt about being away from you, and how someday a man would come into my cell and tell me that I was free to go, and I'd come back here and live near you and Samuel and never ask any favors from you, just to be allowed to see you every day. Then I'd tell you that it was all romantic rubbish, worthless, senseless, and I'd hear your voice quite clearly, just as clearly as I saw you, telling me that my plan was a good one, not foolish at all, and that Samuel would be pleased. After a while, of course, I'd come to my senses and see that it was a lot of childish nonsense.

"Then one day James came to see me, and after he had gone I let my control slip for the first time in months, and banged my head against the wall and cried like a baby, and you came right up to me and said, 'Morgan Connolly, you're only half a man! Give that up at once! Shame on you!' I stopped, but I was shocked and frightened at how real you were, and then I thought I must be really on the edge of madness. But it passed off; I had a dizzy head for a day or two and then began to get hold of myself again. I haven't talked so much about myself in all my life but there isn't much more to say. Soon we'll be married, and then we'll have peace at last. I did a terrible thing to you once, and if I don't tell you now, I never will. I wrote to Samuel when I came back from Aran, that time long ago, and I told him you were a loose woman and that you were a scandal on the island."

"Why? Oh, Morgan, why?"

"Can't you see? So that he'd leave you and I could have you myself. You said to me in Aran that a woman is like a bone between dogs, when the men are after her. I'd have destroyed you that time to get you for myself. That was my sin, and nothing before or after was as bad as that. Many a time in Paris I saw men act in the same way; if they wanted a woman for themselves they'd stop at nothing to get her. Men are the same everywhere. Now I can see you're shocked and angry, because you're really an innocent; you have no idea of the badness there is in the world, or the things people do to each other, even friends. That's why what I did was so terrible. But I didn't know then that Samuel was such a good man, though I'd had plenty of proof all my life, when I was at the school and eating at his table. I thought he'd throw you there and say to himself that he would be better to trust one of his own kind, but he just rushed off to Aran and took you away. He was an honorable man, as Master Fahy would say. When I heard from James in London that he was dead, I felt the same pain that I did when my father died, though Samuel was not that much older than I. Now I'm making you cry, and that's not fair because I know you cried enough for Samuel long before I came. Alice, my dear, sweet Alice—"

"Those were the words he said to me when he was dying. How do you know so much? Here, lean on me. He said, 'I'll be with you.' Wasn't that a strange thing to say? Sometimes I've been angry with him for saying it, but of course it's quite true. He'll always be with us, and I'm glad you told me these things, though they hurt so much. What does that matter? Yes, we'll be married now, though we'll have to ask Master Fahy about it. He'll know what the decencies are. And anyway, you'll be here, under our roof—you see, I can't stop saying 'our' and 'we.' You'll be safe, where I can see you. In a few days things will be easier with the people and we can make our own plans."

Master Fahy advised them to wait a year before being married but Father Brady, who took over Father Kenny's work after his conviction and sentence of five years' penal servitude, forced them to it earlier. He was a huge, coarse, overfed man from Gort, who believed in terrifying the parishioners into heaven for their own good. He met Morgan on the road to Galway one frosty day after Christmas and pulled up his horse to talk to him. The two horses put their noses together, sniffing and nibbling at each other, sending up clouds of steamy breath.

Brady said without ceremony, "Connolly, you'd better get out of that widow's house at once. You're causing a scandal in my parish and I won't have it. There's Ned Fagan has gone to live with Kate Keating's family and he not married to her, and when I told him to get out, didn't he say to me that what was good enough for the landlord's wife was good enough for him. You're there long enough. Time for you to go home to your own place now, wherever that is."

"I'm a guest at Mrs. Flaherty's house," Morgan said mildly. "I've stayed there off and on since I was a child."

"Don't give me that stuff. What an innocent you are! As if the world didn't know you're in her bed every second night. It's an open scandal."

Morgan lifted his whip and his horse danced across the road. "It's not true! By God, you'd better mind your tongue!"

"And you'd better mind your manners! I don't want the like of you in my parish. Bad enough to have that wild woman there, with her ranting and screaming and disturbance, telling the people to stand up to the landlords and hang on to their houses without paying a penny's rent. She got her answer from Mr. Burke but I heard she's going around the country saying the same things to other people's tenants. Faith and if she is, I'm after her telling them the opposite, that if they don't or can't pay, they must get out and give the landlord back his property, and from now on I'll be present at every eviction myself to see that right is done. The people must pay their debts like Christians and there will be none of that French nonsense in these parts. You learned your lesson badly in jail. It's the like of you coming home that turn the people's minds upside down so that they don't know right from wrong anymore."

"There will be plenty more coming home from jail with the same story."

"Ah, so that makes you bold, does it? I thought it might. But it's not certain yet what will come of the amnesty movement, or if Mr. Gladstone will keep his promises if he's elected, but I'm not waiting for that. I don't want the poor foolish people of this parish to be condemned to jail. You saw what happened to Michael Donahue, and now his family is gone to America and God knows if they'll ever live together again or if he'll get out of jail alive. Is that a benefit to the people, to put them in a corner like that?"

"The people must put up some kind of a fight or there won't be a soul left in the country soon."

"In the holy name of God, what kind of a fight can they put

392

up, and they having hardly a rag to cover their backsides with at the present time? Anyone that makes them fight is doing them an injury, as bad as the man that knocks the house over their heads. Better for them to go to America than to jail—any reasonable person can see that. And for a woman to be carrying on the way Mrs. Flaherty is doing is a disgrace to all women. Of course she's not a lady born and I suppose she knows no better. But she knows better than any lady that she shouldn't be keeping an unmarried man under her roof for months together, and if you don't clear out of that house, I'll read her from the altar. Why doesn't she go back to Dublin?"

He sent his horse thundering down the road, a great, unkempt horse, rather like himself.

Morgan rode on to Galway, astonished at himself for not having struck the priest for his insults to himself and to Alice. That restraint was one thing he had learned in jail. If Alice had been a poor woman, she would have been read from the altar long ago, and probably threatened by the priest and forced to go to America. Only a month ago Brady had got rid of a girl from Glann whose crime was that she was so good-looking that all the boys wanted her, and several fights had taken place because of her.

Brady had gone to her father's house, thundering. "We don't want that class of thing here. Either get her married at once or send her off to America."

"How can I get her married and she having no fortune? I can't even give her a pig to start her out in life."

"Then it's America—she's not staying here. There's no one will be satisfied with a decent ugly girl for a wife as long as that one is around the place with her curls and her rosy cheeks, flaunting herself."

"She doesn't," the poor father pleaded. "She's a decent girl but she takes after her grandmother, that was a beauty, they say, though I never saw her."

"Get her out, I'm telling you, or your first grandchild will have horns on him!"

Alice heard the story when the father came to her for the passage money.

"What could I do?" he said. " 'Tis true she's a beauty but I have seven other children to think of and not a bite for any of them. Maybe it's the best thing for Nora to go and make way for the others in time, when she makes her fortune in America."

"Why didn't you refuse?" Alice demanded but he was so shocked that she had to give it up.

"Is it go against the priest? He said he'd put a curse on me and my family, and how could I bring down that misfortune on them?"

When she told Morgan about it he said, "You and I have come a long way, though I never believed in that kind of nonsense—probably because of Father Ned. I wonder why they couldn't have sent us another like him?"

"There are not many like him. One thing is certain, Morgan. I don't want to be married by Mr. Brady."

So they had the wedding in Dublin just before Lent, in Donnybrook parish church, with no one there except Anna and James, who had come over especially for it, and Julia, who was released from her boarding school for the day. But for James, it would have been a sad affair. He sprang about like a little grasshopper, giving instructions to Alice's cook and the butler, Fanning, for a good luncheon with champagne to be ready immediately after the ceremony. He arranged for the honeymoon to be spent in the Lake District so that they could visit Thomas at his school in Lancashire before returning home.

"I hadn't thought of going anywhere," Alice said, "things are so terrible in Ireland, and at our age—"

"I was almost your age when I was married," James pointed out. "You need a rest from all this misfortune around you, and so does Morgan. Next winter you should organize some parties and perhaps have a ball in the house. That's how to keep your end up. It won't do yet, but a year after Samuel's death it will be quite proper and it will be good for Thomas and Julia. Samuel would want that for them if he were here."

"I can't think so far ahead," Alice said distractedly. "How can I think of having a ball? I wouldn't know how to go about it."

"Of course you would. You've been to plenty of them. And Fanning knows. Anna and I will come over to help you if you have it at Christmas. It's important to do this kind of thing properly."

He looked so serious that she did not dare to laugh, as she told Morgan when they were safely on the Holyhead boat.

"He really does think it's important, and that's why he gets on so well at his work. Who would have thought Moycullen would produce a man about town?"

"He's a romantic, is James. It's one of the nicest things about him."

It was a clear, sharp February afternoon, with white horses on the sea and a wind that kept most of the passengers below.

They stood a long time at the rail, close together, his hand over hers under the warm cover of her shawl, watching the evening lights of Dublin appear one by one, seeming to float toward them out of the gloom. The soft breathing of the steamer's engines and the cries of the sea gulls were the only sounds that reached them. It was a blessing to be silent together.

56

Within a few years the Christmas ball at the Connollys' had become a ritual. The back drawing room was cleared of furniture and the parquet floor was waxed and scattered with a white powder that made one's feet fly. Garlands of smilax and ivy were hung against the stucco garlands that decorated the walls; the Waterford glass chandeliers were festooned with tiny colored glass bells; the archway at the end of the room had a platform inside it on which the musicians sat, three of them, two violinists and a pianist; long tables were ranged at the sides with wine cup and lemonade, the glasses reflecting the soft colors of the Chinese lanterns that crossed and recrossed the room. The young people gasped with delight when they came, melting into the dance eagerly so as not to lose a moment, the long fluttering skirts of the girls' dresses flicking and whirling like feathers in the wind and the long black legs of the boys like spiders twitching in and out among them.

In the smaller room beyond the ballroom the older people played cards or rested while they peeked through the open door at the dancers, chatting and gossiping about them, admiring the prettier girls and refraining from comment about the plainer ones. It was an evening to be enjoyed, even by the sourest aunts and mamas, whose tongues were checked by the happy atmosphere as much as by Alice's habit of suddenly appearing and joining the conversation as if she had heard the whole of what went on before her arrival.

The doors on to the long, cool conservatory between the ballroom and the garden were open, and usually one door on to the garden as well, so that people could go out there for fresh air, and Fanning arranged little tables and chairs among the potted trees in the conservatory, with more Chinese lanterns hanging from the glass roof. Fanning supervised everything, calling on Julia for advice and help as far as possible, so as not to tire Alice, who would have enough to do on the day of the ball.

Julia enjoyed every moment of the preparations, filling little bowls of sugared almonds and marshmallows, arranging huge dishes of fruit—apples and tangerines and oranges—which filled the hot room with a sweet smell, bringing plate after plate of petits fours from the kitchen, where the cook carried on a running battle with the housemaids and menservants. Anna came with new ideas from London, mostly impractical, such as a palm tree to be set up in the hall, with real monkeys on chains in the tree, or stuffed deer and foxes to stand among some pine trees on the terrace. That sort of decoration was all the rage in London, she said, but she agreed with a giggle that it looked a bit foolish to see grown-up people playing like children with stuffed animals. Julia did not often make fun of such things, since Anna lived in the midst of them; they were her whole life now, and James was pleased with her for doing him such credit. They were invited out almost too often, Anna said, but they always went, and had lots of parties themselves as well, though it meant she could not be enough with the children. That was one reason why she came gladly to Dublin at Christmas and to Moycullen in summer. It was considered quite a proper thing to visit Ireland sometimes, and there was talk of James being made a colonial governor someday, not in a nasty little place with a bad climate but somewhere nice like the Bahamas. He had thought of standing for Parliament but had changed his mind with things in Ireland being so difficult.

"If we go to the Bahamas, you could come and stay with us," Anna said. "By the time it happens, you'll be quite old enough to travel alone. You would come, wouldn't you?" she added doubtfully, watching Julia, who was high on one of Fanning's ladders arranging a fallen garland.

"Of course I would—don't look so sad!" Julia climbed down and hugged Anna. "Do you think I'd abandon my two nephews? They wouldn't know me when they'd see me again. Now cheer up—it may never come to that."

"I don't know how you manage to be always cheerful," Anna said. "So many frightening things happen in Ireland and the people seem as miserable as ever, and Mama never stops talking about politics now. It's not proper."

"Mama never minded if things were not proper, and she has to do so much for the people, she can't help talking about it. Now just forget all your worries for today and enjoy yourself. Why don't you run up to the nursery for a while? I'll come as soon as I have the last of these done, and we can stay at least half an hour. It's our last chance today."

Anna went off and soon Julia went to find Morgan in his study, the room at the turn of the stairs that used to be Samuel's. Julia walked in without ceremony as she had always done with Samuel, saying, "Uncle Morgan, could you find Mama and ask her not to talk politics and famine and evictions in front of Anna? She's been doing it again, though she knows that Anna can't stand it. She seems to hope to convert her, but it's a waste of time. Anna has the mind of a child or a good little mother—certainly not a politician."

"And what have you got, Miss?"

"I've never thought it out—a mixture of different things, I suppose. You will speak to her, Uncle Morgan?"

"Yes, of course. She does try, but she forgets."

"If she doesn't watch out, Anna won't want to come to Ireland at all."

"I'll tell her that."

"She'll listen to you. Thank you!"

She kissed his hand mockingly and danced out of the room, flying up the stairs two at a time on her way to the nursery.

The three little boys were sitting at the tea table, which the nursery maid was laying with their evening meal. No one could mistake them for one family: Anna's two, Walter and Gerald, were small and fair and docile while Morgan and Alice's son Fergal, almost to a day the same age as Walter, was black-haired and determined, given to glaring at his betters if he was not pleased. Julia saw the moment she appeared that he was behaving well this evening.

"You promised you'd show us the ballroom if we're good," he said, rolling his big blue eyes at her.

"So that's it!" said the nurse. "I knew he was up to something." Fergal smiled at her knowingly so that she said under her breath, "I declare to God, Miss, that child gives me a turn sometimes."

Afterward, all holding hands, they went down the wide, shallow stairs to the hall and through the little entry into the drawing room, where the children gasped, dazzled at the beautiful sight. Sleepily they blinked up at the colored lights, cautiously walked a few steps onto the slippery floor, as if it were thin ice, and then skirted it carefully to go out into the conservatory.

"I have another promise for you," Julia said.

"What? What?"

"We'll come and show you our dresses if you get into bed

with no fuss and lie as quiet as mice until we come. Will you do that?"

"Yes, yes, yes!"

As they scuttled back upstairs Anna said, "You're a genius with them—I never say anything but '*please*' to them and they take no notice. Nurse tells me they should be whipped but I just can't." Her eyes filled with tears at the very thought of it. "I'm afraid she does it herself from time to time, though I've told her not to."

"Now, Anna, you promised not to worry today. Which dress are you wearing—the gold one or the blue?"

"James says the blue is prettier." Anna brightened at once. "I've worn it twice in London but no one has seen it in Dublin yet. I just love the little rosebuds, such a sweet idea, and the floating scarf. What about you?"

Julia made a face.

"White for young girls. I've got rosebuds, too, though not as elegant as yours."

Julia cared nothing for rosebuds, whirling and prancing around the ballroom for hours without feeling in the least bit tired. She did get warm, though, and at ten o'clock she was glad to retire to the conservatory and let Hugh de Lacy bring her an ice.

"You're an angel," she said as she took it in one hand, taking his other hand in hers and bringing it to her lips.

In a flash she realized that she should not have done it. Hugh was at least twenty-four, not a boy at all, and he was holding her hand steadily now and looking at her humorously, his eyes dancing with amusement and pleasure. Then he let her hand go, and seemed to let her go with his eyes, too, so that she turned away and pretended to be absorbed in her ice, but she felt her face get redder and redder with every moment. Yet she really did like him, best of all the men who came to the house with Thomas. His father had an estate in Kildare and was in the Home Government Association for which everyone had such hopes. Though he was older than the rest, Hugh was a law student at Trinity College—all the young men seemed to be studying law or medicine.

"Let's go back," she said foolishly.

Instead Hugh sat down beside her, saying, "No. Finish your ice and we'll just sit here and watch. Can you see?"

"Yes, of course."

Other couples were sitting about on the benches and little chairs in the dimness. The light from the ballroom fell brightly through the open doorway, and while they watched, the floor was cleared and an accompaniment was started up on the piano.

"Oh, how tiresome! Someone is going to sing!" Julia said in an undertone.

Hugh peeked out into the room and drew back in a moment to say, "It's all right—it's Lily, my sister, quite a good voice. You won't suffer."

Poor Julia covered her face with her hands at this. What an unfortunate remark. She would never learn to be quiet, as Alice and Morgan, and Samuel in his lifetime, had always warned her.

She felt Hugh take her arm and heard his kind voice say, "I suffer, too, I assure you. We'll both suffer later, but not now. Lily really has a lovely voice, and good taste, too."

She sang well, "The Last Rose of Summer," in a clear, well-taught voice that was pleasant to listen to. But after she had finished, girls and young men were pushed forward, one after another, to give their songs, which they had been practicing for the occasion under the supervision of governesses and tutors for weeks past. Soon Julia was wildly clutching Hugh's hand, stifling her giggles, while Molly Shaw sang in a wavering soprano "The Meeting of the Waters," cracking on every top note, which she held with demon stubbornness much longer than necessary. The climax came when her brother Charlie began to pipe:

> " 'When in death I shall calm recline, O take my heart to
>   my mistress dear;
> Tell her it lived upon smiles and wine of the brightest
>   hue while it lingered here.
> Bid her not shed one tear of sorrow to sully a heart so
>   loving and kind,
> But brightest hue of the red grape borrow, to bathe the
>   relic from morn till night.' "

By the time he had finished, Julia had fled out of the conservatory into the garden, covering her mouth with her handkerchief, as if she were trying to quiet a fit of coughing. She fetched up in the deep shadow of a cypress tree, her white dress shining like a moth in the darkness. Hugh darted across the grass after her and found her leaning against the tree trunk in a silent paroxysm of laughter, wiping her eyes with her tiny handkerchief.

When she could speak she said chokingly, "I'm really not able to stand it—I have no manners—I'll come to a bad end—

everyone says so—but they're so funny—and I can't help loving all those songs—especially Thomas Moore—'Take this cup which is now o'erflowing to grace your revels while I'm at rest'—isn't it gorgeous?"

"So are you," Hugh said softly, taking her in his arms so gently that she could not be shocked or displeased in any way. Just to be held like that was amazingly pleasant, to feel the warmth of another person so close, to smell the sweet, flowery smell of his hair and his clothes, to lean her head on his shoulder, which seemed broadly made to receive her, to hear his gentle, low voice, still with the sound of laughter in it, whisper in her ear, "Julia, may I kiss you just once? I've wanted to for a long time."

She turned her head to look into his face and then his lips were clinging to hers, and more surprisingly she was responding with the same clinging, which sent a wonderful flow of joy right through her body, a delightful sensation, like the tingling that came when she drank a glass of wine. She drew her lips away from his and peered into his face but it was too dark to see him properly.

Quietly she put up one hand to feel instead, and he held it against his cheek until at last she said softly, "Hugh, we must go back. This is not allowed."

"I think you love me too."

He sounded astonished and she chuckled with delight.

"Why should that surprise you?"

Then she buried her face in his shoulder again, though it was too dark for her blushes to be seen. Her tongue should have had an inch clipped off, Miss Conroy had often said. How right she had been about so many things! She would never have approved of a girl being alone in a garden at night with a young man, even one she had known all her life. In fact she had said that those were the more dangerous, as they felt they could presume. Julia had never quite known what she had meant by that: it must have been what Hugh had just done. She began to giggle again, so that he asked what was so funny, and then she had to tell him, else he might have imagined all sorts of much ruder things.

Now there was Mimi D'Arcy coming to the conservatory door alone, probably looking for them. Mimi was in love with Hugh but he seemed hardly to notice her, treating her like a child, though she was twenty-three, much nearer his own age than Julia was. She had confided in Julia only last week, causing Julia to observe Hugh more closely for the first time, so that she saw how right Mimi was. Not only his looks, which

400

were all anyone could ask for—tall, thin, soft fair hair—but his warmhearted expression, borne out by everything he said and did, made a tiny inner voice tell Julia that he was not to be wasted on Mimi. She had not consciously led him on, or at least she had only begun in the very smallest way to think of doing such a thing, when he had made the first move and saved her all the trouble. What would happen now? Most girls were trotted off to the Castle over and over again before anyone made an offer for them, and then it was usually a man that the girl hardly knew, who might or might not turn out to be amusing. As for the other side of things, everyone agreed that if the man was clean and reasonably considerate, not rough or demanding, the girl would not find the experience too unpleasant. Julia had asked Anna about it, since surely she should know by now, but Anna had said vaguely, "Somehow it's all right when it happens, though I never like the idea in advance. James is a man of the world—he knows so many things—I leave all that sort of thing to him. That's what a woman must do."

Which made Julia take a long look at James in a new light. She could not share Anna's admiration for the "man of the world," though she was fond of James and knew he approved of her. He looked after Anna well but Julia noticed that he was given to patting other girls as they passed him by at parties, not in Dublin, but in London, where this seemed almost to be a convention. Dublin was provincial, by comparison with London. Julia watched out lest anyone should do the same to her, but no one did, and she concluded at last that this was just James's way of being genial. For the last two years, since Miss Conroy was gone, she had spent a month in London with the Fahys in the autumn. The first year, she had not been invited anywhere, but since she had reached the magical age of eighteen, all the invitations included her. Some of the people were nice, though they all patronized her, both for being young and for being Irish. Anna said the Irish part was inevitable and that after a while one began not to mind.

As they strolled toward the conservatory door they could hear the "Blue Danube" start up inside. Julia felt all her bones go soft, the usual effect on her of a waltz, and she was relieved when Thomas came to the door, took Mimi by the arm and led her inside. By the time Julia and Hugh reached the ballroom it was a mass of whirling skirts whose colors changed over and over again as they passed under the different-colored lights. Morgan and Alice were dancing together, which they did beautifully, like a single body, as light as any of the young people and with an amusing high step of which Anna had tried in vain to cure them. Julia did not want them to learn better, or differently, they looked so happy together.

As she and Hugh flowed into the dance, she saw Anna and James together, too. She felt sure he must be enjoying himself, his feet moved so neatly and his rhythm was so perfect, yet his little chest was puffed out, and his chin was up so that his eyelids drooped, and the corners of his mouth were firmly turned down. Soon the band would play "Sir Roger de Coverley," a signal to end the evening; that would be the time to watch James, to see if he could stamp with dignity. The boredom of being married to a man like that! But Anna loved him, and as Alice said, where there was love, there was nothing to fear. No other mother was capable of making such forthright statements, and Julia knew that the habit was regarded as an oddity of Alice's, proof that she was not quite a lady, no matter how rich she was, no matter how she might be envied for having caught a second husband when so many could not manage to catch even one.

Spinning around the room, Julia became lost in the joy of Hugh, her eyes closed and her whole body given over to the piercing new sensation. Everything came together to heighten it, the three-four time of the waltz, the scents the girls used, the smell of hot wax from the candles and of hot cloves from the mulled wine that Fanning had just brought in, the gritty feel of the floor under her thin shoes, even the faint headache that was more a feeling of exhaustion than pain.

She put her mouth to Hugh's ear and whispered, "Do you feel it too?"

"Yes, yes!"

"What do you feel?"

But he only held her closer and whirled faster so that her head spun and she seemed to go into a trance that lasted right to the end of the ball, through "Sir Roger de Coverley" and the inevitable "Auld Lang Syne," which someone always started up just before all the guests flowed out of the ballroom, out of the house, into the carriages, like a long, colored wave, calling farewells and thanks as they went. Then she was somehow lying in bed, exhausted and bewildered, feeling her head throb and her limbs ache and her eyes burn with fatigue, letting Mama's maid open the window a crack and put out the light and then tumbling headlong into sleep, a glorious, blank condition without memory or responsibility or hopes for the future. It was such a complete collapse that when she awoke next morning she had to lie there for half a minute before recalling exactly why she was so wonderfully, crazily happy, why everything in the world had changed, what marvelous news she had for Alice and Morgan this morning.

Still she did not get up for a long time, but lay there recalling the things that had happened, Hugh's gentle, penetrating kiss, the joy that it had released in her and the new understanding of why she was alive at all.

57

A strange and monstrous quirk in Alice's mind prevented her for hours together from remembering the existence of Fergal. She knew he was safe with his nurses; he didn't feel neglected but was always glad to see her when she came to visit him. She consoled herself with this but all the same she felt guilty about him.

She said to Morgan, "It must be because I was always thinking about you. I had no time for him. When you first came back, I was waiting for you to be arrested and put in jail again. I used to run into the house in fear that I wouldn't find you there. Then I'd be ashamed of being such a fool and try to cover it up but I think you knew about it."

"Yes, I knew."

"It was foolish."

"Not so foolish. I might have been arrested again when we began to fight the evictions. I've never found out why I wasn't —perhaps it was because of you."

"How could that save you? They don't love me."

"No, but Samuel is taken for a martyr in the cause of landlordism. It's hopelessly complicated—you're not a clear-cut case of sedition—they don't know what to do about you."

"Long may they stay that way."

She compensated Fergal by taking him with her when she went to organize the tenants against an eviction if the distance was not too great, setting out from Moycullen in the early morning, closely wrapped in rugs, driving the gig or the big tub trap herself if the weather was fine, in the carriage driven by the coachman and a groom if it was wet. As they drove along she answered his questions as best she could, pleased when he understood and angry, impatient when he seemed to be trying to see the landlord's point of view.

"They're wolves, jackals, devils, going around seeking whom

they may devour, dragons, ogres," she said, trying deliberately to arouse him to hatred and glad when he shivered with emotion. "It's not just Irish people who are in this, but the poor of the whole world. All over the world people are watching Ireland, waiting to see how we'll succeed. We must never give up the fight until we put an end to the whole system—"

"What's a system?"

Brought up short, she realized that she was speaking to a small child.

"There will always be landlords and tenants, but the landlords must learn to treat the tenants well."

"Hugh is a landlord. Nanny said so."

"Hugh is a good landlord, and so was Samuel. There are some good landlords but most of them are—" She stopped, defeated by his excited, questioning expression. "Open your eyes, keep your mouth shut, listen—that's how you'll learn. The people live in filthy hovels, slaving day and night to gather the rent for the landlords. They must learn to fight for their homes, to hold on to what they have, not to give up without a fight."

So she repeated the word until it became part of Fergal's life. His lonely games were battles between landlords and tenants, in which the tenants always won and the landlords were chased away with a brandished sword; his nightmares were filled with fiery-eyed twenty-foot ogres who ate up fields of corn and knocked over the cottages with a push of a toe. He kept silent as only a solitary child can do, recognizing this advice of Alice's as the price of being allowed to come with her, and to remain in the room unnoticed during the exciting discussions that followed every encounter with the enemy.

This was why he was present, when he was nine years old, one evening when the men came back, Morgan and Hugh and Thomas and Dr. Conroy, ravenously hungry but starting at once to tell Alice and Julia what had happened at the great meeting in Irishtown. It was a soft April evening, so warm that the French windows had been left open in the afternoon, and even after they were closed again, the dining room seemed full of the songs of blackbirds and the scent of grass and earth. Fergal stayed huddled in the dark-red armchair beyond the mahogany table, well out of the lamplight. There was only one lamp and that was on the table, and everyone sat there while Fanning and Tom brought a huge plate of roast beef for the men who had been out. Julia and Alice had dined at six o'clock as usual.

While they were being served, Morgan said, "I wish you

could have seen it, Alice—fully seven thousand people, and five hundred men on horseback to guard the speakers."

"Was Mr. Davitt there?"

"No, but he sent the resolutions and the speakers to propose them. They made fine speeches, and the people listened carefully to every word. Mr. O'Connor-Power said that public opinion must be organized, and that there's nothing tyrants dread so much as exposure. He said evictions must be stopped and no more emigration must be allowed unless the people want to go. You should have heard them cheer at that—I wonder if they really believe anything will come of it, but at least the thought did something for them. Mr. Ferguson made a speech about breaking up the big estates so that food can be grown at home instead of buying it from America. That idea got a cheer of its own because they say it's going to be another bad year for the potatoes."

"Isn't it rather early to tell?"

"The growth is too slow and there are patches where nothing has come up at all. It's like the years of the blast. A lot of the people are planning to go to America before the hunger starts in the summertime. But the best part came at the end when the whole crowd began to shout together: 'Down with landlordism! The land for the people!' I've never seen them so united—and against a priest landlord, too, and in spite of having been warned on all sides not to have the meeting. In a way, you could see that the demonstration was directed against the old landlord, not the new one."

Afraid to ask questions lest he might be sent to bed, it took Fergal the whole evening before he had succeeded in piecing together what had happened. An old Protestant landlord named Kirwan had sold his estate fifteen years ago to a Catholic named Walter Burke, who doubled the rents immediately. Of course the people could not pay, and when Walter died, last January, a lot of rents were owing. His brother, Canon Geoffrey Burke, was the new owner, and though he should have known better, he began to evict the tenants who owed more than a certain amount. Today he had seen that the people would not be cowed any more, Dr. Conroy said. They would no longer consent to die of starvation here below in the hope of a prize in heaven. Fergal liked Dr. Conroy much better than the doctor in Dublin, though he looked exactly like a fox, with his slanted eyes and soft red hair. He had a soft voice, too, as a fox would have if it could speak. His wife was called Mimi and they had three boys. She was always very friendly and cheerful, though Fergal had heard the servants say that her mother hadn't spoken to her for years because she had married beneath her.

"Then what is going to happen next?" Julia asked. "Did you see Canon Burke?"

"We didn't see him but Mr. O'Connor-Power and Pat Nally went, and a few others who had organized the meeting. They said the Canon was impressed, and he's promised to cut the rents by a quarter."

"And that means we'll have the Land League in working order in a matter of weeks. When the rest of the country hears what can be got by agitation, there will be no stopping them."

That was Thomas, who always thought that everything could be settled easily and that people would use their brains.

Alice said, "So you'll have other meetings."

"Yes. The Fenians are against the Land League. They say we'll get nothing by agitation. But Mr. Parnell will be told what happened today and Mr. O'Connor-Power thinks he'll give his support. There is to be a big meeting in Westport in June, and he's to be invited to speak at that."

Thomas and Hugh always lowered their voices with respect when they spoke of Mr. Parnell. Fergal longed to see him but he was not allowed to go to Westport. Alice and Julia went but Master Fahy thundered when Alice asked if Fergal might have the day off too:

"Certainly not! His head is turned with all this talk of politics. Do you want him to grow up ignorant? He knows no Roman history and his Latin tenses are deplorable. What use will he be to king or country if he goes on like this?"

"Well, I just thought—as it's such lovely weather—"

"Children must learn not to take a holiday on every fine day. That boy is spoiled."

The sharp edge on his voice frightened Alice and she gave in quickly lest Fahy might beat poor Fergal when they had gone, because of the Latin tenses. She need not have worried. Fergal could have told her that the Master was not such a terror nowadays, that he often fell asleep during lessons, waking up with a start, drawing a deep breath and going on with the subject almost where he had left off. There was a silent understanding between them that Fergal would make no remarks on these lapses. In a dim way Fergal realized that he had a remarkable teacher, and Thomas had told him that he would find himself well prepared for Stonyhurst in two years' time. No need to tell the other chaps where you learned so much

406

Latin, Thomas said, and Fergal remembered this as he remembered every word from his marvelous half brother.

Still Fergal was eaten up with envy as he listened to the account of the Westport meeting in June, where Mr. Parnell had spoken with firmness and dignity to an enormous crowd, much bigger than the one at Irishtown. Over and over he heard the words that Parnell had used: "Keep a firm grip on your homesteads," and his whole being burned to have been there. Soon there were other names—John Dillon, Matthew Harris, Dr. Duggan, the Bishop of Clonfert—great champions of the poor every one of them, but none with the magic of Parnell. Everyone agreed on that but no one was able to describe exactly what it was about him that made him so exciting. He was a silent man, and very sure of himself, as all landlords are—yes, he was a landlord himself, in County Wicklow, and knew every twist and turn of the landlord mind. Yet he had not much real respect for the poor, as you could see by the fact that he never looked at them directly, except for the leaders. A serious man, they said he was, with a strong streak of English blood in him. Set one Englishman to catch another: he was a match for them in Parliament. He made calm, deadly speeches there, and he was not afraid of hog, dog or devil, cleric or bishop, Queen or councilor. Ireland had a leader at last, as good as Mr. Davis, who had died so young and left the people with nothing; much better than Daniel O'Connell, who for all his great speeches was always soaping up the clergy and sold the pass in the end; fifty times better than James Stephens, who had turned out to be foolish in politics, though he might have been good enough in old-fashioned war.

What was needed now was the Land League, the great new movement that had grown out of the meetings and was founded in Daly's Hotel in Castlebar in August of 1879. Six million acres of land were owned by three hundred people; five million people owned nothing. A few thousand landlords were protected by a standing army that was supported by the landless millions of Ireland so that they could be robbed. Fifteen million pounds were extorted from the people every year and sent to England, where the landlords lived; scarcely a penny was spent in Ireland. Fergal's head spun as he tried to remember all this and more. The most important decision of the League was that there was never again to be an eviction without a large crowd to watch it.

Fergal had to read the newspapers aloud in the kitchen and the yard at Moycullen, and it was there that he heard, just after Christmas, that there was going to be great doings in Carraroe in the new year. The family had come from Dublin for the Christmas season as usual and were to go back for the ball, which was already being prepared. The invitations had all been sent out. Anna and James were coming with their four children and Julia and Hugh with their two, Matthew and Daniel.

Fergal burst into Alice's bedroom first thing one morning, saying, "How can we go to Dublin now? There's too much to do here. It's silly to go just for the ball."

"The guests have been invited," Alice said mildly. "We've got to be there. But we're coming back here the day after it."

"Can I come with you?" Seeing her hesitate he went on quickly. "I can do lessons with Master Fahy here—he's much better than Mr. Cox and he's always grumbling that I forget everything when I go back to Dublin. You didn't let me go to Westport or Balla or Castlebar."

"Those were not fit places for a child."

"Johnny Fagan went with his uncles, and Peteen Cooney went, not to Castlebar but to Balla and Ballinrobe. Carraroe is not so far. *Please* take me with you. You are going yourself?"

"Yes, I am going. I'll ask Papa."

"*I'll* ask Papa," said Fergal and went off to find Morgan.

They measured each other. Morgan was reasonable about most things but he was impatient when he was interested in political affairs, Fergal had found. The only way with him was a man-to-man tone, straight from the shoulder.

He began at once. "You're going to Carraroe for the process serving next week. Can I come with you?"

"Ask your mother."

"She said I was to ask you!" Fergal said triumphantly. "There will be hundreds there, including all the boys for miles around Moycullen. If I don't go, I'll be different from everyone else. They're going over from Oughterard and Cashel and even from Cong and Clonbur, I've heard."

"You'll be in the way; you'll be under everyone's feet."

"I'll stay out of the way—don't keep me out of it." He dashed angry, childish tears out of his eyes. "Every boy in Connemara will be there. I can stay with Mama. No one will bother with me."

"All right, all right, all right! But keep your mouth shut and your eyes open and remember everything you see."

"That's what Mama always says!"

Fergal gave a whoop of delight and went off at a run to tell Alice that he could go.

The trip to Dublin for the ball seemed not quiet real, though the house was full of guests as usual and the rooms were decorated with smilax and ivy, giving off that strange, acrid smell mixed with the smell of tangerines that was the embodiment of Christmas. Fergal was lost between the small children, whose nurses had no time for him, and the Fahys, who were so good it was hard to have any fun with them. Their table manners were perfect, and Walter made things worse by pretending not to understand when Fergal tried to shake them up a bit. Gerald watched everything that his older brother did, earnestly copying him as best he could, so there was no fun in him either. Their two little sisters seemed to be eternally whining, and Fergal greatly preferred Julia's two babies, who were the same age as the Fahy girls but a lot more amusing. Julia said it was because they were healthier, but whatever the reason, Fergal found that he had to escape from the nursery now and then, lest he might tear into them all and scream his impatience at them and their foolishness.

On the evening of the ball, he rambled around the rooms, keeping out of sight of the older people for fear he would be sent back to the nursery. He could hear the music begin downstairs but it was still too early for dancing. They always played slow music at first, until enough people had come to make a start with a waltz, always the opening dance. Later there would be lancers, with marvelous music. Fergal leaned over the attic banister, watching the bright ladies flutter into Mama's dressing room with their cloaks. One of them looked up, making him draw back in alarm. She gave no sign that she had seen him—an intelligent lady—but he didn't want to risk it again. He went sliding quietly up the stairs, along the short landing and into the great cold attic that looked out on the garden. It was only a storeroom, full of old furniture and books and the great leather trunks that went on Continental holidays. He left the door open, so that a dim triangle of light lay on the dusty floor, coming up the stair well from the landing below. He walked a step or two into the room and paused, aware of something strange in the feel of the place, a scent that was not the sour smell of dust, a warmth that belonged downstairs, not to this deserted place.

He strode forward without thinking, peering into the dimness, hearing a squeak of fright, too loud for a rat.

"Who's there?"

By some instinct he whispered rather than calling out.

There was no answer but now they seemed to float into his view like a pair of ghosts—Uncle James Fahy wrapped like an octopus around Miss Pauline D'Arcy, Mrs. Conroy's sister, both of them lying on an old feather bed that had been put away to be remade into pillows. As slow and stiff as a turning weathercock, Fergal turned and walked out of the attic, closing the door softly behind him, holding the banister carefully all the way down to the next floor, drifting along to his own bedroom, which he was sharing with Walter this week. The trestle bed that they had put in had a corner that stuck out and had caught him several times on the shin. He avoided it and went to his own bed, where he took his nightshirt from underneath the pillow and began to undress. He had left the door open so there was a triangle of light on the carpet from the landing light, just as there had been in the attic. He undressed very slowly, put on the nightshirt and got into bed, lying perfectly still, closing his eyes to pretend he was asleep when Walter came in with the Fahy's nurse some time later, hearing them whispering so as not to awaken him.

The picture of those two kept coming back to him again and again. So odd they had looked, odd and frightened, even Uncle James, who was always so suave and smooth. Fergal had never seen that expression on his face before, something frightening, almost threatening, like a cornered dog. He wanted very much to find Morgan and tell him about it, and be told it didn't matter, and that everything would be the same as usual, but he could not imagine how he could possibly describe what he had seen. Supposing it turned out that Morgan knew all about it. Fergal would have to include him in the new hatred he felt for Uncle James. Since Morgan knew everything, surely he must know this too; but if he did not, how could Fergal be the one to tell him?

Very carefully he pulled the sheet right up over his head, shutting out the night light that the nurse had lit, glad of the darkness, his hands held softly together, like a baby's hands, breathing evenly and slowly as Alice had told him to do whenever he was too nervous to sleep, and telling himself over and over again that he would never, so long as he lived, tell anyone what he had see in the attic.

58

They came over the mountain to Carraroe on Friday morning, the second of January, 1880, all on horseback, seeing the dark-blue curve of Greatman's Bay spread out below them for an hour before they reached the village. There were eleven horses in the group, Morgan on a bay gelding and Alice on a quiet old gray mare. The trap was out of the question since for part of the way the road was only a track through the bog. Fergal had his pony, which swished its tail and tossed its head with excitement. Hugh de Lacy was there, in his gentleman's clothes and polished top boots, with seven men who worked around the Moycullen stables and farm. Others were to come later but it was not certain whether they would be needed.

It was a windy day with high white clouds in a dark-blue sky, so that the bog holes were patched white and blue with ruffles of white foam on the bigger ones. Morgan was wearing a borrowed bawneen jacket, fisherman's jersey and rough tweed trousers, so as not to stand out among the crowd if it came to a fight. He had not worn clothes like these since he had gone to Paris, more than twenty-five years ago, and the texture and smell of them reminded him painfully of all the things he had left behind him then. He could scarcely understand now how people could grub a living—any sort of living—from the little stony hills by the sea. Even if the landlords, Kirwan of Tuam and Berridge, the brewer, of London, had treated the tenants better, even if there had been no rent at all to pay, the people would have lived in penury. In fact Robinson, the agent for both landlords, was a master hand at devising ways of screwing more and more money out of the tenants: fines for getting married without leave, levies for bringing baskets of turf across the lake from the bog, fines for not giving duty days of free labor if they were sick when they were called on, fines for a brother's or a son's failure to pay his rent—Robinson saw possibilities in everyone's misfortune and needs. At the court in Galway before Christmas, he had been granted four processes of ejectment for arrears of rent, including one against a widow named Mrs. Mackle, who had a good cottage next to the dispensary and the post office. Since her husband's death a year ago she could not work her little holding, and though she asked for time until her brother could come from America, Robinson had promised her land, with another holding, at a higher rent, to a friend of his from Spiddal.

Colman Wallace, the Carraroe man who had come with the latest news to Moycullen, had said, "It's bad enough for them all but you'd think they'd pity the widow. She's a good fighting woman but what can she do? She hasn't a penny to bless herself with. They say she could bring Robinson to court under the new law and get a lot of money back if it can be proved he was charging too much rent. But where would she get the money to pay a lawyer to go to court for her? Sure, if she had money, couldn't she pay the rent? That's how the poor people are always caught out." His tone became savage suddenly. "We had fun on Sunday with young Fenton—we frightened the living daylights out of him, a whole crowd of us. The minute Mass was over, we made a drive for him, right there in the church, God forgive us. We marched him up to the altar and made him swear on the Cross that he would serve no process for the next week, neither himself nor his father. He swore black and white, to get away from us, and I'm thinking he won't be too anxious to be on the road at that work for a good while to come. But the father is a different pair of shoes. Can you come down on Friday, Morgan?—for I'm afraid there will be bad business done there."

"Of course I'll come. Are you sure it's Friday?"

Colman had said. "How can we be sure? They come like thieves, but a man came out from Galway yesterday and he says he thinks it will be Friday for he heard talk of a protecting force that is to be sent out that day to the west. That must surely mean to Carraroe. If you come over the mountain on Friday, we'll have a welcome for you. John Mullan will wait for you on the road."

Half a mile above the village, a man rose out of the ditch by the side of the road, where he had been completely concealed. Morgan pulled up his horse and the others clattered to a halt, hooves crumbling the sand, noses down to sniff at the salty grass.

"It's yourself, Morgan Connolly?" the man said in Irish.

"It's myself. Is all well?"

"All is well. The barracks are full to overflowing and there's more police to come from Galway, a huge army of them with pikes and guns. Word came two hours ago, and messages are gone to Rosmuc and Cashel and Kilkieran for the men to come down."

The singsong accent of Cois Fharraige was like music to Morgan.

"Will Fenton serve the process?"

"The father will do it, he says, because he has the Peelers with him to hold the people back. He's inside the barracks since the rising of the day, wetting his drawers with the fright if there's a just God in heaven. Let there be no fright on you when you hear the horns blowing from the hills around for that is the signal that is given when someone is coming."

412

Morgan shook up his horse again, riding beside Fergal now, having seen the boy's white, excited face while the Carraroe man was speaking. Perhaps he should have been left at home—but who was he to decide that his son should have a sheltered life? By the time he was Fergal's age he had seen dozens of evictions and was a good hand with a sling and a stone to sting the backside of the bailiff and disappear without a trace into a deep ditch, as John Mullan had done while he was waiting for them. Fergal would have his share of fighting to do and the sooner he learned how to do it, the better.

At the edge of the village a boy came running up, panting, "They're drawn up outside the barracks now, eighty policemen with bayonets and carbines. You're to leave the horses at my mother's house."

He skipped off before them, looking back over his shoulder every moment with little shrieks of excited laughter to see if they were following him. The mournful sound of the horns was borne down to them on the wind, lying on it naturally, like the voice of a storm. Opposite the lane that led to the sea, the boy darted into a miserable cottage and a moment later a middle-aged woman appeared at the door. Alice dismounted stiffly and followed her into the house. Morgan and Fergal eyed each other.

"You said you'd stay with your mother," Morgan said. "The women will be out later."

"Very well."

He stumped inside without another word, obviously furious. The horses had to be led around to the back of the cottage and tethered there out of sight. Then Mullan led them up a lane behind the house and across three fields until they had circled back to a point above the village. Crowds of men, women and boys were moving toward the barracks, a large, square, slated house with iron-barred windows set on rising ground with a view of the village. The men signaled to Morgan to come down, and when he did so, they placed him at their head and marched to within twenty yards of the building, taking up positions in a double line opposite it. Morgan estimated that there were about five hundred men there. The women and boys moved in behind the men, not in any disciplined formation but darting in and out like swallows and calling out to one another.

He glanced down the road and saw that Alice and Fergal and the woman who had received them were coming up to the barracks together. He could imagine the scene in the wretched cottage, with the animals sheltering from the January cold, while the guests would have to drink some milk for the sake of hospitality. Fergal could be trusted not to show disgust. Morgan knew that he had not been spoiled for Moycullen and Connemara by spending part of every year in Dublin. He slid easily into each life as if it were the only one that interested him. Now Morgan noticed that approving remarks were made about him as he came nearer, how tall he was for his age, how bravely he marched beside his mother, how much he resembled his father, how Ireland was going to need boys and men like him for a long time to come.

The men stood tensely, watching the barracks' main door, at either side of which a threatening army of police was drawn up. Suddenly the door was flung open and a man stood there on the threshold. The police were taken by surprise and all turned their heads to look at him. He took a step forward.

Instantly a voice called out, "Fenton, you devil!"

The watching men ran forward until they were close enough to let fly a fusillade of stones, which bounced all around the process server and occasionally struck him, so that he covered his head with his hands and shot inside the barracks again. The police rallied and made a short rush at the men, who retreated, jeering, to their former position.

Then one of them called out, "God save Ireland!"

The whole crowd took it up, even those who had no English to speak of, and soon they were all chanting the slogan over and over.

"God save Ireland! God save Ireland! God save Ireland!"

Half a dozen began to move forward but were recalled by the rest, and they waited silently again, expectation and tension rising with every moment.

A shout went up when the barracks door opened a crack and a conference began between Gibbons, the subinspector of the police, who was near the door, and the men inside. Gibbons gave an order and the police moved right across the doorway, bayonets at the ready, pointing toward the crowd. Then Fenton appeared for the second time, slipped quickly in among his protectors and the whole guard moved in a body down from the barracks door to the road. The crowd fell in behind them, gradually moving closer, until they were marching on either flank of the police. The women and boys darted ahead, bounding like goats along the grassy verges of the road.

"Faherty is the first process to be served," said Colman Wallace, who was walking beside Morgan. "Should we attack now?"

"Not yet."

In fact the women beat them to it. At Faherty's cottage, Fenton stepped forward with the document in his hand and several women rushed to seize it from him. There was a mad moment in which they seemed almost to be fighting one another for the piece of paper and then it flew into the air like snow and was scattered on the wind in a dozen pieces. The police charged, prodding wildly with their bayonets. There were several shrieks of pain.

"Now, now we'll attack!" Colman said, but Morgan would not let them.

"Not yet. Let them get away. Hold your patience a while."

The men were growling but no one charged the police. The guard moved on to Mrs. Mackle's, Fenton walking among them like a bird in a cage, all marching faster now. Excited by their success the women were running nearer now, some armed with blackthorn sticks that they had taken from the men and with which they made sudden sallies, whacking at the legs of the policemen so that one or two turned on them angrily. There was no general attack, however, and soon the whole party had reached Mrs. Mackle's cottage.

The door stood open. As they approached, a tall, skinny woman appeared on the step, her arms folded on her breast. Why was her door not shut as Faherty's had been? Morgan pitied her, facing that ugly army headed by the narrow-eyed Gibbons. She stood for a second only, then turned and darted into the house, reappearing just as Gibbons and Fenton walked boldly up to the door, the process held in front of him by Fenton as if it were a snake. Gibbons had no time to save himself. She had a shovel piled with burning turf in her hands and with a sudden upward movement she flung it over his head. He shrieked with pain and fright, and an answering moan of sympathy went up from the watching men, quickly followed by loud, appreciative laughter as they fully realized what had happened. Gibbons was hopping from foot to foot, shaking the ash and burning particles of turf from his clothes, while his men made a wild attack with their bayonets on the nearest women, who had closed in at once.

Morgan called out, 'Now! Now!"

The Connemara men plunged forward, pushing the women aside, forcing their way through the bayonets with their sticks and with big stones held in their fists. The police began to fall back and the men succeeded in getting between them and the house. Morgan looked around desperately for Alice but she was not there. He had seen her behind the first attackers and he knew the Carraroe women would prefer to keep her clear of any rough-and-tumble. This was all the comfort he had. In any case he had to attend to the men now, calling to them to keep together in front of the house, shoulder to shoulder.

The police had been driven down to the road below, and while Morgan watched, Gibbons shouted an order. Instantly the carbines went up and a volley of shots flew over the heads of the men, lodging in the thatch. As if at a signal, with a roar of fury the men plunged forward, a solid mass, irresistible as a wave in a storm. The constables turned and fled, the unfortunate Fenton pounding along ludicrously among them, his face and neck as red as a turkey cock's wattle.

Morgan held back, watching the chase from Mrs. Mackle's doorstep. A sound inside made him turn and look into the kitchen. The woman was there, on her knees in front of the fire, her head covered by her shawl to stifle her moans, while three terrified half-grown girls clung to one another against the far wall.

Morgan stepped into the kitchen, saying, "They're gone. They're running back to the barracks. Stand up. Come and look."

He lifted her up and took her tottering to the door, where they watched the police charge up the hill to the barracks, bundle inside, tumbling over one another in their hurry, and slam the door, while their pursuers deliberately slowed their pace to give time for their escape.

Morgan said, still holding her bony shoulder against his, "Look! Our men couldn't have done better if they had been under orders all the way. We don't want a massacre."

"They'll come back," she whispered, her eyes fixed on the barracks door as if she expected it to burst open again at once. "I don't know what came over me, to throw the fire over the poor man."

"If they come back, we'll be waiting for them. We're not leaving the district until they go. Word has gone out to the islands and to all Connemara. We'll have two thousand men here by Monday morning. Even if they get reinforcements, they won't be able to reach that number."

"They have guns and pikes."

"True for you, but even those are not much use if they're outnumbered ten to one."

She turned wearily back into the kitchen.

"What use is it all? Won't I have to get out in the end, just the same? The priest says I owe the rent and I must pay or go to hell. Isn't it all the same which of those two things I do now?

And my man dead on me and no one to give a curse what becomes of me."

"We give a curse, and ten curses," Morgan said softly. "I heard you're a good fighting woman, but you're not asked to fight alone. If we keep the process off until Tuesday, you must have another three months of peace."

"Three months? It's better than nothing. My brother might come in that time. I was a fighter once but now I'm tired." But her tone was more reasonable and the three girls had begun to relax. "Who are you? I haven't seen you before but I know you're a Connemara man from your clothes and your talk."

"I'm Morgan Connolly from Cappagh, living in Moycullen now."

"Morgan Connolly, the Fenian?"

"Yes."

"You suffered your share."

She began to put the scattered fire together, sweeping the hearth neatly with the wing of a goose, hanging the kettle on the crane so that the rising smoke curled all around it. The familiar tasks quieted her with their rhythm so that her expression softened and lost its look of terror. He left her soon afterward, promising that he would come again.

59

He went at once in search of Alice, asking the excited group of men who were standing about if they had seen her. It was Hugh de Lacy who told him that she was at the cottage where the horses had been tethered earlier. As they came near they saw that the calves had been put outside and were huddled against the gable wall out of the wind. Alice was sitting on the hob, close by a huge fire, with Fergal on a stool beside her. She sprang up and came to take Morgan's hands while the woman of the house said, in English out of politeness to Hugh, "They'll have to sleep here with me. We can't ask the priest to take them into his house for he's all against us. Miss Alice says she won't mind it—God bless her, she's one of our own—and the boy is the image of yourself, Morgan. Come in, the two of ye, and I'll pour ye a glass that will warm your hearts. I've only stools to put you on but you're welcome all the same."

They calmed her down as best they could while she fussed with glasses of poteen and buttermilk. John Mullan and his brother Donald were there and a few minutes later Colman Wallace, Stephen O'Brien and Pat Sanly came in. The kitchen was stiflingly hot. Morgan recognized O'Brien and Sanly as leaders of sections of the savage army that he had just seen in operation.

"You're well organized," he said by way of compliment.

"We are," Sanly said, "at long last. There's new heart in everyone since the Land League. The only trouble is that Gibbons knows us all by sight, but sure we can't be worse off than we are, I say."

Morgan remembered Dartmoor with a shiver of terror for them but he said nothing.

Sanly went on. "They'll be telegraphing from the barracks for support, to Galway and Clifden and Ballinrobe and maybe even farther. They can gather three or four hundred at the most. Our men are coming in from all over Connemara but I wouldn't like to swear that they'll be a useful army, except that there will be so many of them."

They had a plan that Morgan said would have done credit to a regular Army general—to destroy the bridge south of the village, cutting off communications between the police and their base so that they could be overwhelmed by superior numbers.

"But that would be a massacre," Hugh de Lacy said in English. "Mr. Parnell won't like it. It would be foolish to sacrifice his support so early."

"Is the gentleman afraid?" Wallace asked in Irish.

"No. Didn't you see him in action at the barracks?"

"That's true, indeed, but I think he's not really a fighting man."

"There are many ways of fighting. His way, and Mr. Parnell's way, is a quiet one but a good one. The first thing you must do is to send around to all the houses and tell the women that they are not to give as much as a cup of milk or an egg to the police who will be coming, or to those who are in the barracks now. The women won't like that; they'll be getting sorry for the men and wanting to feed them but they must be stopped. Have a guard at every house if necessary."

Alice went with Donald Mullan to organize this while Morgan and Hugh consulted with Wallace and Sanly about the next moves. The Carraroe men, excited by their success, wanted to attack the barracks and chase the police along the road to Galway, and it took hours of patient argument to convince them that this would not fit in with the new policy. They had heard a great deal about it but they had to be told of exact cases in which it had worked. The most effective persuasion was that Michael Davitt believed in it. They agreed that you could trust a man who had been such a good fighter and that this was a new and dangerous kind of fighting. Why spill the blood of Irishmen—the police were nearly all Irishmen—unless it was strictly necessary?

When Alice came back, the woman of the house cooked a pot of potatoes, which were washed down with more poteen and buttermilk, and at last Morgan and Hugh went with John Mullan to spend the night in his cottage near the quay.

"We have a bed," John explained, "that the mother left us when she died. We are only two men in the house so it's not a palace but we have this bed that you can share."

Alice was to stay where she was, with Fergal, since the woman of the house would not trust them to anyone else. She would make a straw bed by the fire where they would be warm, and she would stay up all night to attend to them, she assured Morgan as she herded all the men out of the house.

Morgan caught Alice's eye on him and said solemnly, "Thank you. I'm sure you'll do your best for them."

Saturday was a peaceful day, with neither side wanting to make a move until reinforcements arrived. Morgan spent the day talking to small groups of men who gathered in the village and in the fields, encouraging them, telling them more about the Land League, and welcoming those who were beginning to arrive from the surrounding countryside.

Sunday morning was quiet. Cleanly dressed, the whole population went to Mass and sat demurely through a long sermon in Irish on the text "Blessed are the peacemakers." Toward the end of Mass, just before the blessing, a sound of many hooves was clearly heard. Heads jerked, eyes met, not a word was whispered but the men of the congregation rose in a body to their feet and galloped outside with a whirring of soft cowskin shoes on the stone floor. The women hitched their shawls piously forward so that only their noses showed and received the blessing on their bent heads from the anxious priest, who paused with his right hand raised to say, "I ask every woman here to do what she can to restrain the men from crime on this holy day. What will you have at the end of it all? Some men in jail, a lot more evictions, weeping and wailing on the road to the Cove of Cork and perhaps the guilt of blood on your souls. You are being used by people who love power more than wealth, by people who don't care what becomes of you or your men or your children, by people who don't want peace and prosperity but turmoil and war. That's what they

419

learned in France, the home of revolution and godlessness. I see people here in this church today who are leaders in that movement and I say to you all: don't follow such people. Remember that the poor will inherit the land and God will comfort those that mourn."

Still all the heads were down and no one would have dreamed of saying a word in the church, but as they trotted outside on their bare feet Morgan heard several of the women say, "Doesn't the skin grow fine and soft on him? Easy to see he doesn't go hungry—chickens for dinner every day, sides of bacon hanging in his kitchen, two cows milking for him so that he's never short of butter or milk. What does he know about the long hunger? If they have these ideas in France, then France is the country for us."

One of the boys began to sing a drinking song in Irish that Morgan had often heard in Cappagh.

> " 'Rise up in your might, you dashing young blades,
> Fix the head of a pike on all your spades.
> . Follow them back, the black-hearted rabble,
> And set up the law of France at home,
> And O woman of the house, what's on your mind?
> O woman of the house, I'll say it three times,
> There'll be land without rent from this year out
> And O woman of the house, what's on your mind?' "

A small, fat, white-haired woman said in a scandalized tone, "Out of the church ground, you young scoundrel! That's no song for the holy ground!"

He was hustled out onto the road, where he began on the second verse.

> " 'I sat myself down beside my love,
> Drinking my quart like any free man.
> The woman of the house said, rough as you please,
> "If I don't see your money, you're out the door!"
> And O woman of the house, what's on your mind?
> O woman of the house, I'll say it three times,
> There'll be land without rent from this year out,
> And O woman of the house, isn't that a fine thing?' "

"Good man, Paudeen! There's nothing like a good song to rouse up our hearts. Land without rent! That will be the day!"
And they swung off down the road in a body.
Morgan paused at the church door with Alice and Fergal,

peering along the road toward Galway, attracted by a movement there. A strong wind was blowing but it was one of those January days that hold a promise of spring, either through a real softening of the air or through imagination and longing. Greatman's Bay was indigo blue, emerald green farther out where the big waves were. Not a single glint of growth showed on the rocky fields for which the battle had taken place on Friday.

"A sour place," said the priest's voice at Morgan's elbow. "God help them. Why do you come here to make things worse for them?"

They measured each other but in a moment Morgan turned away, full of pity for this huge countryman with the meek blue eyes. The contrast between him and Father Kenny was too great to be borne: one leaving a comfortable life to give himself to poverty for love of the people, the other—probably —sent to Maynooth by an adoring mother who thereby ensured at one blow her son's salvation, provided him with a well-paid profession and avoided for herself the pain of seeing his affections transferred to another woman. Then he blamed himself for being a cynic. He had no evidence for any of this —in fact the priest had spoken like a true Christian.

Fergal was pointing excitedly down the road toward Galway, where a little army of mounted constables was approaching, perhaps a hundred men, armed with carbines, riding in formation and raising a foam of sand from the road. Up by the village, a great crowd was beginning to gather. The horses that had passed by during Mass were tethered to the corners of houses here and there and more were arriving as they watched. Many men were coming on foot, down the road from the mountain and up from the quay, where they had tied up their boats.

Tormented with sudden anxiety for them all, Morgan said to his family, "Look, you must take care of yourselves today as best you can. Don't do anything dangerous or you will cause trouble to the men. Stay with the women and try to keep them from running into danger."

"Of course, Morgan. Go now, at once. Forget about us. We'll be safe."

He said desperately, "What will come of all this, Alice? Not just today, but the things that are happening everywhere. How can we hope for anything? Sometimes I feel that the priests are right and we should let the people alone, and then I see the starvation just as bad as when we were young, and I know we must do something, however small—"

"The speech he made at the blessing disturbed you," she said calmly. "It was nonsense—you know it well. Go to the men now. They're waiting for you. God go with you."

Astonishingly, he did forget about his family for the rest of the day. There was so much to do, and everywhere he went it seemed that the people had elected him as their leader. No one was willing to fight on Sunday, especially after the sermon they had heard, and they were all worried on behalf of the Catholic policemen who had been afraid to come out of the barracks and go to Mass. It didn't matter about the Protestants, since they were all going to go to hell anyway, but how could they have a blessing on their battle when it began so badly? Morgan quieted these fears and tried to make sure that all the men at least had shelter for the night and that there was enough food to keep them going until they would get home again. The islandmen had brought bags of good potatoes because the islands were usually free of the blight, and they shared these with the men of Kilkieran and Rosmuc and Carna, most of whom had come empty-handed. The islandmen, who looked well-fed and comfortable by comparison with the others, would sleep on their boats. As night fell, the heavy wind dropped so that the doors could be left open for ventilation, a great blessing since every house was crammed to bursting point with visitors.

Early on Monday morning, Morgan and Hugh came up from John Mullan's cottage by the quay to find that a crowd of two thousand or so had already gathered below the barracks. They were very quiet, not through fear so much as from excitement at what they were doing. With Sanly's and John Mullan's help, Morgan went among them and picked out a hundred who knew how to fire a gun. There was a small dump of arms, not to be used except in the last resort, and the men who handled them had to be trusted not to tell where they were kept or even that they existed at all. For this reason, Morgan tried to choose mostly men he knew, from the Joyce's Country and the district around Moycullen. With these he went a short distance up the mountain road and took up a position from which they could observe the front door of the barracks, laying the guns in the thick grass at their feet. The Mullans had gathered them earlier—old-fashioned flintlocks and pistols with such a short range that their usefulness was very doubtful. Everyone hoped that they would not have to be used, since the League's policy was against it, but if the police fired to kill, they would have to be answered.

Not a sign of life came from the barracks. Yesterday several constables had come out demanding eggs and milk, and at last appealing in the name of God for as much as a potato, but the women had told them that a little fasting would do their souls good. Then doors were shut and the few cows and goats were kept indoors, so everyone was sure tempers must be mighty short in the barracks this morning. Not even smoke showed down there.

"I wonder are they all dead with hunger?" Sanly said sardonically.

"Now it's beginning," said Morgan. "Look!"

The men had begun to move in toward the barracks in blocks of three and four hundred, marching in loose formation until they had surrounded the building. The wind carried the voices up the hill chanting together, with sometimes an isolated voice among them.

"Come out, you womanbeaters! Come out, you heroes! Fight someone your own size! Women yesterday, men today! Up the rebels! Come out! Come out! Fenton, how are you today, my love? Serve your process, you black devil! Give him out here to us! We'll give him a good run today!"

But it seemed that Fenton had had enough. When the barracks door opened, everyone made a threatening step forward but they stopped when they saw that only a single unarmed constable had come out. Colman Wallace went to meet him and after a short conversion he waved the men back and then walked with the constable to the barracks door. The men on the hill watched hungrily. The women, who had been at a safe distance, surged forward and took up positions on the outcropping rocks above the road, from which they could clearly see the barracks. Minutes passed slowly. Morgan saw Alice moving quietly among the women and hoped that she was obeying his instructions. It was infuriating to be so far off but to have courted arrest would have been madness, since he would be sent back to jail at once without trial.

A cheer went up from the crowd when the door opened again and a long, slow file of constables began to leave the barracks, heads down, tired and hungry and dispirited, almost enough to arouse pity. No one attacked them, no one spoke to them, and the cheering was quickly suppressed by the leaders of each group. Silently they watched while the horses were led around to the front of the barracks and the constables who had come on horseback mounted. Many had marched all the way from Galway, twenty miles, and must now march back again through the unfriendly countryside.

Sanly said, "It's a taste of what we have all the year round. It will do them nothing but good to go hungry."

Coldly the others agreed, and they watched steadily until the long column disappeared around the last bend of the road.

60

The last dried chestnut leaf of the year twisted fluttering to the ground, like a little old hand. It made James feel uneasy; it seemed so sure of where it was going, settling after all its maneuvers at a point almost exactly underneath the scar on the branch from which it had fallen. Now the tree was quite bare, ghostly gray against the gray December morning sky. Moycullen was full of silences and sounds, immemorially old, twined through his bones like ivy. A late, dispirited bee hummed past, looking for the long-dried flowers of summer, a symbol of himself, just when he least wanted one.

He had a genius for making a mess of things, there was no doubt about it, and yet he seemed always betrayed by something so obvious that it should surely have been easily avoided. Moycullen was good for him, in certain ways, helping him to see clearly. It was like going to Confession in the old days before he finished with all that nonsense, when he went into a dark box and notified the priest in a terrified whisper, full of disgust, that he was a fraud, a sex maniac, a cheat, a dishonest, scurvy, ambitious, grasping worm, on the watch for every opportunity to advance himself and take advantage of others. The reactions were interesting: some offered comfort, some the fires of hell, all agreed that the solution was in his own hands, as if he could remake that stinking little sod that he was into a good-living, honorable Christian gentleman overnight. The glass had darkened, not cleared, with time, and here he was in 1890, at fifty-five, in the same kind of crass mess that he used to create for himself when he was in his twenties.

How the devil was it that his judgment was so bad in personal matters when it was really good in things that didn't concern him? In his work, even in getting the wretched Irish out of political messes or out of jail, he moved with the prideful certainty of a stag on the mountainside. In his love affairs he was a mouse at bay, squeaking futilely in defense of a lost position, a lost life. Once he had been masterful with women, overcoming his small size with a large attitude, so that they looked down at him with awe. Remembering this, he knew that his size had nothing to do with his present ridiculous state. Age perhaps accounted for it to some extent, or more precisely the lack of youth, since youth gave authority by its unselfconsciousness. He was thinking in paradoxes now because straight reasoning no longer made sense.

He felt hot and weak at the thought of some of his mistakes, but out here by the edge of the lake, under the ghostly tree, there was no one to see him. There was hardly anyone who mattered at the house now, either, all strange servants, as efficient as in the old days but without the warmth that was always there in Kate's time. The welcome she used to give him! He had never sat in the kitchen since her death. It was too painful, almost more than he could bear, even to go through the baize door from the hall and down the short passage, to see the huge glowing fire and the old scrubbed table where he had sat so often with her. Kate was above being concerned with what he did while he was away from Moycullen; when he came back, he was at home, and home was for rehabilitating the soul, not for describing the irrelevant, peripheral activities that took up his time in London.

To some extent Alice and Morgan continued the former atmosphere at Moycullen, but since they spent so much of the year in Dublin and were so taken up with politics, they could not possibly reproduce the old restful feeling. But how could he ever have thought of it as restful? Murder, famine, evictions, his own miserable childhood with only Kate to comfort him—these should have been his memories of Moycullen. Samuel's death was a horror from which he still recoiled. Clearly it was a false nostalgia, nothing to do with reality, rather a dream of prenatal bliss. Sitting on a damp tree stump, he clutched his head between his hands while he tried to work it out. Moycullen itself, no matter what happened there, was his home. A thousand times he had tried to break away from it and had come creeping back like the lost mongrel he was, to lie whining against the back door, hoping to be let in.

But was that such a despicable thing? His father thought it honorable, and quoted du Bellay and Goldsmith to prove it. James could hear his slow, deep voice intoning the lines on one of his last days, his eyes fixed on James and his meaning extremely clear:

" 'And as an hare whom hounds and horns pursue
Pants to the place from whence at first she flew,

425

I still had hopes, my long vexations past,
Here to return, and die at home at last.' "

The question was: Were his long vexations passed? Heaven knew there had been enough of them. He was almost certain now that it had all been started by Angela, who for all her blasé ways must have been put out at his marriage to Anna. She might have stomached a woman of her own age and she had certainly not wanted James for herself in any permanent way, but Anna's youth had been a slap in the face to them all. They hadn't shown their claws at first, so that his fears had been dangerously soothed. Then, after his first infatuation with Anna had cooled, the rumors had begun to float around, and Walter Lawrence, now a worried lawyer, had said to James, "It could damage you, old man. There's just a little too much of it. Better be extra discreet for a while, be seen about with your wife, all that sort of thing, until people lose interest."

He had been married seven years when this had happened, and the rumors had been current for a long time. No doubt he had been indiscreet, and for some reason the women had changed in their attitude to him, no longer taking his advances in good part, as a joke between the two of them. That certainly had something to do with his age. He became very careful indeed, in London especially, and as Walter had predicted, people did lose interest until this new thing cropped up. Then they remembered it all, or too much of it. Anna was happy in those days, he recalled now, never away from him for long if they went out together, immensely proud of him, gradually gaining in confidence. She had not believed any of the rumors. He knew this for a certainty, because he would have known if she were unhappy. It was a good thing for him that she was not very intelligent. On the whole she had made an excellent wife, and deserved the rewards of it. How she would suffer if she were disgraced now, at this late stage! He had got over so many things, even that terrible occasion when Morgan's beady-eyed child had seen him in the attic with Pauline D'Arcy. James had sweated for weeks over that, but Fergal was a closemouthed brat and had turned into a closemouthed man.

All over again, James had to work out his exact attitude to Anna. It could only be called love; it was not the same love as he had had for her when she was an infant, neither was it gratitude, though that was part of it. He was well able to see that his more recent advances would not have been possible without her, and most certainly his being offered a governorship was partly a compliment to her. A governor's wife was very well inspected indeed and Anna was a perfect little lady, commanding respect everywhere she went. There was a lot of Samuel in her, unconscious pride and uprightness. She had always said she would enjoy their position if this opportunity came up, the warm climate would suit her, and she had a real zest for travel, which she had never been able to satisfy because of her eight children. He knew she had fretted over the three who had died but her five remaining ones were a comfort to her. Their passages would have been paid if his appointment had been confirmed.

At first he had thought it would be all right but the old man had been unexpectedly severe, looking down at the carpet as he said in a low voice, "We always stand up for our man, Fahy, but there are some things that won't be tolerated by the electorate. At least it's not an open scandal. If you can bring me evidence that the stories are untrue, we'll reconsider, but it's hard to disprove that sort of thing, as you know."

"Yes." James did know. "You've been very kind about it." He hesitated, embarrassed as hell, wishing himself outside the door as he used to do when he was a junior clerk and had copied something wrong, a rare occurrence indeed but still painful to the memory. "You haven't quite decided yet, then?"

"No. The decision is partly up to you, in fact. I'll tell you what I'll do. If you can tell me straight that there is no truth whatever in what I've heard, then I'll take your word for it and back you to the limit. I know you well enough to say that. Part of the trouble is that the Irish are not very popular just now but that can be got over. After all, there are so many fine Irishmen in the public service." He seemed almost to be talking to himself, in a soft, reminiscent tone, so that James was shocked when he looked up sharply and said, "Well? Were your relations with Mrs. Swift innocent?"

With his back to the wall, James had to say, "I can't disprove the rumors, sir. It's true that I've been indiscreet. I shouldn't have visited her alone."

"Late at night?"

"Yes."

Damn that maid! She hadn't that bright eye for nothing. James had warned Carla about her but she had laughed at his caution, even saying the idiotic thing that most women say, that she would prefer if people knew about their liaison. Well, now she had her wish. She would not be left alone again—but that had been part of her plan, as he knew very well. He put up his chin and narrowed his eyes and enunciated his words clearly—no point in mumbling when you're cornered.

"Mrs. Swift resented not being taken by William on his foreign trips. I've come to the conclusion that she was using me. I should not have allowed myself to be used, of course, but that's my weakness."

The old man was pleased by this frankness but he said seriously, "Weakness—that is the unfortunate thing."

James realized that he had spoken unchivalrously about Carla. She deserved it, the bitch, leading him on, inviting him to the house, giving him to understand that she always had 'some man in to liven things up when William went away, then letting him down afterward by boasting to her friends—or perhaps it had been the maid. It was all the same now. It looked as if he was to pay dearly for that little piece of entertainment, which had not been so very wonderful, by the way. At least he had written no letters—she was the sort of woman who would keep letters, just in case they might prove useful.

The old man gave a long, tired sigh and said, "I'll need time to think. It seems the rumors go back a long way. I doubt if we'll be able to get over this."

They had not got over it. A week after that conversation, James was advised that the governorship would not be his and that he should take a holiday of several months in Ireland, with the option of retiring then on an excellent pension. So here he was in Moycullen House with nothing to do all day but listen to endless arguments about the rights and wrongs of the Parnell divorce case, which had rocked Ireland for a year. There was an advantage here, however, in that no one wanted to talk about James and his future. They were embarrassed by his position as a pillar of the British Empire, and Anna made things worse by telling that James had been offered a governorship and was considering whether or not he would accept it. James had burned the letter and had never had the courage to tell her that he had been passed over.

He ground his teeth with the boredom of it all. How could they still be talking about Parnell? The case was finished and done with since the spring but all day and night, it seemed to him, everyone trotted through the details of it as if no one had ever slept with another man's wife before in the history of the world. They were so shocked, really, genuinely shocked, though Parnell was acquitted by the more simple on the grounds that he was a Protestant. At the dinner table last night, Morgan had rumpled his white hair in exasperation and pointed out that Protestant puritanism is at least as formidable as the Catholic version and that anyway that was not getting rid of Parnell, who had proved immovable by other forms of trickery.

Julia's husband, Hugh, thought that Parnell should stand down for a while and come back later when Mr. Gladstone and the English Non-Conformists had agreed to the new Home Rule Bill, but Fergal said that Morgan was right, that the elections should be fought one by one and that Parnell could be forced on the Catholic Church if the people would only stand up for him. Every dinner table was fouled with the controversy, Alice and Morgan and Fergal against Hugh and Julia and Thomas and Conroy, the doctor, who heard what the country people were saying in the course of his work. Thomas' wife Letitia kept out of the argument, making mercifully one voice less. Conroy said that the people would follow the priests this time, partly through feelings of guilt because they had stood up to them before. Now they had been proved to be wrong in trusting themselves and their children to the leadership of a man whose moral standards were low.

"And by moral standards they mean only one thing," Conroy said. "In Ireland it doesn't matter what other vices a man has—his sexual morals must be above reproach. It's a symptom of national tension, probably, the fear of being laughed at by outsiders."

When the ladies had gone up to the drawing room, James said with a chuckle, "My father loved to quote Swift, though he wouldn't have quoted what you reminded me of, Conroy. You remember?"

"I haven't read Swift."

"On the foolishness of becoming a slave to the sexual act— I've forgotten the exact words—something like 'the position is ridiculous and the expense damnable.'"

Conroy laughed but James could see that even he was shocked. Since then, James had felt lost and lonely, as he had felt from time to time in even the most friendly foreign country. How on earth would he accustom himself to living with these innocent people? He could reform, but it was a dreary prospect. He was fond of Morgan and Alice but it would take time to get used to the unsophisticated company that one met in their house. It had always been so, but he had not minded it when he knew that he could escape to London again. He would just have to take on protective coloring if he intended to spend the rest of his life in Ireland. This had certainly not been his intention when he came but now he found himself seeing it as his only escape hatch.

Then like a lightning flash a gloriously crazy idea came to him. He sprang to his feet so fast that he almost fell over a mossy root of the stump. More cautiously, he marched homeward, along the grass-grown lane, past the broken wall of Jerome Burke's demesne, over the stile into the paddock where the Moycullen horses were grazing, onto the avenue that ran by the side of the house. There he paced up and down for a long time, thinking it all out. He could see no flaw in it, yet a recurring weakness in his stomach warned him that it might not be as perfect as it looked on the outside. There was glory in its recklessness, a sense of flying above ground, a sense of freedom, and he was sure of the most essential thing, that Anna would consider him a hero.

He found Morgan in his study, which used to be Samuel's study, bent over the mill account books just as Samuel used to be. He spoke strongly, so that Morgan looked up in surprise.

"Morgan! I'd like to lend my weight, as far as I can, to get Parnell's man in at the Kilkenny election."

Morgan laid his pen down deliberately and gazed at James, then said, "Are you offering to take part in the campaign?"

"Yes." Sudden panic seized him. "Would I be useful?"

Morgan sprang to his feet and came around the desk to take James's hands, saying, "Of course you would be useful—in fact you'd have enormous value. I can hardly grasp it yet, it's such a surprise."

"Why should it surprise you? I've always been a good Irishman."

With his chin in the air, he challenged Morgan with his eye.

Morgan said quietly, "You know it will ruin you with Gladstone? You know you'll never be made governor if you openly oppose him?"

"I know very well. I know exactly what I'm doing."

He saw Morgan's eyes light up with affection and admiration, and he clapped James on the shoulder, saying, "Sit down, then, and we'll pool our wits. You know the position about the candidates?"

As they had scarcely talked of anything else for days, James said rather sourly, "I should hope I do."

Since the split in the ranks of Parnell's party, under pressure from the Catholic priests the candidate whom Parnell had chosen, Sir John Pope-Hennessy, had changed sides and had agreed to stand for election as the anti-Parnellite candidate for the same constituency. The whole affair had taken on the appearance of a crusade or a witch-hunt, depending on how you looked at it. Parnell had been a thorn in the side of the Church for so long, it was only natural that the unholy element of revenge should be present, but while one could make some excuses for the men of God defending the sheep and lambs of Ireland, James felt nothing but contempt for the vulgar jealousy displayed by Parnell's former right-hand man, Timothy Healy. It would be a real pleasure to expose him in the course of the campaign, he said.

"I don't expect ordinary people to recognize Healy for what he is, or even to object to his ranting vulgarity. They've had so much of that, they've become accustomed to it. I think they'll swallow him in the name of religion and orthodoxy, as they always do. In a way, I suppose we can always expect this in Ireland."

"Always?"

Morgan sounded disbelieving but James said firmly, "Yes. Coarseness and vulgarity have the appeal of strength. If Mr. Parnell could manage it, he should try a little of the same himself."

"I've been told that Healy is a religious man."

"There's no charity in him. He has an animal energy. I met him once in London and found it unpleasant even to be near him. One thing I must say for his type is that they're usually to be found on the winning side. It's a bad outlook for Mr. Parnell. They'll stop at nothing to get rid of him now, if only because they couldn't bear the sight of him marching triumphantly back into the House if they fail."

"I had no idea you were such a close observer of politics," Morgan said.

And James answered nonchalantly, "It's been my job for more than thirty years."

61

James and Morgan arrived at Kilkenny station at half-past four in the afternoon, two days before Parnell was expected. Morgan was cool enough but James was sizzling with excitement. A dozen local men were on the platform to welcome them and Morgan seemed to know most of them, greeting them by their names as if he had been hobnobbing with them the week before. James kept in the background, walking a yard or so behind Morgan out of the station, but on the very steps a great bearded bully rushed forward and shrieked, pointing a finger into his waistcoat, "It's Pope-Hennessy, the bastard! The turncoat!"

Instantly the air was filled with boos and groans, all unbelievably directed at him. James shivered with alarm, but only for a moment. He tightened his mouth in fury, glaring around at the ragged mass before him, stood up on his toes to give himself the extra height he needed and let out a thunderous roar.

"I am *not* Sir John Pope-Hennessy!"

The nearest voices were silenced and gradually the whole lot died away. James stuck out his chin and narrowed his eyes, puffing out his chest so that he felt himself swell up like the mother frog in the fable. He compelled total silence with the power of his eye and thundered again, aware of Morgan's astonished admiration.

"I came here to fight for the plain people of Ireland, to fight for the leader, the chosen leader of the people, the man who has carried our country closer to freedom than it has been in six hundred years, and that man is Mr. Parnell!"

A voice called out, "Three cheers for Parnell!"

While they were cheering, James was aware that the nearest men to him were looking at him oddly, almost as if they doubted his statement. One man, a little better dressed than the rest, came close and pulled at Morgan's sleeve, whispering to him softly.

James heard Morgan say, "It's James Fahy, a good friend—helped a lot of Fenians out of jail."

"Three cheers for Wexford and '98!"

Again they were cheering, and the man who had spoken to Morgan had gone down through the crowd and was obviously passing on the news he had heard. Morgan and James climbed onto an outside car, whose horse was side-stepping in fear at the noise all around its ears. The driver flourished his whip and the crowd fell back to let them pass through, then closed in behind them and set out at a run to escort them to the hotel. The car swayed from side to side on the cobbled street, threatening to throw them off at any moment. James held on to his top hat with one hand and clutched the slim metal bar with the other, feeling all his inner organs being jumbled up together. Down one hill and up another they went and drew up at the Victoria Hotel, which stood on a small square. Above the square, the huge, ugly limestone castle of the Butlers showed through the bare trees. There was more cheering as they got down, and they paused on the doorstep to wave acknowledgment before entering the sudden silence of the hall.

Morgan said softly, "Well done, James! I didn't know you were an orator."

"Neither did I," James said happily, almost giggling with pleasure. "I didn't like being taken for another man. Am I so like him?"

"You are, rather. Have you never met him? He was suborned by the priests. A pity, because Mr. Parnell thought well of him. He always stood up for the native population everywhere he went."

Alone in his bedroom, James gloated unashamedly over his triumph. Now Morgan knew him for what he was—a man among men, a free man when he was away from all those women. To give her her due, Anna had behaved extremely well, saying only that he must follow his conscience. Alice seemed puzzled by his behavior but she too regarded him as a martyr.

With his trained eye, he still admired Alice tremendously as a woman, tall and straight and at fifty-eight only a little less slim than she had been at nineteen, when he had known her first, her hair dressed high in the dignified style she had always worn, with two white wings now where once it had all been as black as a sloe, moving as swiftly as she had always done, her voice still low and sweet. How did she do it? Most of the women he had admired when they were young had coarsened as their confidence had increased, with horrid, loud, sharp voices and a shaming lack of delicacy, and loud, heavy laughter. His life seemed to have been wasted on such people. To be free of it all! He threw his arms wide and smiled broadly. He was free now, truly free, of every crafty consideration that had cramped his life until now, free because nothing could possibly damage his career more than what he was doing now, free as a snake without its old skin, free as a chicken just out of the egg, free as a race horse out of the womb.

The hotel drawing room was full of people when he got there, so that he felt suddenly shy. They were so big and hairy, he could not possibly feel at home with them, but their eyes were kind, like friendly dogs'. They seemed much less frightened than the people of the west, so that he did not feel quite so superior to them. This was the city of James Stephens and Fintan Lalor, and nearby Tipperary had produced fighters of the caliber of John O'Leary and Thomas Luby. These names were in the air all around him, and he had to rack his brains, while looking intelligent, to remember their exploits.

Most of the men were concerned only with the present battle. Anger was in the air, too, bursting out in puffs of savage irony against the cynical exploitation of the people's innocence and devotion to the Catholic Church. The priests of the deanery had met at St. Kieran's College a few days before and had issued a statement saying that they "supported and followed the anti-Parnellite leader Justin MacCarthy, rather than countenance or recognize the moribund faction led by a man convicted and befouled by reason of the decision of the London Divorce Court."

"That's open war, if we didn't know it already," Morgan said. "It's a pity the election is not in Dublin. Dublin will always be behind Mr. Parnell, as he knows well."

James almost smirked at the notion that had been foisted on the simple priests that Parnell was the one immoral man in the whole Liberal alliance.

He said to Morgan, "Don't they know that quite a few of them are keeping little bits of fluff? Lord Hartington has had a mistress for years—surely they know that."

"Who knows what they know?" Morgan said. "The people who want to get rid of Parnell certainly know these things but they will ignore anything that doesn't suit them. I don't have to tell you about bishops and cardinals."

"No. Could we use some of the information I have in the campaign?"

"I'm not sure. I'll ask some of the local men."

But he came back later to say that it would not be allowed. The Kilkenny men, knowing their own people, said that the effect of throwing mud at other politicians would be a loss of dignity for all the Irish Party members, and it would inevitably raise the question of why they had associated with the Liberals in the first place.

The candidate was a worried-looking man named Vincent Scully, who told James privately that a baboon would have supplied as much personality as he needed for this campaign. The people were voting for or against Parnell. Scully and Pope-Hennessy were only names. James could see that Scully was given very little attention by the busy men who hurried in and out of the hotel, and he was the last to be thought of when the French windows were opened on to the balcony and half a dozen of them went outside to address the roaring crowd. The early winter darkness had fallen and a bitter wind grabbed them by the ankles. James sheltered in the high collar of his coat, which he had prudently seized as he was being taken outside. Below them, the faces of the crowd looked ferocious in the glare of torches held high and occasionally waved about by cheerleaders, who set up a yell as soon as they saw the windows open.

James felt his skin crawl as the first speaker, a Mr. Fitzgerald, to whom he had been introduced inside, began his speech in stentorian oratorical style, pausing between phrases for dramatic effect.

"Men of Kilkenny, I come here tonight to tell you, to make clear to you, that when you vote in this election you vote not for Mr. Parnell, not for his candidate, but for the total freedom of Ireland, for the final severance of the ties that bind us to our ancient enemy, for a free and united Ireland, self-governing, independent, the Ireland of Wolfe Tone and of the men of '98 . . ."

Treason! Sedition! And here was James Fahy on the same platform with this old firebrand who was clearly stating that the Fenians were still to the good, waiting their chance to kick the British Empire into kingdom come if they could manage it and to set up a republic in Ireland. His boats were burned, all right. Down there in the crowd there were certainly several policemen making notes to send to the Crime Special Branch in Dublin Castle, with a list of names of people to be watched. James Fahy would be one of them. Could they put him in jail? Could they cut off his pension? He must talk to Thomas and Morgan about a job in the mill or in one of the Dublin offices for Gerald when he came down from Oxford, since he would probably be blackballed for the Civil Service now. Walter was in already and he could change his name if necessary. Alice's nephews were all working in the mill, or so it seemed when one went in there.

And then, on top of this general feeling of alarm, once again he experienced a wave of exhilaration and recklessness, accompanied for the first time by real understanding of the reason why these apparently harmless men spent their whole lives working for the helpless, hopeless people of Ireland. It was too complicated to be put into words but he sensed that it was mainly a wish to share their knowledge of what it was to be honestly Irish, without compliment or apology, as a Frenchman or an Englishman is. This was the whole concept of freedom, an essential basis for honest daily living.

Presently Morgan was making a speech, his white hair blowing in the wind, his usually soft, resonant voice now as sharp as a dog's bark.

"Men of Kilkenny, remember that you have a great fighting tradition behind you. Remember Fintan Lalor and his ideal

435

of a republican Ireland. Remember James Stephens and the Fenians. Remember the best friend of the poor man in Ireland, Parnell, the only incorruptible Irishman, the man who forged the tool that will bring us freedom from foreign domination, the man who never bowed the knee to landlordism, to imperialism, to intimidation, Parnell, who was the first to tell you in that historic phrase to keep a firm grip on your homesteads, Parnell, who was maligned often before now and proved himself innocent, Parnell, who has been a thorn in the flesh of the British Empire for the last ten years, Parnell, who is the strongest man in the Irish Party, the only man who can lead us to freedom at last, Parnell, who is our last hope of getting our freedom by constitutional means, Parnell, who is such a danger to Westminster that the foulest means will be used to break him, Parnell, who is not merely the leader of the Party but the leader of the Irish nation. Parnell, who suffered in jail as all good Irishmen do sooner or later. As John O'Leary says, let Mr. Gladstone screech and his followers howl—we will never abandon Parnell!"

Cheers and roars broke at this and Morgan went on.

"What are we to say about the attempt to make you sit in judgment of Mr. Parnell? Did he sit in judgment on you? Did he not rather treat you with Christian charity when some of you were weak and had not the courage to keep up the fight against the power of the landlords? Surely you remember what he said, that when a man who had let down his neighbors by buying an evicted farm or by paying an unjust rent, when that man came back to sense and reason he was to be treated like a lost sheep returned to the fold. Why should you listen now to the priests who tell you to vote against your one true leader, remembering that it was those same priests who told your fathers and grandfathers to pay the rent to the landlords and be glad to die of starvation on their own hearthstones. Let the men of God attend to the business of God, and we'll attend to the business of the world ourselves."

Over the heads of the frantic crowd, James saw a scuffle where a procession had come swiftly out of a side street. They had their own torchbearers, four at either side, and appeared to be carrying a flag, which the nearest men of the Parnellite crowd were trying to tear down. The flag swayed and fluttered as it was jerked up into the air to get it out of reach, and then with a sickening shock James saw that it was a woman's torn petticoat. Shock began to silence the crowd under the balcony, too, as heads turned one by one to see what the diversion was. The procession plowed on, pushing and elbowing and jostling, until it was well into the square. Then a man was lifted onto the shoulders of his companions to call out, "Will the petticoat of Kitty O'Shea be the flag of Ireland?"

Immediately it seemed that the square below became a battlefield as the two factions fell on each other and the police moved in and began to batter heads on all sides. Down the street from the direction of the station a troop of cavalry was trotting and at a shrieked command from their officer they charged the crowd. James covered his eyes with his hands, and when he dared to look again, he saw people pressed against the walls, crawling across the square, hiding in doorways, even shinning up drainpipes to get away from the murderous hooves of the horses. The torches were gone, either carried away up the hill or trampled on the roadway, so that only the greenish gaslight lit the scene faintly.

James dragged at Morgan's arm like a child, saying, "Morgan! Morgan! What can we do? God help them, this is murder. There's the officer—can't we do something?"

"You can try. It's always like this."

And James, the little hero, safe on his balcony, went to the railing and yelled out in that new voice that he had not known he possessed, "Officer! What the hell do you think you're doing? Call off those men of yours!"

His accent was the best you could buy in London. The young officer looked up in astonishment, his soft face outlined in his ridiculous helmet, like a baby's bonnet. Once again James had proof of his power over the human race: the officer shouted almost hysterically to his men and amazingly the whole thing stopped, the horses were turned around and went trotting off down the hill again, rattling and clattering long after they had mounted the next hill and had gone out of sight.

James felt quite ill as he stumbled over the threshold, back into the drawing room, seeing as he turned away that the people were creeping out of corners into the square again. Morgan clapped him strongly on the shoulder, almost knocking him off balance, laughing excitedly.

"James, you have the heart of a lion! This will go down in history. I'd fight a war with you!"

James smiled weakly, hoping that his feeling on the subject of wars did not show. What had he got himself into? This was much worse than hunting, much worse than house parties. He felt unfit to skip about at the pace of these people, and yet he was successful at it because each crisis was all over by the time he was aware of what was happening. Now he was being slapped on the back and having his hand shaken by everyone

437

in the hotel, it seemed, all laughing and joking and telling one another what an asset James was and what a victory he had won. He was to be taken to as many meetings as possible so that he could make use of his great talent—to Gowran, to Thomastown, to Kilmanagh, to Tullaroan, to Freshford, to Urlingford, to places James had never known existed but whose populations were seething with excitement.

He heard one man chuckle as he said to another, "Fahy is the answer to the maiden's prayer—he looks like a Protestant!"

62

From then onward, James let the whole situation whirl him along like a river in flood, taking instructions and carrying them out as he was told, playing himself to the crowds in all the little villages as if he were a trained seal, so that he heard many more compliments to his fighting spirit.

" 'Freedom comes from God's right!' " thundered James. "Those are the words of Thomas Davis. Is it possible that you have forgotten them? Do you remember the rest? 'And righteous men shall make our land a nation once again?' " A pause for the cheers and then he quieted them with his fiery eye. "And who are these righteous men? Are they those who direct you now to turn against your leader? Are they those who hate Parnell first and foremost because he is a Protestant and secondly because he has a different code of behavior, entirely consistent with the operation of his Church? Are they those who give grounds to the fear that Home Rule will be Rome Rule? Are they people who care more for their Church than for their country? Are they bishops and cardinals jostling for power? 'Render therefore unto Caesar the things which are Caesar's and unto God the things that are God's—that's the only way for Ireland, and Ireland has proved over hundreds of years that her faith won't suffer or be any weaker in the end. If you want Ireland to be free from the center of the sea, you'll vote for Mr. Parnell and he will carry the whole nation as he has done for the last ten years!"

Howls and cheers of delight again. That was at Callan, the morning after he and Morgan had arrived in Kilkenny, and afterward Morgan said, "You're a wonder, James, though you sailed close to the wind there. The old-timers are asking where you have been all these years."

A rumor reached the hotel that John Redmond and others of Parnell's supporters would arrive on the afternoon train from Dublin, and without waiting for confirmation, they all set out to walk to the station. They had to force their way through a crowd, already ten deep around the little stone building and flowing out into the station yard. James stayed close to Morgan for protection, like a meadow pipit behind a cuckoo, he said to himself, as he let Morgan do the elbowing. When they were recognized, the stationmaster helped to clear a way for them, and they found that the platform itself had been kept rather free, though the railings bordering it were crowded. James turned away to look down the tracks. It was freezing already, so that the rails glittered like silver, curving off into the beautiful green fields, peaceful and remote from the affairs that tortured the men all around him. Mr. O'Keeffe, the most active of the local organizers, seemed almost to be in physical agony, poised for failure already, suffering it in advance, with his hands clasped behind his back, at the very edge of the platform, frowning at his boots.

In the far distance, the slow puffing of the train punctuated the air. The stationmaster came running forward and stood watching anxiously as it sailed in, the passengers in the dark carriages looking out like fish from a bowl, unreal, beheaded.

When the train halted, the stationmaster bawled, "Great Southern and Western train from Dublin!"

Everyone scurried like hens and James peered into the thickest part of the crowd for a sight of Mr. Parnell but he was not there. All the excitement seemed to surround a small, worried man who turned out to be Mr. Scully's campaign manager, a solicitor named Moran from Limerick.

He pushed his way testily through the crowd, amid the cheers prepared for his leader, then seemed to recollect himself and called out, "Come again in the evening! Bring the band!"

Other city men were trooping out of the station, velvet-collared, top-hatted, high-buttoned, suavely professional. They were the London M.P.'s, with foxy eyes and sharp mouths developed from years of watching.

Suddenly the crowd outside the station was shrieking and howling like a pack of dogs.

James asked Morgan, "In the name of God, what now?"

"It's the Waterford and Central train from Maryborough. By the sound of it, someone else has arrived."

They crossed the platform to the other line, and there, sure enough, a second train had pulled quietly in. Outside the railings the crowd was chanting insulting words accompanied by groans and boos led by half a dozen men who kept the front positions and gave out the words like a litany.

"Rat!"

"Renegade!"

"Traitor!"

"To hell with the place hunter!"

"Go to the Carlton Club!"

Each of these was answered in chorus by the crowd, first with groans and then a repetition of the words used. The ceremony was directed at one part of the train where a small, white-faced man sat like a rabbit, afraid to move. So this was Pope-Hennessy! James gazed at him, fascinated, the attack on himself still fresh in his mind. He saw the little man stand up with a jerk, fling the door open and face his tormentors. Their yells became louder. He was shaking with fear but they had no pity on him.

Another set of angry voices joined in, and about twenty top-hatted priests were suddenly released onto the platform by the stationmaster, who then stood by like a man who has just unleashed greyhounds. They went at once to Sir John, almost lifting him to the ground, escorting him outside, loading him onto an outside car, while two of the priests climbed up to ride with him and the rest tried to hold the people back. All around them the crowd pressed, booing and jeering, while the unfortunate passengers kept their heads lowered into their coat collars as the horse was driven away. The Kilkenny horses had strong nerves, James reflected, as strong as the Kilkenny priests. That piece of fun over, everyone turned back to the train, where a tall, thin, sharp-faced man was standing watching the departure of the priests and their candidate with a sardonic eye.

"It's Pierce Mahoney! Up Kerry! Three cheers for Pierce Mahoney!"

James peered into the crowd and thought he spotted the ringleader, a stocky, fair-headed man with unnaturally pale-blue eyes, a ruthless, hateful person. Mahoney was making a speech that could scarcely be heard for cheers. He used such a rabble-rousing delivery that it was hard to believe he meant a word of what he said, but he was not talking down to the people, and they seemed well able to understand him.

"We are here to fight for the independence of the Irish Party, so that it will not be the tool and the lackey of any English party, however friendly. The secessionist members of the Irish Party are selling out to England, led by that able dealer Tim Healy—"

"Healy the renegade!"

"Healy the Gweedore traitor!"

"Tim the Falcarragh traitor!"

What in the name of heaven had happened in Gweedore and Falcarragh? Then there were three cheers for Parnell and Mahoney, and the whole lot of them were climbing onto outside cars and driving precariously to the hotel. After a wretched supper the comedy began again, with a deputation to meet the train, though word had come that Parnell would not be on this one either. James wondered if he could manage to stay away altogether but there was no hope of that. The politicians gathered themselves up like actors about to appear on the stage, putting on their public personalities as they emerged onto the street, Mahoney swashbuckling, with his overcoat swinging free from his shoulders like a cloak. James had never had good feet and all this walking was beginning to tell on them.

A fife and drum band was pounding away outside the station, the drums drowning out the little whistling fifes so that it was impossible to make out the tune—something with a strong beat to it, certainly. The crowd around the band leaped up and down, cheering and waving several dozen torches. Morgan took James and hurried him inside where it was warmer—not that anyone but himself seemed aware of the piercing cold. They were a rugged lot, these politicians, their brains less important than their muscles and hearts and lungs, and very strange company indeed in which to find Mr. Parnell. James had glimpsed him more than once in London, walking near the House of Commons, aloof and aristocratic but accepted by society in much the same way as they would accept a man who had a fancy for collecting monkeys. Oddity was the prerogative of the upper classes, James knew, but it would not be tolerated in him or his kind, hobnob as they might with the titled and the great. If he had been made a colonial governor it might just have been possible. Pope-Hennessy had managed to get away with it but then he had faint connections with French aristocracy, remote enough to be romantic. He had a tough mind, but now, having seen him, James wondered how his body would stand up to the rigors of political life. For one thing, Pope-Hennessy was no bigger than James himself, who was now positively frightened by the mass of huge men crushing all around him.

"We'll get in a corner," Morgan said in his ear. "Leave them to it—they make me sick."

James turned to him in amazement.

Morgan lifted an eyebrow, saying, "That surprises you? I loathe politics and politicians and political tricks. Yes, they're all on Parnell's side but for all the wrong reasons. We'll talk about it some other time."

Skillfully he placed himself and James in a corner from which they could see along the tracks. James could not wait for "some other time."

"Do you think Parnell is a political trickster?"

"When it suits him. There isn't a single man out there who understands him—perhaps that's why he's always able to make them obey him. He orders them around like schoolboys. You'll see. This time some of them have got out of hand."

The train was gliding into the station and the pattern was repeated, cheers, boos, speeches, the agonizing drive on outside cars, with a pause outside the Imperial Hotel, where Pope-Hennessy was staying, while William Redmond of the Irish Party stood up on his car and called for three cheers for Parnell. When these were given, he called for groans for Pope-Hennessy, then cheers for Wexford and '98, then cheers for '67. It was grotesque, that a grown man should behave like this. Where was his sense of dignity? Could he possibly be sincere about it all? Was this the game that he, James, would have to play if he were to be taken up and made into an M.P. as someone had already suggested? God forbid! He would never be able to do it. Parnell must be a good deal of an actor to have got away with it so well, but he was a strong man, one who had never served anyone.

When Parnell arrived a day or two later, James watched him closely all the time, trying to make out how he was able to turn himself into the kind of person that these dirty, vulgar people admired. One of the secrets seemed to be never to speak to anyone on intimate terms, never to confide or relax. How was he in his bedroom? The divorce case had proved that he became almost childish in love, but now James could see why: it was because he was compelled to act like a god in public, poor devil. The cracks were showing, however, and as the days went on, his rhetoric became wilder and more abusive so that even his supporters looked at one another in alarm.

"Send that mongrel skinner back to Cork!" he said bitterly of Pope-Hennessy, whose family background included a tannery in Cork.

The pace grew hotter. A handful of lime was thrown at Parnell, striking him in the eye, and Dr. Hackett immediately took him into a nearby house and licked it clean, burning his tongue slightly in the process. Afterward some of the men said they had heard Tim Healy state that it was flour, not lime, and that Parnell was pretending to be injured to excite sympathy for himself. Nothing was too low for Healy, who frequently called for three cheers for Kitty O'Shea at his own meetings. Later he fell into sentimentality, saying in tones throbbing with false emotion that he was no place hunter, that the only place he had sought was in the hearts of the Irish people. A plague on both their houses! James longed to be out of it all, yet this was the price he had to pay for Anna's happiness. He had to remind himself constantly of the reason why he was here at all, and that it would soon be over. Though he had spent his whole adult life in close contact with politicians, he had never before seen how they came to be elected. He could hardly bear the thought of the great Mr. Gladstone facing a crowd of Scottish villagers, no doubt all shrieking and screaming like their Irish cousins.

Then, on one of the last days, he heard a plain speech that moved him unexpectedly, bringing him horribly near the bones of the people's grievances. It was given by a quiet countryman named Walter Dalton, at Gowran, a village on a river, a few miles from Kilkenny.

Dalton said simply, "On behalf of the evicted tenants of Tipperary, I advise the people of Gowran to stick by Parnell. The battle we are fighting is the old battle and I can tell you straight that the men of Tipperary would never have made such sacrifices if they had thought the victory that was to be won was the victory the secessionists seek to win now. I'm proud to stand on the platform with Mr. Parnell, and he is the man who can be trusted to care for the poor people of Ireland. We have proof of it over and over, how he emptied his own pockets without a thought for himself, how he went to jail in cold Kilmainham, as the song says, and how he still comes to our rescue in spite of insults and attacks from the people who used to be his friends. You have heard Mr. Davitt say that he would not willingly hurt a hair of Mr. Parnell's head in this contest, but Mr. Davitt has done a terrible injury to us all in letting the people of Ireland be divided among themselves. You have heard Mr. Parnell say that he appeals to no section of his countrymen, that his appeal is to the whole Irish race. Let the Irish race stand together and we'll have peace and some kind of prosperity at long last."

The frost continued right up to the polling day, Monday, December 22. James had taken to wearing two sets of underwear, on Morgan's advice, and still the cold chilled his bones. It would be crazy if this were to cost him his life. He did what he could to save himself, with hot toddy at night and a good fire in his bedroom, yet he cursed Kilkenny every morning as he dragged himself out of bed and creaked downstairs to the chilly dining room. Then, on Monday, he woke to hear water trickling through all the eaveshoots of the aged building and looked out on streets deep in mud.

There was no rain that day. From the drawing-room windows he watched the cabs and traps go past, loaded with voters in charge of the local men. All day long he kept reminding himself that it was nothing to him which of the candidates was elected, but by evening he knew that he longed for Parnell's victory. He was a truly great man, as great as Gladstone or Lord Granville or any of the others who had inspired him in his youth. To be near him was a privilege, to be addressed by him was an honor. He was a man whom James could have loved as he had never loved anyone in his life except Samuel.

He stood near Parnell at the counting the next day in the Court House. Michael Davitt and John Redmond were there, uncomfortably silent, embarrassed by Healy's bouncing and sneering. The two candidates behaved more politely, chatting to each other like old friends. At three o'clock, when the count finished, Pope-Hennessy looked almost apologetic as the sheriff gave the figures, two thousand five hundred and twenty-seven for Sir John, one thousand three hundred and sixty-five for Parnell's man, Vincent Scully.

There was perfect silence for a second and then Sir John, in a low voice, gave formal thanks to the sheriff and his staff, and Mr. Scully seconded it in rather firmer tones. Parnell crossed to the window, outside which they could hear the murmurs of a still-excited crowd. How did they keep it up? They had energy for ten more elections, judging by their cheers as the balcony doors opened and Parnell, Scully, Morgan, James and several of the local men came out. Parnell walked to the rail and leaned on it, the knuckles sticking out of his thin hands like battlements. Now James realized that Parnell was ill, that the bright red of his cheeks was caused not by excitement but by fever, and that he was holding himself upright with painful determination. He gazed down silently at the people below, bowing gravely, seeming to examine their faces as if they were friends, then lifting his right hand slowly in a gesture that asked for silence. Gradually the shouts died away. Parnell straightened his shoulders and was about to speak when Timothy Healy strode out onto the balcony, walked to the railing and, taking off his hat in a sweeping gesture, bowed ironically to the crowd below.

Screams of fury flew upward, the Kilkenny men on the balcony made a rush at Healy while the outsiders started back in amazement, then several policemen came out of the room and shouldered his attackers away. Parnell began to speak calmly, turning his back on the scuffle.

"I want to congratulate the courageous people who resisted clerical intimidation in this election—"

Again Healy came forward and bowed, clowning and aping Parnell, waving his right hand in a mock elegant gesture. Parnell turned sharply to the Resident Magistrate who was hovering with a sickly expression in the doorway.

"Mr. Considine, can't you take this man away and allow me to address the people?"

"I refuse to leave," Healy snarled. "I have as good a right to be here as anyone else."

He looked around arrogantly but there was an element of uneasiness now, which Parnell deliberately increased with a long cold stare before turning to face the square, speaking a little faster than before but in his usual strong, clear voice.

"Men of Kilkenny, Mr. Healy is staying to prevent me from speaking to you but I would ask you to take no notice of him. We have more important affairs to consider. What are the component parts of this great conspiracy to strike me down, and through me the cause of Ireland? The main part of that conspiracy was based on the knowledge that if I were deposed from leadership of the Irish Party, the Irish race would be divided, and once divided, the more easily set aside. Some weeks ago John Redmond asked a question to which Mr. Healy and his friends were not able to give a satisfactory answer. Mr. Redmond said: 'If we are asked to sell our leader to preserve an alliance, we are bound to ask what price we are getting for him.' To that I answered: 'Don't sell me for nothing. If you get my value, you may change me tomorrow.' They have not got my value. Instead they have become the discredited and powerless tool of the Liberal Party."

Groans and angry shouts came from various parts of the crowd. James saw Healy turn to slip quickly through the balcony door. If Parnell saw him he gave no sign of it. With his chin up and his eyes bright and determined he was going on.

"But I say we still need courage, as we always needed it. I am still your leader, and the leader of the Irish Party. I would rather perish than do anything to make you regret for an instant that you have befriended me, and I shall go forward with your help and with the knowledge that I should be a dastardly scoundrel if I deceived you, and with your warm hearts cheer-

445

ing me forward I shall leave this town tonight confident of the near approach of victory."

He stepped back, keeping close to Morgan, who seemed prepared to have him collapse there and then. They shepherded him down the stairs, pausing in the hallway to marshal themselves for the last time. James kept his eyes fixed on Mr. Parnell, aware that he might never see him again. James felt that he had done what he had come to do, to destroy himself in the eyes of the Unionists, to become an apparent martyr in the cause of Ireland, to provide himself with a ready explanation of why he need hope for no more plums within the structure of the Empire. Why then was he consumed with a black poison of shame, the most conscious of all his life? The people had unhitched the horses so that they could pull the carriage, with the whole party, back to the hotel. All the way there, James suffered agonizingly, as if with physical pain, so that he knew it showed on his face even before Morgan said softly in his ear, "You did your best, James. We're toughened to this game. The Chief appreciates you—he has said so. Don't take it so hard."

Unable to answer, James closed his eyes. Good, unsuspicious people! God help them, how could they ever hope to defeat the powers that were ranged against them? They were compassed round about with enemies, and as if that were not enough, they had enemies in plenty inside the gates, people like himself who took advantage of their innocence. No one had the least idea of what his motives had been, and there was no reason why they should ever find out.

63

It was Fergal who first noticed that James was completely changed by the Kilkenny election. Over Christmas in Moycullen he sat gloomily reading old copies of the Kilkenny newspapers that he had brought back with him, and others that kept coming by post, going over and over the accounts of the election. If anyone came into the room he would look up sharply and say, "Listen! Listen to this!"

Then he would read the piece in a high, shocked tone, waiting for the hearer to express disgust or astonishment, always disappointed. Everyone had moved on to something new, tired of their own anger. A few days after Christmas, Fergal found him in the drawing room, lost in a wing-backed armchair that could easily have contained two men of his size.

James said, "Fergal, listen to this! It's the editorial of Christmas Eve—it's just come by the post: 'December 24, 1890: To us Conservatives and Unionists the result of the contest is indeed of no consequence whatever, and we have already devoted so much of our space to its consideration that we leave the matter between the two contesting Home Rule factions, whose quarrel has had one result whereof we may rejoice—namely, the smashing of Home Rule.' How can they crow over their own destruction? Have they no political vision? How can they pretend that they're not Irish at all? But earlier they were saying that at least Pope-Hennessy is a gentleman, as if that's all that matters."

"You've been away so much. Of course it seems mad. But they always write like that. They hate the idea of Home Rule."

"But they can't help admiring Mr. Parnell. Another day they said 'A mastiff is a mastiff and a pug a pug no matter how many agree to call the former a pug and the latter a mastiff.' "

"That's certainly a horrible use of the English language."

But James was already picking up another paper, clawing at it with his little rat's hands and peering shortsightedly. Mumbling an excuse, Fergal hurried away to find Morgan, saying in exactly the tone he would have used about a sick horse, "Papa, please come and look at Uncle James. He's behaving awfully strangely, scrabbling through the newspapers. He shouldn't have been taken to Kilkenny at all. What on earth happened to him there?"

"He wanted to go, and he seemed able for it," Morgan said rather impatiently, but he went and sat with James for a while, trying to give him some comfort.

Anna worried about him but was not able to do much, though Fergal saw that she understood the problem.

"This visit to Ireland has changed his whole life, Fergal," she said pathetically, "and mine, too. We liked it in London, and we were going to go to one of the Crown Colonies—it was not settled which—and there would have been balls and all kinds of chances for the girls when they were old enough. And then he saw Mr. Parnell."

St. Paul on the way to Damascus had been stricken in much the same way. The presence of all his children for the Christmas holiday only provided James with a new audience for his sorrowful recitation of the perfidy of Parnell's former friends, and he became furiously angry when Gerald said with unusual intelligence, "But Father, surely the Party members must first be loyal to the Party and then to the leader. Parnell taught them that himself."

"What use is a party without a leader?" James snarled, his eyes narrowed with hatred of anyone who seemed to doubt that Parnell was indispensable. " 'Divide et impera' was the plan, and the whole lot of them fell into the trap."

Alice and Morgan had many consultations about him, and Morgan agreed that it might help if he were told what was happening in the negotiations between the two sections of the Party. These took palce in Boulogne early in January, and when he came back from them, Morgan had to explain—so little did James know of what had been going on until now—that they could not meet in Ireland because John Dillon, who was an important member, would have been immediately arrested. He moaned when he heard how Parnell had proudly refused to retire even temporarily.

"He was the only one who was able to get anything done. He held everyone spellbound. He was everything the English admire, though they wanted to despise him. This will set back the cause of Ireland fifty years, if not a hundred."

Morgan asked Alice. "Have you ever heard James mention the cause of Ireland before?"

"Never."

"It's true, as Fergal said, that he should never have been taken to Kilkenny."

In the spring, Anna was diverted with buying a fine Georgian house and some acres of land a little south of Dublin, but after they moved into it, James sat all day brooding, refusing to take any interest in it. All through the summer he seemed to get smaller and smaller.

Morgan remonstrated with him. "You'll have to get over this, James. You're a family man. You must remember your responsibilities to your wife and children."

"Children!" said James. "Not one of my children cares about Parnell."

"Perhaps they don't show it, or don't know anything about him."

"I've tried to tell them. They won't listen. Children are a doubtful blessing, Morgan. They desert you when you need them most."

"They need you, too. You should go out and drive in the park with Anna. She's suffering a great deal because of you. And she wants you to take charge of running the gardens. You always said you would like to own gardens."

"You think I've been neglecting Anna?"

The narrowing of his eyes was a warning to Morgan of some danger, he knew not what. He denied that he had accused James of neglecting Anna and went back to telling him to pull himself together. He seemed to improve, until the dreadful day when they learned that Parnell was dead.

James brought the news himself, one miserable October morning, cold and windy, the air full of protesting birds blown off their course, thick, ugly rain spilling inescapably so that James looked like a little wet fly when he appeared on the doorstep.

Alice had seen him arrive and had come running out to ask in alarm, "How did you come? What has happened? Why didn't you bring the carriage?"

"I walked." He sat weakly on a chair in the hall, shocking the parlormaid who had opened the door. He lifted his head after a moment and said, "Parnell is dead."

The girl gave a shriek and ran off toward the kitchen, clutching her apron to her mouth. The sound brought Morgan into the hall, so that he was able to help Alice get James into the drawing room and make him take off his coat and sit shaking by the fire. For one wild second he thought that James was out of his mind but when he looked closer he saw painful sanity. Then James began to tell them what had happened, tears running freely down his cheeks.

"Our man Michael came into the dining room while we were having breakfast—he had the news from the milkman, who had heard it at the station. I don't know how. Perhaps it came over the telegraph. He died last night in Brighton. His wife was with him. He was ill only a day or two, Michael said. But when we saw him in Kilkenny he looked dreadfully worn, do you remember?"

"I remember."

Alice said bitterly, "They have their wish. They wished him dead, but they were afraid to kill him in cold blood. Now they'll regret it, you'll see. They'll pity him and be sorry they hounded him to death."

"Who will pity him? Who will be sorry?"

"The priests and bishops."

"They will not. Perhaps Gladstone will be sorry, but not the priests."

Morgan was right. Not a single priest was to be seen at the public funeral on Sunday and Catholics were warned at Mass not to go, but thousands came from all over the country to march in the procession just the same. Morgan took James with him, afraid to leave him alone. All through the day he said never a word. He stayed close by Morgan, like a child with his father on a long day's outing, his mouth screwed up with pain and grief and his eyes fixed on some invisible, distant object. Early in the morning they went to Kingstown to meet the steamer from Holyhead, watching it move in to dock in the ghostly dawn among the bouncing, rain-soaked fishing boats. As the coffin was carried down the gangway in its plain wooden case they heard the angry voices of the watching crowd.

"Healy the murderer! Traitor Healy!"

On the short train journey into Dublin they sat with some of the Lord Mayor's party, who eyed James curiously but took charge of him at Westland Row Station and made sure that he was not trampled on by the huge crowd that was waiting, especially in the stampede for pieces of the casing, which was broken off before the coffin was put into the hearse. When the procession set out for St. Michan's Church, he was handed carefully into Morgan's carriage, with John O'Leary and James Stephens, and still he did not speak, though he twitched his shoulders when the three old Fenians agreed that Parnell was the greatest Fenian of them all.

"He was destroyed by his own party," Mr. O'Leary said in his quiet, precise way. "Once they allowed priests in politics, they threw away the second half of their independence. It will take a long time to get them out again. Sectarian politics are a curse everywhere—that was the one thing the Fenians had achieved. Mr. Parnell is a great loss, a great loss."

"I should have seen what was happening to him," Morgan said miserably to Alice afterward. "I never took him seriously. None of us did. We insulted him always with our indifference. In Kilkenny I watched him as if he were a performing dog, not a real full-blooded man, full of feeling, as sensitive as any of us. Why couldn't I have seen it? After the service, we went to the City Hall and there was the coffin draped with the Volunteer flags from Avondale, and the great big Celtic cross of flowers and all the wreaths, and he went and stood by the terrible one from the Belfast Committee that had 'revenge' and 'murder' worked into it, and he stayed there while thousands of people passed by the coffin. I got uneasy when we went outside and I began to tell him what the different groups were but he wasn't listening. I asked him if he would like to go home but he gave me such a look that I didn't suggest it again. I told the General that I couldn't walk with the I.R.B., that I'd have to keep an eye on James, and he agreed, of course. They were all grateful to him for what he had done in Kilkenny—they didn't know him at first but then they began to ask who was the little man who was crying so much. It was hard to watch. It wasn't that I was embarrassed—lots of people were crying. In a way I envied him. I wished I could cry as I did when I was a boy, when I hurt my toe on a stone. I thought he would get over it better that way—I could see he was suffering terribly, but I remembered that old wives' tale that you can cry your way out of sorrow. He seemed to be a little better in the carriage. We were with Mr. O'Leary and Mr. Stephens, just behind the Lord Mayor's carriage, and we were all disinclined for talk though we might have been doing some planning if he hadn't been there. It seemed indecent to say much in front of him, and there was the doleful music and the sound of the hooves and all the people marching so solemnly. We could hear everything very clearly because the rain had stopped.

"When we got to the cemetery, we had to wait while the whole procession came inside and he saw Mr. Parnell's old black horse being led along with the riding boots reversed. He stopped crying then and I could feel him shivering. I thought, perhaps that's a good sign. It's a change at least. We had the prayers, and they began to lower the coffin into the grave, and then the worst thing of all happened. A lot of us saw it, though if we had been near enough, we should have been looking into the grave. A falling star, Alice, swooping down across the sky. It sent a shiver through my Connemara bones, I can tell you. Suddenly everyone was looking up. It was a pale sky, not dark at all yet, hardly dark enough to see the stars and a little piece of moon. Then James gave a squeak and fell against me. I thought he had stumbled and I held him, expecting him to right himself, but he just sagged lower, and then I laid him on the ground and we cleared a space around him. Several other people had fainted, too, but they made way for us to get him out to the carriage. Fergal and Thomas weren't far away and they saw what was happening and came over. They carried him and I walked along beside them, and just as we got to the gate I saw that he was dying."

"Poor little James. Samuel told me once that he never saw him cry, even when he was very small. It used to worry him. He said that James would have to cry someday. He said that the time for crying comes sooner or later."

"Samuel was a very wise man."

"Morgan, I'm worried about Anna, she seems so lost and helpless. She depended on James for everything. It's strange because I never taught her to be like that. It's either heredity or Miss Conroy's teaching."

"Perhaps it's just as well. It's a great thing to have had such love."

Morgan hated secrets between himself and Alice but he had never been able to bring himself to tell her what he had learned from time to time about James and his capers in London. Something extraordinary must have happened just before he came back to Ireland, making him act so differently in every way that Morgan could scarcely recognize him for the same man. Poor little devil. How he must have suffered, all alone. Could he have helped him or comforted him in any way? He doubted it. James had always kept up such a front, there was no getting at him.

Without warning, over miles and years, the pain of his own first love for Alice struck him in the heart, so that he felt again the agony of the journey along the rocks on that mad, bright evening when he had found his way into her room and into her bed. Was it possible that James had felt the same flaming passion for each of his London ladies? Anna had loved him devotedly, as anyone could see, and he had loved her. What did it matter if he loved half a dozen others as well? Who could arrange to love only one? And now, anyway, none of it mattered.

PART
SEVEN

On a summer day in 1907, Fergal was lying on the short grass of the side lawn at Moycullen, waiting for Grace Burke. He lay so still that the blackbirds came bouncing close to him. Beside him a hedge of tiny roses attracted dozens of bees and he watched them butt their way into each flower, hang there guzzling for ten seconds, then dart out and into the next. The roses were two colors, cream and pink, so small that the bees weighed them down. Grasshoppers ticked all around him and strange, slow insects climbed through the grass beside him. If he lifted his head, he could see over the low beech hedge that curved in front of the house, down to the shiny line of lake water below. At this time of day he should have been in Galway at the mill, but he made a point of not going there on days when old Morgan went. At seventy-eight, Papa was getting crusty, given to asking suddenly: "Now just what do you mean by that statement?" His hawk-eyed smile was unwavering but you had to be careful not to let it become quizzical, as he allowed you to hang yourself expertly with you own rope. He was gentle with every failing except laziness and lazy thinking. Thomas especially roused him to fury with his continual defense of the Irish Party, so that Fergal had come to dread their arguments.

They began within minutes of Thomas' arrival from London, as inevitable as the stiff whiskey that Morgan poured for him, while the servants were rumbling the trunks upstairs and Letitia and the children were hugging Alice and asking about the cats and dogs.

Morgan would turn his head sideways and upward, looking out of the corners of his eyes at Thomas, and say, "Well, how are things in the mother of parliaments?"

"Much as usual."

Thomas represented a Dublin constituency that had been loyal to Parnell, and he had been a determined nationalist from the time of the Land League and the Battle of Carraroe, but Morgan frequently told him that he was pitifully ignorant of the true state of Ireland.

"How can you know what's happening?" he would ask reasonably. "You live in London—you must live in London, under present conditions, so of course you're out of touch with thinking at home."

This was perfectly true, and they would settle down uneasily in two armchairs in Morgan's study—"Let the women get on with their gossip"—while Morgan told Thomas what had been happening since his last visit. Thomas really wanted to know everything and he had no better way of finding out. He always tried to have a talk with Morgan before anyone else, especially before meeting his agents in Dublin. For this reason, if the family was in Moycullen he came there for a short visit first, and then took the train to Dublin for a few days each week, returning thankfully to the country on Fridays.

They were all at Moycullen now, and would stay for at least a month before going to Mrs. Blake in Galway. Letitia divided the time scrupulously between the two grandmothers so that both could have an equal chance at spoiling the children. There were six of them, a year or a year and a half apart. They were a cheerful lot and had forced Mrs. Blake to make friends with Alice, insisting that they exchange visits all summer long. They called for Mrs. Blake and made her come with them when they drove into Galway to shop, and later went to MacDonnell's to stuff themselves with Bath buns and éclairs before going home, or when they went on a picnic to the riverbank at Dangan, settling the two old ladies together on a rug while the rest rowed across to the old Blake castle at Menloe. Since Thomas was one of the richest men in Connacht, Mrs. Blake found it easier to be pleasant than Alice did. Fergal had been on these outings several times and had seen how they needled each other harmlessly, no longer caring about converting each other.

On the last one, three days ago, Mrs. Blake said in her Grandmother Bear voice, "We all know you encourage the beggars—it's no wonder you have them in droves on your back avenue. They'll always go where they get a welcome and then they'll raid the chicken yard as soon as you've gone to bed."

"The poor people must eat," Alice protested. "When we have Home Rule they'll be better off and they won't have to steal."

Mention of Home Rule silenced Mrs. Blake. She feared the idea so much that she didn't trust herself to speak of it. The country would be handed over to ragamuffins and mass agitators, big-eared louts from Connemara would walk in and take the jobs from people like her late husband, who had mismanaged the accounts of the Flaherty mills all his life and died at last respected by all, a perfect gentleman. The County Balls would be filled with people like the Connollys, whose son Fergal was a dangerous rebel. It was all in the sidelong glance she gave him where he lay under the shelter of his hat, digesting the good luncheon that they had brought with them. It was peaceful on the warm grass, listening to the river gurgling past, the dry rushes rattling in the softly moving water at its gravelly edge, and the two old ladies bickering. Then the children came back and they climbed into the sun-warmed traps and drove to Moycullen House for tea, to find Morgan and Thomas in the middle of a blazing row about the future of Ireland.

Fergal listened to them in despair. The futility of it made him want to roar at the two of them, dingdonging over their glasses of whiskey when they should have been soothing their digestions into the right mood for dinner.

Morgan was moaning, "Parnell was the last Irishman in the world, according to you! He's dead, man! As dead as poor Jamesy Fahy, sixteen years ago, *sixteen* years ago! Do you think Ireland can be saved by a ghost? Your precious party turned on him and rent him asunder, with the enthusiastic help of the Holy Roman Catholic Church, aided and abetted by the great and glorious British Empire. Are we to sit around on our bottoms forever, waiting for him to rise again? Is he perhaps transmigrated into the body of John Redmond? He's surely not in his brain. I'm sick and tired of telling you about the clubs that are rising up all over the country—cultural clubs, Irish language clubs, sports clubs, every damned kind of club, all with one single aim and object, to get the Empire out of our backyard once and for all so that we can make our own arrangements. How can you talk about Ireland being loyal to the Empire when Dublin Corporation refused to give a royal welcome to His Royal Highness King Edward only a few years ago? Nothing has changed in Ireland, nothing! Can't you see what's in front of your nose, man?"

"Papa, what is all this about?"

"Tell that mutt of a brother of yours that he'll have to listen to reason."

Morgan slumped back in his chair and glared at them both, his chin on his chest and his blue eyes sparkling with rage.

Thomas swung around toward Fergal and raised his eyebrows, safe out of Morgan's view, then said peaceably, "I didn't want to upset you, Uncle Morgan. Let's talk about it quietly."

Morgan growled and waggled his shoulders and shot furious looks from side to side, missing both of them deliberately every time.

Thomas said to Fergal, "Uncle Morgan has been telling me

that we're all going to be asked to abstain from Westminster."

"It's Arthur Griffith's idea—the Hungarians did it with great effect, refusing to go to Vienna."

"So I've been told," Thomas said with forced restraint.

"It's an idea worth examining."

"And just tell me, Fergal, what influence we're going to have in the Westminster parliament if we're not there?"

"Griffith says the Irish M.P.'s have been corrupted in Westminster. He believes that it will force them away from playing the parliamentary game and make them concentrate on squeezing Home Rule out of whatever government is in office."

"How? By setting up a parliament at home, without by-your-leave? That would destroy the work of years. I've been trying to tell Uncle Morgan that we're on the brink of getting Home Rule at last. We even have hopes of the Ulster Unionists. Almost everything that's being done in Ireland now is a danger to it. No one minds all the little clubs because they can be useful when Home Rule comes eventually. I can see their national value as well as anyone, and the poetry that's being written is quite good in its way. But Sinn Féin is a horse of a different color. That's not Home Rule as it's understood in Westminster. Everything is there except a declaration of rebellion: demands for protection of industry, a consular service, a national bank, a national Civil Service. Next thing they'll want is a national army."

"It would be logical," Fergal said cautiously. "We're already campaigning against Irishmen joining the British Army. There's not much secret about the aims of Sinn Féin. It's in all the propaganda: 'to re-establish the independence of Ireland.' How we go about it is a matter of judgment. And those harmless little clubs are all amalgamating with the same idea—once you study the culture of Ireland you're led naturally to one conclusion. The Dungannon clubs are strong in Ulster. Hereabouts we have mostly Cumann na nGaedheal. The National Council was Griffith's invention. We'll all have the same idea, in the long run, as Papa was saying."

"We? Are you mixed up in this kind of thing?"

Thomas sounded genuinely puzzled but Fergal said sharply, "Some day soon you and your colleagues are going to have to face reality. Better do it now. Do you know that the Westminster Parliament has passed a hundred coercion acts for Ireland in a hundred years? What can we possibly expect from it? Every time you come home we tell you these things but when you go back to London it all seems to become unreal, or a kind of joke. It's not a joke. Griffith's idea is to have a council of three hundred, to include the M.P.'s, of course, making decrees that would be carried out by the County Councils. That was Daniel O'Connell's idea, too. Yes, it's a national parliament, no question about it. But what else can we do? We don't believe we'll ever get Home Rule, or if we get something called by that name, that it will be anything like what we want or what we need."

"What do you need?"

"Good government."

Fergal noticed that Thomas said "you," as if it were not his problem at all. That was how the Irish M.P.'s always talked, as if they were benevolent inspectors from the center of the Empire, kindly listening to the grievances of the colonials. He had decided long ago that he would never fall out with Thomas, no matter what seemed to divide them, so he continued his argument in the same low key, though he could feel exasperation boiling.

"There's no secret about the Government's policy toward Ireland either—all governments—we're to produce flocks and herds and servants in saecula saeculorum in the south, and Belfast is to have shipbuilding and linen and woolen industries as a reward for past loyalties. The poverty and unemployment in Dublin are disgusting to any thinking man, ignorant or educated. The workers are going to strike there soon, and they'll have a full-scale rebellion if things don't improve. They have nothing to lose, remember."

"But Dublin has always been poor. Nothing will be done about that in our lifetime."

Morgan growled from the depths of his chair, "Something will be done, all right."

"Gerald says there has been trouble in the mill in Dublin."

"A man called Larkin is organizing the workers there, but we've come to terms. Gerald is surprisingly good, especially with people. The workmen are fond of him, partly because his father died at Parnell's funeral, but there's more than that in it. Larkin is reasonable—we cut down the hours of work and raised the pay of the senior men. He said the good example is worth a fortune to the cause." Morgan snorted. "He wanted to take me on a tour of the slums to let me see what it's like to be poor. I told him to take Gerald instead."

"Wasn't that a little unkind?"

"It did him good. Gerald is always anxious to do the right thing, God help him."

Fergal knew that whenever Morgan visited the Dublin mill,

Gerald streaked out by the back entrance and went to the Kildare Street Club for the rest of the day. Morgan had the same effect on everyone except Alice. The moment she appeared, he stopped growling and demanding quick, intelligent answers. She had broken up that session in the study the other evening, insisting on what she called civilized conversation during dinner and afterward, quoting Ellen Hussey as proof that it was improper to discuss politics in the evening. Fergal loved to get her to do this, not only for the glimpse it gave into that vanished world but as a clue to Alice herself. He needed to know a great deal about her just now, to understand why she was so furiously opposed to his friendship with Grace Burke. The reasons were expressed in her most forthright way.

"She can't be any good with that drop in her. Her father was a rogue and a scoundrel who never did a day's good in his life. And at sixty-five, to marry a girl of twenty-two! It's only the like of him would think of it."

"There's no disgrace in that if she was willing. Plenty of young girls marry older men in these times:"

"Who knows if she was willing? Or how he got her to agree? She was a sweet young girl and he was a bedraggled old goat. It wasn't decent."

"Then her mother should have stopped it."

"Her mother was only glad to be rid of her, always wailing about her three daughters that she'd never see married. It was the price of her that Pauline married the way she did."

She would say no more then but he got her back to the subject another day by asking, "Did Jerome Burke treat Pauline well? Was he good to her?"

"Fairly good, for Jerome," she admitted grudgingly. "He was better than he was with Lydia but that's not saying much. Besides, he was getting old and he was depending on her. You should ask if she was good to him."

"Was she?"

"A wonder to us all. How she put up with him and his tantrums no one could make out, but she let him have his way in everything and in the end she wound him round her little finger. When he got the stroke that finished him, you'd think she had lost the best husband in the world."

"Now, Mama, that sounds nasty," he said to rouse her.

"I could never stick him," she said between gritted teeth, quickly adding, "God rest him. He was a rotten landlord and a cruel father and a mighty poor husband to Lydia, though she was no great shakes herself. Perhaps he improved, or perhaps

Pauline had a good effect on him, or perhaps he looked at her and saw how lucky he was to get a wife like that at all. She was the prettiest little thing you ever saw."

"I remember Pauline well. She used to come to our Christmas ball. I always noticed her."

Until the last time, when he found her in the attic with Uncle James, and she never came again. He heard voices say that Pauline was to marry Jerome Burke, that Pauline had married Jerome Burke, that Pauline had a daughter, two daughters, that Pauline and Jerome had come back after many years to live in Moycullen in the old Burke house, that Jerome had a stroke, that old Jerome was dead, and always he slid away from anything to do with Pauline, until one sunny day this very Easter when he found a girl walking by herself on the banks of the lake, and her name was Grace Burke.

She was a small, fair girl with elegantly shaped chin and particularly neat hands and feet. At first he thought she must be a visitor but she walked right up to him and said, "Good morning, Mr. Connolly."

Fergal gazed at her with rapture, aware that his mouth was slightly open and his right hand lifted foolishly, his eyes fixed on hers until she looked down uneasily, blushing very beautifully all over her face and neck. When she looked up, there were tears of mortification in her eyes, which were flashing with anger as well as embarrassment as she said in a low voice, "I'm sorry. I seem to have made a mistake. I took you for a neighbor, Mr. Connolly."

"I am Fergal Connolly."

"Then why— Oh, well—I'm Grace Burke. You've forgotten me, I've been away so long."

He crawled with apology then, in terror that she would walk off and leave him and that he would never see her again. But she had no airs at all and was soon sitting beside him on the grass telling him all about herself quite naturally. She was twenty-seven years old and had done nothing in particular except be a companion to a rich old cousin of Jerome's, a Mrs. Clarke, who had been traveling in Italy for four years. The offer had come a week or two after Jerome's death and her mother had urged her to accept it, though she had not wanted to leave her so soon. Her younger sister, May, was there, so she had been persuaded to go, since it was not the sort of chance that came twice in a lifetime. It happened that the old lady was cheerful and patient, so it really had been a pleasant experience.

"And now you're back for good."

"I'm to go to her in London soon. I've just come for a short visit."

Then they looked at each other in alarm, realizing a thousand things at the same moment. Fergal felt as if he were falling over a precipice. Grace put out her hand, which was hot and dry, taking hold of his fingers, saying in a shaking voice, "I can put it off. I can write to her. I needn't go at once."

Quickly he closed his fingers over hers, longing to kiss her lips and hold them gently with his, to feel her shoulders and then her whole body soften in his arms. He drew away from her and looked again, as if he had never seen her before.

"Grace, Grace. Was that wrong?"

"No."

Now he could see only the top of her head, the soft, fair hair, like an infant's hair, gold in the sunlight as she leaned against him for one delightful moment before moving away and beginning to stand up. She watched him compassionately while he made more apologies and then said softly, "Please stop, Fergal. It's all right, really it is. You didn't do anything." And then, so quietly that he hardly heard it, "Don't spoil it."

He walked with her to the back entrance of the Burke place and watched her as far as the wicket gate of the stable yard, then he bounced home as lightly as a bird—Fergal, thirty-seven years of age, behaving like a boy of seventeen, already halfway to being in love with a girl he scarcely knew.

65

He began to question Alice about her and was brought up short by the sharp, sour answers he received, with something personal in their disapproval. At last he said, "But you're talking about the girl's father, not about the girl herself. Who on earth can be responsible for a father? I scarcely remember Burke but I can tell you she's not in the least like him. He was a great, coarse, black man. Once when he came here he cut at the dogs with his whip for fun—I remember that very well—and he laughed when they howled. I hated him for that. It must be that she takes after her mother."

"Her grandmother, Mrs. D'Arcy, had the brains of a hen but there was no harm in her. She was too easily frightened, that's all. When Mimi married Dr. Conroy she came complaining to me—to me, imagine it—that the other girls would never get gentlemen for husbands now because of him, but I knew she was glad enough to get rid of Mimi. I always thought that was why she allowed Pauline to marry Jerome. I haven't seen Pauline for at least two years. I'm told she doesn't go out anymore, not even to church, but there isn't much life around here now anyway, compared with the old times."

Fergal remembered that he had always liked Pauline when he met her at those ghastly parties for children at big houses, where you were driven for miles in the carriage, dressed either in tight velvet with unmanageable buttons, so that going to the lavatory was agonizingly embarrassing, or in ridiculous fancy dress. He particularly hated a clown's costume that he had had to wear several times. Pauline had found him weeping with rage because of it at the Bateses' one Christmas when he was eight years old. She had sat on the stairs with him then and dried his eyes and advised him to tell Alice that he didn't enjoy dressing up, and that it would be quite proper to go in ordinary clothes in the future. Even a velvet suit was better than this. He had followed her advice and had shortened his sufferings, and had almost forgotten that she had been so kind to him.

After several days of meeting Grace at the same time, both gravitating to the bank of the lake without an appointment, at last he said, "We're not children, Grace. I must take you home and speak to your mother. I've known her all my life, after all."

Pauline had dimmed with age, though she was barely fifty years old. She had developed a habit of stroking her forehead with the fingers of her right hand, as if she had a perpetual headache, and looking blankly into distant parts of the room, her eyes widened as if she were seeing a ghost. The second daughter, May, was hefty and tall, with smooth black hair and thick eyebrows and a long, striding walk, the antithesis of Grace in every way. Her loud, managing voice grated on his ears. Her mouth had a downward curve at the corners, too firm, giving her a sardonic look. The room they sat in was shabby, the covers and curtains faded to a grayish white, almost the color of Pauline's hair.

A slatternly parlormaid poured the tea into rosy old china cups and then May sent her away. Grace sat close by Fergal on the edge of a low chair. Casting around for something to say, he remembered that Pauline had been a good horsewoman, and he asked her if she ever rode now.

"I'm not strong enough anymore," she said pettishly and then brightened. "You remember how I used to love the hunt?"

462

Grace said in astonishment, "Did you really, Mama?"

"Before I was married, yes. It was not so easy afterward. I've often thought of going out again, just to see it."

"Nonsense, Mother!" May said heartily. "It would look ridiculous. And anyway, you'd never stand a day on horseback. You'd want to come home halfway through."

Her laugh was like the neigh of a horse.

"You hunt?" Fergal asked expressionlessly of May.

"Yes, with the Blazers. I live for hunting. It's all over now till September. I don't know how I'll survive till then." Again that neighing laugh. "What about you, Mr. Connolly? Why don't you come out with us? But of course, the Connollys never hunt."

"It's not a family tradition."

"You're all more interested in politics."

The sardonic tone and the wrinkled upper lip forecast a bitchy old woman, and in a flash he saw a resemblance to her father in the hate-filled dark-brown eyes turned on him like the cold eyes of a snarling dog. Still she smiled, showing two upper teeth like tombstones. No wonder Alice was alarmed for him. He dared not glance at Grace to see how she was taking it.

Pauline said unexpectedly, "Every reasonable person is interested in politics. I'll never forget how I felt when Mr. Parnell died. It was like the end of the world. Until then, we had something to live for."

"What nonsense, Mother!" May said sharply. "You often heard Father say that it was Parnell who ruined us."

Pauline turned on her and said softly, "You know nothing about it. You're speaking of things you don't understand."

May flushed and after a second's hesitation reverted to the laugh, which seemed to be her method both of defense and attack. She was angry with Fergal now, as the cause of her mother's rebellion. Easy enough to see that she had the life bullied out of the other two, with her horses and her dogs and her hearty ways. How could she be the sister—the younger sister, too—of gentle, sweet Grace, who was sitting so still beside him?

He was on his way home before the explanation occurred to him, so suddenly that he gave a shout of laughter almost the equal to May's. The more he thought about it, the more logical it seemed. He had to consult Alice at once. He found her in her favorite place, the upstairs drawing room with the view out over the avenue and the lake, her chair by a tall, wide window. She was pretending to crochet a purse of green-and-red silk but it could not make much progress while she kept glancing toward the avenue gates.

She made a move to get up when Fergal opened the door and then sank back disappointed, saying, "Oh, Fergal. I thought Papa might have come by the back way. He's late."

"No, he's not late. It's only five, and Eddie is driving him. Mama, I want to talk to you."

He looked with affection at her, sitting up so straight, her white hair neat, her dark-blue eyes measuring him as if she suspected him of having all kinds of secrets.

She laid down the crocheting on the table at her elbow with an air of being glad to be rid of it and said, "Well? Here I am."

"Mama, you're the only person I can ask."

"Well? You're like a girl. What is it?"

"It's not easy to explain." He chuckled suddenly. "You should be pleased." He watched her control her curiosity and exasperation until he had her at simmering point before he said, "I think that my Grace is not Jerome Burke's daughter at all. I've just been there and I've had a close look at the other daughter, a big, black, horsy one with a graveyard smile, the image of Jerome Burke."

"That's no way to speak about a lady. Perhaps Grace takes after Pauline."

"Yes, of course, but there's more than that. She should have some resemblance, however dim."

"Then what— who—"

"James Fahy. Years ago, when I was nine or ten, I saw them together in the attic the night of our Christmas ball."

"You always saw too much."

"I'm glad now that I saw that. Mama, when Pauline was married off to Jerome Burke, perhaps she was already—"

"*Enceinte?* That was her mother's word. Poor little Pauline! But James— I sometimes wondered about him and I wanted to ask Papa what he thought, but I didn't want to make trouble between them. Papa can be very proper at times. James— yes, that could be it." Alice sighed. "I'm sorry now that I never had a proper look at those girls. Grace is the fair one— I have seen them only at a distance. That would make Grace a half sister of Gerald and all the others. What about Anna? I wonder if she suspected any of this?" She was beginning to look agitated now, as all the implications began to make themselves felt. "It means that Jerome had nothing to do with Grace. That's something to be thankful for, though some of Amy's children were nice enough. Heredity is a funny thing. If it

464

could stop at one generation it wouldn't matter, but a throwback to Jerome would be bad business."

"Aren't you rather running ahead, Mama?"

"Life runs ahead and it carries you along with it. You think you're going to be able to change it but you can scarcely do anything."

"You've done plenty."

She was gazing at him with an odd expression, her mind on some distant thought from which her next words sprang spontaneously.

"You're so like Papa. Poor James was never really happy, though we tried our best. Do you think Pauline loved him, or was it just a passing madness?"

"That was what gave me the first lead. It was something she said about Parnell, some tone in her voice that made a link with James. I think she was in love with him. Mama, can you imagine how it would be to love one man so much and be married off to another? She must have been through hell."

"I can imagine it very well."

"So there can be no more objection to Grace on the grounds of heredity. If James was good enough for Anna, he should be good enough for me."

She glared at him for a second, suspecting a trap, not wishing to make the point that she would not have agreed to the marriage of James and Anna if she had known what his morals were like.

"I'll bring her to see you," he said after a moment.

"Are you going to tell her what you think?"

"Good heavens, no! Why should I? She seems to have accepted Jerome as her father, and obviously Pauline wanted it like that. Grace seems to have been quite fond of him. I can't help wondering if he knew she was not his child."

"You seem quite certain of it, on very little evidence," Alice said sardonically. "I wonder if that was the one good thing that every man does in his lifetime. Years ago, just after Samuel was killed, I met Jerome in his own house and tried to make him do his good deed but it was no use. He turned the people out into the rain and the cold without mercy, and all the same there was something soft and pathetic about him that I've never forgotten. He seemed to be lost in the world. If what you say is true, Pauline may have done as much for him as he did for her." She broke off to turn toward the window, her eyes shining with excitement. "It's the motorcar. Can you hear it?"

"Yes."

He listened, watching her with amusement, and a minute later they heard it distinctly, chugging up the last part of the avenue. It stopped while Eddie got out and slowly opened the lawn gates. Morgan moved over into the driver's seat and drove furiously up to the steps, stopping in a cloud of dust and flying gravel. He loved the motorcar but had promised not to drive on the road again after he had struck two donkeys in one day. Alice stood at the window looking down, until he climbed out, pushed his goggles up onto his forehead, swept off his cap so that his white hair stood on end and waved to her.

She sat down slowly, arranging her flowing black skirt in a seemly way around her ankles, saying, "Do you remember Mike Sherwin?"

"Of course I do. I used to spend hours with him in his room, hiding from Master Fahy. I even hid under the bed once when the Master came up there looking for me and nearly choked trying not to sneeze."

It was the old cook's room above the kitchen, which had been Mike's later, until he died. They had heard Fahy stumbling up the stairs, so Mike had been able to push Fergal well in out of sight before the old man had appeared in the doorway breathing fire and threats against the little good-for-nothing idler. Fergal had been terrified of the beating that Fahy would give him when next they met but Fahy had quite forgotten what had happened, though he was vaguely aware that there had been something. It was the first time that Fergal had realized that he was breaking up.

"You were a little devil," Alice said dispassionately. "Well, Mike used to go to D'Arcy's when he came here, but he didn't stay there, just spent a few hours in the kitchen and had something to eat, and of course he picked up all the news. Now I'm remembering that he came and told us that Pauline was to be married, and that she was crying all the time, and the servants were worried about it and couldn't make out why. They didn't know all about the D'Arcys as ours knew about us. They were made to keep separate, and when they were in the room, sometimes the family would speak French, very rude, of course, but it seems it's often done in England. Mike thought it natural that she should cry at the notion of being married to a cranky old widower. He knew Jerome well enough from going to his house on his rounds, though he got precious little there. The strangest thing was that Mr. D'Arcy never spoke to Pauline after her engagement was announced—every time she came into the room, he got up and walked out. Mike told us that. Yes, it all hangs together. And it seems the marriage must have been Pauline's own idea, or her mother's. It was certainly not her father's. We'll never find out now, unless Pauline tells us, and that's not likely after all these years. Did she welcome you?"

"Yes."

"Then let's do things properly. Tomorrow you can bring Grace here to see me." She reached out suddenly and took his hand. "I'll be glad to see you married. You've been swallowed up in politics so long, I was afraid you'd never have time to find a wife. I thought I had ruined you by dragging you around to those meetings when you were too young for it." She seemed to be talking to herself, still holding his hand absent-mindedly, looking every minute of her age. Then she glanced up sharply, saying, "And let me tell you, a huge secret between married people is a curse. Don't make up your mind that you'll never tell Grace about James."

"Later on, perhaps."

She let him go then, saying, "Go and find Papa and send him here, please. I haven't seen him since morning."

66

"So there really will be a rising," Morgan said.

They had come back exhausted from Glasnevin Cemetery, and he knew that Fergal was watching him anxiously to see how he had fared in the heat and the crowds. Alice was resting in her room as she always did at this time of the day, and he was glad to be alone with Fergal, who kept glancing at him while he poured the whiskey, holding the glass up to the light as if he needed to check on the measure.

Morgan had learned to sit very quietly when he had done something dangerous, but going to the funeral of his old friend O'Donovan Rossa today had been so exciting that he felt himself beginning to chatter. It was no joke being eighty-six. In the cemetery, while Father O'Flanagan was saying the prayers, he had noticed uneasy looks directed at him by many of the younger men, as if they feared he would collapse.

"Poor old Jerry!" he said as Fergal handed him his glass. "I never thought I'd have the pleasure of burying him—I thought he'd lie in foreign soil. So many died away from Ireland in the end." Hearing his voice shake he sipped the whiskey carefully and settled back in his chair. "That was a good show today, as good as Parnell's. John O'Leary would have been pleased. So would my brother Martin. I'm sorry they didn't live to see it, but we were well represented."

"What makes you say there really will be a rising?"

"I read the signs. When I see a turnout like that at the graveside of an old Fenian, and hear a speech like the one young Pearse made, I know where I am. That was a fine speech. 'The fools, the fools, the fools, they have left us our Fenian dead, and while Ireland holds these graves'—whatever the words were—'Ireland unfree can never be at peace.' Great stuff. He has an ear for rhetoric as good as Parnell and better. That has a Biblical sound about it, though he gave it off so quietly. And the Volunteer uniforms were very businesslike, and the men who weren't in uniform were well drilled. I know the look of a countryman who has been taught the use of arms. I'm reminded of John Mitchel's prayer: 'Send war in our time, O Lord.' There is a war, and here is the opportunity. Everything points toward it." He paused and after a moment asked softly, "Are you in their counsels?"

"What a question for an old Fenian to ask!"

"Then you can tell me about Connolly and the Citizen Army. He should be with you—will he be?"

"He's suspicious of us, naturally, because we're not workers, but we hope to bring him round. He'll realize that we must get our freedom first and all the others things will follow." Fergal stopped and then said ruefully, "Now who's gabbling?"

"I told you I had guessed it already," Morgan said. He sat in silence, trying to calm himself. At last he asked, "How old are you, Fergal?"

"Forty-five."

"I was thirty-six when I went to jail in '65, and there were many men older than I."

"Pearse doesn't think it will be jail."

"What about Grace?"

"She knows about it and she agrees that there's nothing else we can do."

"When will it be?"

"Before the war ends. We'll have to get representation at the peace conference, whenever that comes. If there's a real threat of conscription, the rising may be quite soon. You'll have to read the signs, as you said."

Of course they would never tell him more than that. How could they? At this stage of his life he could be no more than a mascot. In the last few years he had gradually become aware of what the young men were planning and had noticed the changed tone of the speeches as they abandoned hope of getting Home Rule by peaceful means. Three years ago he had listened to Pearse make a speech in Sackville Street, at a Home Rule meeting, using Irish so that his words were understood only by those for whom they were intended. "If we are cheated now there will be red war in Ireland." That was in 1912. A year later he was writing the same thing openly, urging every man to learn to handle a gun in preparation for the glorious day when they would rise up against foreign domination and prove their manhood. On a different level, Connolly was saying the same thing to the workers, maddened by the confident cruelty of the bosses during the great strike. They were every bit as bad as the landlords, in their way, and the landlords had never learned anything except by force. Pearse had been to America and old John Devoy had recognized a kindred spirit. Where else could it all lead? The air held the same tang as it had done in the days of *The Irish People,* when John O'Leary was writing his editorials.

Had those things really happened to him? Morgan shivered still at the memory of the police bursting into the offices of *The Irish People,* moving out the printing press, dragging them all off to jail, and afterward the horrors of the trial when they had fully expected to be hanged.

With a war raging in Europe, what mercy could there be now for the leaders of an Irish rising? The Irish who favored the English war would do nothing to defend them. In Dublin Morgan had heard many middle-aged men of the upper classes declare emotionally that they had "sent their sons to fight." What did they know about fighting? The young men looked dashing in military uniforms for a few days and then disappeared by transport to France, whence presently a telegram came to announce that they were dead. If conscription were introduced into Ireland, the work begun by the great hunger would be completed, the Irish race would be exterminated once and for all, to the great comforts of the British Empire. All the young men would be called up, since there were no reserved occupations in this down-and-out country. If the Irish had to die, at least they should die for Ireland.

This, to Morgan's mind, was the strongest argument in favor of a rising. It could never be more than a protest but at least it should have the old determined look. The Irish Party seemed a spent force and the promised Home Rule Bill was a farce—the native government, if it were ever established, would be no better that a Country Council, after all that effort. John Redmond's speech at the beginning of the war, in which he pledged the support of the Irish Volunteers to the Empire, had raised a horselaugh of pure derision from the old Fenians, yet thousands of Irish Volunteers had joined the British Army because of it. The wheel came round and round, and so it would do until the unlikely day when Ireland would take her place among the nations of the earth, as Robert Emmett had put it so neatly.

Morgan felt old and tired and confused, that day of O'Donovan Rossa's funeral. What was left for him now? He was two years older than O'Donovan Rossa, about ready to do his last duty as a Fenian by providing an occasion for a demonstration and a stirring speech. Old age was even more distressing than youth, and God knows that was bad enough. At least there had been health and strength then, too much of both at times, and always there had been so much to do that there had scarcely been time to think, except during the nightmare of Dartmoor.

His own rocky legs and Alice's near-blindness kept them close together now, thankful that their hearing at least was good. Without that, they could not have had the long chats they both loved, when they sat close by the fire, Alice's knees covered by a rug—she was always cold now—and Morgan in his slippers and the velvet jacket that she had embroidered around the collar while her sight was still good. In Dublin they sat in the big drawing room, in Moycullen in the study, with a fire even in summer, waiting for everyone to come in for a visit. Alice kept a box of fudge at her elbow for the small children and an embroidered black satin bag full of crown and half-crown pieces, and even half sovereigns, for the older ones, pressing them into their hands and folding their fingers down on the coins with a devilish, conspiratorial twinkle in her eye. Even Thomas's eldest son, Sam, who was now twenty-five, enjoyed this ritual gift and told her that he would spend the money on cigars and wine. Sam was to be married soon and then there would be more babies, happy occasions, since they were healthier than they used to be long ago. The great-grandchildren were the most amusing. Walter and Gerald had provided five each, and the girls had seven between them. Morgan had noticed that Alice got a sensual pleasure from holding the babies in her arms, the same as a child gets from holding a smooth, well-shaped stone. Morgan himself just examined the shape of their foreheads and the width of their hands to see how they were likely to turn out, and traced resemblances to Alice or Samuel.

Most of all, he just wanted to have Alice to himself, and when Fergal had gone that day he went to find her. She was pottering around their bedroom, collecting things she imagined she would need for the rest of the afternoon.

As he came in she said, "I was thinking, Morgan, of how I used to sail downstairs when I was young and strong, and then ring the bell for my maid to bring me one thing after another as I thought of it. Such selfishness! The girls were perpetually trotting up and down stairs, carrying silly baskets of needles and thread and all sorts of other rubbish." She peered at him, arching her still-elegant neck like a bird in an attempt to see him better. "How did the funeral go? There are too many funerals nowadays."

"It was an old-style funeral except that long ago we wouldn't have dared to wear uniforms."

"Did Fergal wear his?"

"So you knew he had one!"

"Well, was he wearing it?"

"No. Pearse and several of the others did." Morgan sat down in the armchair and pressed his hand to his eyes. "I was talking just now to Fergal about the whole state of things. Have you talked to him?"

"A little, but mostly to Grace. Sometimes I wish we could have brought Fergal up like Thomas, nice and conservative, never getting dangerously involved in anything, always on the sidelines."

"That's not fair to Thomas. It took great courage for him to abstain from Parliament. He's like Samuel in that way. It's as near as he could go to fighting. Samuel was a man of peace."

"Yes, and he suffered more than the fighters sometimes. Do you know, Morgan, today I was thinking that if Samuel were alive now he would be exactly one hundred years old. He was born in the year of the big battle of Waterloo. Well, let's not think about Samuel. I've seen Fergal's uniform. Grace showed it to me one day at the house, beautiful dark-green stuff, made to keep out the rain, she said, and a slouch hat. What do you think is going to happen, Morgan?"

"There will be a rising."

"Yes."

"They'll be beaten into the ground, just as we were."

"It's never quite the same. This time it feels different. Of course it will be different."

"Yes, yes, of course."

Stupid of him to have spoken his mind. Though she still had some vision, she had developed that unnerving way of blind people of not concealing her tears, as if not seeing the changing expression of others had made her forget that her own would show.

"Every rising is different from the last one," Morgan said. "The reason is the only thing that remains the same. If the British Government would make even one big gesture, or even show one sign of good will instead of this perpetual contempt and prevarication, there might be no need of a rising at all. But they've proved up to the hilt that they'll never give away anything without a fight. It has become a virtue to them, to hold on to what they have. Nothing but bullets and blood will convince them that we must have freedom. That's how it will be until the day of judgment. Every generation will have to make its protest because it will be driven to it, and every one will fail. If I were young again, I'd be in this one up to my neck, and so would you."

"Yes, I'd be in it."

"Let's be glad we're represented, then. Father Kenny would tell us very firmly, if he were here, that there's no escape from conscience."

"Poor Father Ned. I'm glad I was with him in his last fight. He was laughing when he came running up the boreen that day, elbowing everyone out of the way."

"Grace is a blessing," Morgan said, still thinking of Fergal. "She has all the children speaking Irish. They really love it, and speak it so well now. I had a long conversation with little James the other day and he didn't make a single mistake. How can they be the grandchildren of that bastard Burke?"

"They're not," Alice said with a chuckle. "Grace's father was James Fahy—his best mistake."

"What are you saying, Alice!"

"It's true. Fergal guessed it before they were married, and now when I see the children I have no doubts at all. Little James and Michael and Tommy and Ruth—even little Morgan has a look of James."

"And you never told me! How could you keep a secret like that?"

"How could I tell it either? Supposing you had let it slip some time, or supposing you— I don't know what could have happened but I just couldn't bring myself. Now you're furious, but try to see my side of it. Wasn't it one of those secrets that must be kept between two people?"

"Yes, I suppose so. Does Grace know?"

"I don't even know that. I never spoke to Fergal about it after the first time he asked me what I thought. It seemed indecent. But I often thanked God that we hadn't the Burke drop in the family. Pauline doesn't seem to have told Grace— she was very faithful to old Jerome. Now the proof is there in the children, if you look for it. Morgan, will you be able to pretend you don't know this? Perhaps I shouldn't have told you."

"Of course you should have told me. Have you any other secrets like that?"

"Morgan, please don't glare at me. I can't bear it."

"All right. I won't."

With a tremendous effort, twitching his mouth angrily at the corners, his eyes darting furiously from side to side, he went to her and took her arm. How could she see he was glaring? She couldn't but she felt it, and it took a full minute of stroking her hair before her arms stopped quivering and her hand felt its way into his.

Then he could say lightly, "Now give me some of that junk to carry and we'll go down and sit by the fire."

67

Morgan was looking for Fergal but Sackville Street was so crowded that he had lost hope of finding him. The stories were crazy—that all the railway stations had been seized and that thousands of rebels were marching on Dublin, that men, women and children in dozens were manning barricades and shooting down unarmed policemen, that the Volunteers were marching into private houses without by-your-leave and turning the inhabitants out or making them prisoners, that the shops were all being looted by the mob. He knew that bit was true. He had seen it himself—men and women dancing along, wearing pyramids of hats and festooned with gold bracelets and necklaces.

Several dead bodies of civilians lay here and there in the street.

The sunlight bothered him but otherwise he felt well enough. Alice would be furious with him for going out like this, wandering about at his age, asking for trouble. He would be careful, but he was a long way from being exhausted yet. Sackville Street already looked a wreck. From the steps of the hotel he could see the barricades of sandbags at the broken Post Office windows, with rifle barrels poking out over them, and the overturned trams and motorcars at either side. Inside the Post Office, people were hurrying about, and then several Volunteers came out and tried to move the crowd back. It was the strangest thing of all to see how the ragged women whose husbands were at the Front came rushing forward again and again, screaming curses, even kneeling down in the street with their hands clenched high to curse more effectively. The Volunteers fired several shots over their heads but no one took any notice.

"Come to the Imperial Hotel on Monday at twelve," Fergal's note had said, "and we shall see what we shall see."

It was a quotation from the fairy tales that used to excite him so dangerously when he was small, and it had become a sort of password between them. Morgan had had no doubt that this was the promised rising. He was in good time to see the green, white and orange flag hauled up, and the cavalry charge in which the first shots were fired. Now while he watched, Pearse came out of the Post Office and walked to the middle of the street, accompanied by several others, all wearing Volunteer uniforms. Their purposeful manner made the whole unruly crowd fall silent. Morgan felt a stab of jealousy as he recognized Tom Clarke, the old Fenian who kept the cigarette and paper shop in North Frederick Street. But Tom was not yet sixty, though he looked much older—a child by comparison with Morgan.

He moved closer and found himself wedged between a flamboyant-looking middle-aged Englishman and an excited girl who kept lifting herself up on her toes to see better. Pearse had a document the size of a small poster in his hand, which he began to read in a clear, resonant, unhurried voice.

" 'The Provisional Government of the Irish Republic to the people of Ireland. Irishmen and Irishwomen: In the name of God and of the dead generations from which she receives her old tradition of nationhood, Ireland, through us, summons her children to her flag and strikes for her freedom.

" 'Having organized and trained her manhood through her secret revolutionary organization, the Irish Republican Brotherhood, and through her open military organizations, the Irish Volunteers and the Irish Citizen Army, having patiently perfected her discipline, having resolutely waited for the right moment to reveal itself, she now seizes that moment, and supported by her exiled children in America and by gallant allies in Europe, but relying in the first on her own strength, she strikes in full confidence of victory.

" 'We declare the right of the people of Ireland to the own-ership of Ireland, and to the unfettered control of Irish destinies, to be sovereign and indefeasible. The long usurpation of that right by a foreign people and government has not extinguished the right, nor can it ever be extinguished except by the destruction of the Irish people. In every generation the Irish people have asserted their right to national freedom and sovereignty; six times during the past three hundred years they have asserted it in arms. Standing on that fundamental right and again asserting it in arms in the face of the world, we hereby proclaim the Irish Republic as a Sovereign Independent State, and we pledge our lives and the lives of our comrades-in-arms in the cause of its freedom, of its welfare, and of its exaltation among the nations.

" 'The Irish Republic is entitled to, and hereby claims, the allegiance of every Irishman and Irishwoman. The Republic guarantees religious and civil liberty, equal rights and equal opportunities to all its citizens, and declares its resolve to pursue the happiness and prosperity of the whole nation and of all its parts, cherishing all the children of the nation equally, and oblivious of the differences carefully fostered by an alien government, which have divided a minority from the majority in the past.

" 'Until our arms have brought the opportune moment for the establishment of a permanent National Government, representative of the whole people of Ireland and elected by the suffrages of all her men and women, the Provisional Government, hereby constituted, will administer the civil and military affairs of the Republic in trust for the people.' "

"By God, they mean business!" said the Englishman in an awed tone at Morgan's elbow.

Pearse was going on.

" 'We place the cause of the Irish Republic under the protection of the Most High God, Whose blessing we invoke upon our arms, and we pray that no one who serves that cause will dishonor it by cowardice, inhumanity, or rapine. In this supreme hour the Irish nation must, by its valor and discipline and by the readiness of its children to sacrifice themselves for the common good, prove itself worthy of the august destiny to which it is called.' " He looked up and said in a conversational tone, "This proclamation is signed on behalf of the Provisional Government by seven people, Thomas Clarke, Sean Mac Diarmada, P. H. Pearse, James Connolly, Thomas MacDonagh, Eamonn Ceannt and Joseph Plunkett."

"Those are the others," the girl said, clutching at Morgan's sleeve. "Look, he's giving out copies of the proclamation. I'm going to get one!"

She elbowed her way vigorously to the front and got one of the documents, waving it triumphantly above her head as she pushed her way back.

Morgan said, "Hide it. It looks dangerous."

"A good idea." She glanced at it quickly and then stuffed it, roughly folded, into the pocket of her skirt. "You're Mr. Connolly," she said then. "You've forgotten me."

"Shouldn't I have?"

"Eleanor de Lacy."

"Of course—forgive me." Hugh's niece, of course. "What are you doing here?"

"I might ask the same of you. Is there anyone with you?"

"No. I got word that something was going to happen and I came along to see."

The crowd was pushing and jostling again, the street clearing gradually as they realized that sniping had begun. Some people were running into the hotels but Morgan thought them a poor refuge.

"I've got a motorcar in Marlborough Street," he said, "if Johnny has waited for me. I can get him to drive you home."

"What about you?"

"I can't go yet. I've got to find out where Fergal is."

"I'll stay with you, if I may."

She hooked her arm through his elbow and propelled him across the street, past Nelson's Pillar where a Volunteer was pasting up a copy of the proclamation and tearing down recruiting posters, surrounded by a curious crowd of men and women. They took the last bit at a run and arrived panting on the steps of the Post Office where their way was blocked by a boy of about sixteen, carrying a rifle and wearing a slouch hat, the only other mark besides the rifle of his soldiering.

Morgan looked past him to where the tall doors stood partly open and heard the boy say eagerly to Eleanor, "The whole country is rising. They're marching from Cork and Donegal and the midlands. The Germans have landed to help us. We'll have Dublin taken in no time. Such a beautiful day, and all the Army officers out at the races."

A man in Volunteer uniform, whom he remembered vaguely from some meeting or other, came out of the building, saying, "Mr. Connolly, it's good to see you here. Have you come to give us your blessing?"

"That's easy—you have it. Thank God I've lived to see the day. Is my son Fergal with you?"

"No, he's at Boland's Mills with de Valera. Don't go down there—it's a hot spot already. Have you a way of getting home?"

"Yes, and I'm escorted, as you see."

"I came to ask if you need help in there," Eleanor said, leaving the little sentry to join them. "Cooking, nursing, anything? Please let me in."

"We're all right here," the man said, smiling. "You could try the Four Courts. Anna Flaherty is there. Ask for Ned Daly."

"I will, I will!"

Overjoyed, she dragged Morgan away, her only concern now to get to her assignment.

As she trotted him along he was saying to himself, "Clarke, Daly—how many more Fenians and sons of Fenians? Anna Flaherty—Thomas' daughter—where are all my grandchildren? Fergal—I ought to be there—it would be ridiculous even to offer myself." That had been his thought at the Post Office but he had had the wit to stop himself, foreseeing the understanding smile, the unwelcome sympathy for his decrepit condition. The girl would leave him with his driver and go off to her work, whatever it turned out to be, but he had to go home like a good boy and tell Alice what he had been doing. What would happen next? Anything was possible. How could he wait quietly at home to hear it?

They were in a side street off the quays. He pulled Eleanor into a doorway and turned her around to face him, saying, "Look here, all my life I've worked toward this day. I don't feel tired. I'd say I'm in better health than some of those men who came out with Pearse to read the proclamation. Did you see the tall, thin one with the white face? I'm going with you to the Four Courts!"

"You are!"

"Yes, and dare you try to stop me."

"I won't." Her eyes were dancing with amusement and delight. "Come along, then."

They kept away from the quays after that, walking quickly through a maze of back streets, hearing rifle fire intermittently and hiding in doorways whenever they caught sight of running soldiers. Green Street was down there—he felt his heart bound at the thought.

He clutched Eleanor's arm closer and said, "We'll be each

other's alibi—I'm protecting you, you're protecting me. I was driven here in the Black Maria for my trial in '65. That's fifty-one years ago—I can hardly believe it. Did you know young Anna was in this?"

"Of course. Letty and George are, too, and Sam is a big shot. He got us all into it. He's in the G.P.O. with Commandant Connolly."

"Sam!"

Rightly called Sam, the image of his grandfather, tall, angular, determined.

"How are you feeling?"

"I'll be all right. I just hope they'll let us in."

At the big arched gateway at the side of the Four Courts they were challenged by the sentry, older and more anxious-looking than the last one.

"We were told to ask for Ned Daly."

"Who told you?"

"A man at the G.P.O. For God's sake, let us in!" Morgan shouted as a burst of rifle fire fluttered up the street.

He let them pass and they found themselves in the courtyard, then running for the steep steps at the side where someone was holding the door open. Inside the building it was oddly quiet but they went quickly along a passageway to the great front hall where the windows gave a view of the street. Over by them, a number of young men were standing by sandbag barricades over which their rifles pointed out into the street. One of them fired a shot, then another, carefully aiming at some target across the river.

Almost at once he saw Eleanor disappear by way of a small door at the back of the hall, while a tall, thin-faced young man in Volunteer uniform came over to him, asking sharply, "What's this? How did you get in?"

"The sentry let us in, under pressure. We were sent here."

"Who sent you?"

"Someone at the G.P.O."

"You're Morgan Connolly?"

"Yes."

"I remember you. I met you in Limerick with my Uncle John."

"Ned Daly!" Morgan grasped his hand. "I wish to God I were twenty years younger. This is a great day for Ireland!"

"How are things at the G.P.O.?"

"Exciting. We saw Pearse read the proclamation and before that I saw the Lancers charge down the street. There's ructions, all right. No one can stop the looting—"

"So they're looting!"

"Of course. It's to be expected. It will stop when things get more serious. You have a good position here, right on the route from Phoenix Park."

"Yes, and Heuston is across the river at the Mendicity Institute. He won't be able to hold out long but it's well worth it all the same." Daly laughed with pure joy. "It's good to have an old Fenian here. What are they saying in Sackville Street?"

"That the Germans will land and help and the English will be beaten—a young lad said that."

"God help him. What do you think?"

"As you do. It's worth it, all the same."

"They'll shoot us all afterward if they catch us. I'd rather fight to the death."

"That's every soldier's dream."

"You know you'll have to go?"

"Yes. As I came along with the girl, I had a foolish idea that I could stay with you but of course I'm too old. All I could do now is take messages."

"We have the boys and girls for that. But you can go back and tell that you've spoken to me and that we're all in good spirits. I'll let you out myself."

68

He went with Morgan to the same door of the courtyard, opened it a crack and then let him out quickly. A minute later the whole episode seemed unreal. As he made his way back toward Sackville Street he felt horribly alone. Now every doorway was a threat. He kept away from the river sneaking along Mary Lane to Capel Street, until from the corner of Mary Street he could see the length of Henry Street and into Sackville Street. If only he had better sight—but in any case Nelson's Pillar obstructed the view just there. It also made a shelter, under which he was able to cross Capel Street and so reach the corner of North King Street and Bolton Street. He was beginning to feel very tired, and hungry, too, and was surprised to find that it was almost three o'clock. He wondered what Johnny had done, whether he had been able to wait in the street all this time. A good job they hadn't brought the horses. To get to Marlborough Street, Morgan would have to cross Sackville Street by the Parnell Monument, which had been used as cover by the cavalry a short time ago. Other people were walking along by the walls of the houses now, instead of out in the street as they had done at first. He followed their example and reached the corner of Sackville Street.

Down by the Post Office, several trams had been blown up, blocking the way into Talbot Street. It would be crazy to cross Sackville Street. He began to move down toward the Post Office but felt his old knees totter in the most maddening way. He was thankful that he was still as thin and straight as he had always been. Something of the old excitement filled him, the ugly excitement of the night he had fled on horseback from Moycullen House, something that belonged to youth. It gave him the extra wit to keep out of plain view, dodging from doorway to doorway. Several times he heard bullets crack off the walls and realized that a sniper had spotted him. Despair filled him at the thought of dying here in a city battle, by accident. He crouched as he crossed the wall space from one doorway to another, ducking in and spreading his hands flat on the panels. One particular doorway was narrow, beside a shop, not set deeply enough to conceal him, but now he felt it give behind him and a hand drew him inside. He was in a narrow, dark hallway, covered in old linoleum, with rickety stairs leading up to the floors above. A bent old woman was looking up into his face, her eyes shining oddly in the gloom. She gave a cackle of amusement.

"You're as old as myself. I thought you were one of the young fellows, with the way you were sprinting along. Here, lean against the wall. You'll be all right in a minute. It's no exercise at our time of life. That's right—in two shakes you'll be singing 'God save Ireland,' like the jokers in the Post Office. They have to keep their hearts up. When the legs is under you, we'll be going upstairs. Come on, now, my hearty."

He straightened up, still shaking but well able to follow her slowly up the stairs, hanging onto the banister as she did, hauling themselves along like two slugs traveling up a branch. She stopped for breath on the first landing and then continued on her way, wasting no more energy to talk. How high was this place of hers. A memory came into Morgan's head, of seeing some Volunteers with pikes in Dublin, only a few months ago. Pikes! They'd be as well armed with bows and arrows. Another flight, then another and they were at the top of the house, with lower ceilings and a door hanking askew, with a latch instead of a lock to keep it shut. She was moving faster now and was inside before he had climbed the last three steps. He could hear her talking to someone in there, and as he walked into the attic room he saw three young men crouching behind a barricade of sandbags at the front windows. One wore full Volunteer uniform and the others had bits and pieces, a belt, puttees, a bandolier, a hat. All had some sort of firearm. They looked very young.

A fair-haired one with a Mauser automatic pistol hanging loosely in his hand said, "We saw you trying to get down the street. You'd never have made it. Where do you live?"

"In Donnybrook. I left my man with the motorcar in Marlborough Street."

They looked at one another with raised eyebrows. He hurried to explain and saw them relax their suspicions gradually as they realized who he was—not he but his descendants, and Samuel's descendants.

The fair-haired man said, "We decided to pull you in when you'd come to the door. We wondered what you were at. This is Auntie Ellen. Give him some tea, Auntie."

She did, while they consulted among themselves. The oldest of them, a lanky, dark man with a strong Cork accent, never took his eyes off the street while they talked. On the side wall there were two high windows, no more than a foot square, with a single pane of glass that could be moved in and out. A soapbox stood under one of them and from time to time the fair-haired man would stand on this and take a look out into Henry Street. The gray stone of the Post Office walls cut the light out of the little room. It was furnished with only an iron bed, a makeshift wardrobe consisting of hooks and a flowered curtain on a string, and several upended orange boxes on one of which stood her gas ring. Her water can, a milk jug, two pots, a frying pan, two mugs and several chipped plates were kept in the boxes.

"It's a palace," she said sardonically, watching him, as she handed him the tea. "Are you hungry?"

"Yes."

"I'll make some flannel cakes for the lot of yez."

They were pancakes, which she made expertly, using flour out of a large bag that she said the boys had brought her when they came. They tasted delicious, though they were only flour and milk, and he felt strength come back. While she was cooking, one of the men laid down his rifle and went out of the room.

The fair-haired man said, "He'll get a message to your Johnny, if he's still there, to go home and tell your family that you're safe. You won't be able to leave here for a while."

"You should have told me what you were doing! What the

hell do you mean by wasting a man like that? Johnny would have gone home by himself. I have a message for the Post Office garrison from Ned Daly—it would be more fitting for him to take that. Don't you know—"

The fair-haired man was grinning.

Morgan said apologetically, "All right. I'm speaking out of turn. You know what you're doing. I can watch the side window for you, at least."

That became his task. Until darkness fell he watched intermittently from his soapbox at the little window, with a view down Henry Street for a few yards and out into Sackville Street if he craned his neck and placed a second box on top of the first. The side door of the Post Office was almost directly opposite, with a window beside it, half filled with sandbags. Over the tops of these he could see right into the building but it was too dark to make out more than the shapes of the men moving about in there. More men came into the room behind him, sniping from the front windows with a deafening echo. One of them exclaimed "Oh, Christ! Oh, Christ!" every time the kick hurt his shoulder.

He could see that he had got himself into a hot corner. Since the Post Office was the main position, it would be heavily attacked as soon as the military reinforcements could fight their way through. This eagle's nest across the narrow street would be right in the line of fire. He felt very old. He was a nuisance to the young men, who were glancing at him now and then. They would be polite, of course, but they had no time to take charge of a decrepit old hero.

All night long, rifle and machine-gun fire rattled from the direction of St. Stephen's Green, but that Monday night was the quietest of the whole week. On Tuesday morning Morgan, who had been given the bed to lie on in deference to his age, woke stiff and cold and dreaming of Pentonville Prison. He came to himself in a second and saw most of the Volunteers sleeping on the floor in different parts of the room, while three watched from the windows. The old woman had gone out last night saying she would sleep at her friend's house in Moore Street and would come back in the morning. She appeared carrying three loaves of bread at eight o'clock and made tea for them all. While they were drinking it, she gave them the news she had picked up.

"Thousands of soldiers is coming in from all quarters, poor little bastards from England that thought they were in France when they got off the boat in Kingstown, and fellas from The Curragh and from Belfast and every barracks all over the country. They can't get into town because the railways is all blown up—"

"That's good news, anyway."

"So they're marching in along the roads and there was a fierce fight at Portobello—Davy's public house is gutted but they didn't catch the men that were in it, whoever they were. Mrs. Brady's daughter came down out of Rathmines Road to stay with her mother, to get away from the fighting, and where has she landed but in Moore Street! That's going to be a queer place, I told her, but she's afraid now to go back to her own place, and she has the baby with her, four months old, and three more at home and no one to see to them with the daddy out in France—"

"What's happening in Sackville Street?"

"Sure, can't you see that by sticking your head out the window?"

"I can't see much. Were you up at the Monument?"

"I was, and they were fixing a big gun up there. There will be no holding out against it. Jesus God! Listen to that!"

There was a tremendous boom a little distance away. The whole building shook and a shower of plaster fell off the ceiling above the stove. Auntie Ellen ran like a beetle to blow it out of her pots, then shook them angrily upside down.

"That's the class of thing that's going on. A woman out in Sackville Street told me she heard one of the officers telling the soldiers to shoot anyone in a green uniform but they're shooting anyone between fifteen and fifty, if you ask me. Sackville Street and Henry Street is strewn with corpses. A dirty pack of thieves is going around grabbing everything out of the windows of the shops. The kids is carting home toys in their arms. I know what I'd have done to one of mine if he brought home something he didn't pay for, but the mothers and fathers are just as bad. There's snipers on the roofs of a lot of the houses and they shooting at the troops whenever they show their noses."

The big guns sounded all day, mixed with the sound of fireworks that the looters had discovered in Lawrence's toyshop. With idiot delight they took these out into the street and set them off, shrieking in mock fear when each one exploded. As darkness came on, the rockets were sent up in the air to light the sky with showers of colored sparks, and smaller fireworks were set off on the ground, whirling among the feet of the crowd. The Corkman fired shots over their heads from his position at the window but they only turned and shook their fists up at him, knowing well that he had no intention of killing them. Morgan leaned out for a look but as the shop was in line with the window he could see very little. Then a different note, a long-drawn-out, high-pitched moan of real respect came from the crowd as an orange glow, too big for a firework, flooded the street with sudden light.

"They've set it on fire, the lunatics!"

They had, and now they moved backward to watch the effect of what they had done. Auntie Ellen was sent down to investigate and came back in a few minutes almost hysterical.

"All the kids is playing soldiers with toy guns out of the shop. It's burning down—there won't be a stone of it left."

"Should we get out now?"

"No— I don't know—"

They looked at her helplessly as she collapsed on the bed in a fit of weeping, defeated at last.

Morgan said, "She shouldn't have been sent down. That's a job for me."

"Very well."

None of the younger men could go. Every move they made, as well as the expression on their faces, would give them away if they were stopped. They let him go, calling after him to bring back some bread if he could. He groped his way down the dark stairs and cautiously let himself out into the street. The crowd had moved back from the fire and were watching it with the strange, unworldly, vacant gaze of people watching a fire anywhere. He moved in among them and worked his way to the middle of the street, where he had a good view. All along Sackville Street the buildings were of varying heights, and Lawrence's being slightly lower than those beside it was burning independently. This was what saved its neighbors. The roof had already fallen in and the side walls of the adjoining houses showed no sign of catching fire. He could report that the snipers' position seemed safe for the moment, though other houses were burning fiercely lower down the street.

No one took notice of him—at his age he might as well have been a woman or a child. As he moved away he saw that the crowd were beginning to run as some heavy artillery shots fell nearby. He went into Henry Street, keeping to the walls, glad that his legs were carrying him so well after what he had seen—a whole building shudder and collapse in a slow, outward movement, dreamily, filling the air with feathery dust. Leaning against the wall of the Post Office he heard singing from inside, a lone voice first and then some others joining in—"Who Fears to Speak of '98." He had hardly believed Auntie Ellen when she had said that they were singing.

The noise of rifle fire and artillery seemed to grow louder by fits and starts, most of it coming from the direction of the river. He turned into Moore Street and was immediately seized by the collar of his coat and held tightly. Then the hands relaxed their hold and a wondering voice said, "Sorry. You walked so straight. What are you doing here?"

Other men were in the street, some in Volunteer uniform like his captor, who now pushed Morgan into a doorway, saying, "There's a machine gun up at the top. We'll have to get in."

"I came out to get some food for the men on the top floor at the corner of Henry Street."

"Who is there?"

"I've only heard their first names—Kevin and Jim and Barney and some others who came later. There's an old woman, too, the tenant of the room."

"I'll get you some bread."

Holding him firmly by the arm, the man pushed him along the passageway to a back room where there was a table covered with oilcloth, a family kitchen table. Several men were sitting at it, on kitchen chairs, studying a street map, bent close over it. They looked up quickly when Morgan was brought in, then one said mildly, "That's my grandfather you've got there."

"Sam!"

"What are you doing here?"

"I haven't been home since yesterday morning. I went down to the Four Courts first and now I'm with a bunch of snipers on top of the corner house at Henry Street."

"*On top* of the house?"

"Well, not exactly. We're in the attic. The old woman got nervous and I came out to get some food and find out what's going on."

He was enjoying Sam's astonishment. It was like talking to Samuel again. At this notion his nerve slipped and he said, "Do you mind if I sit down?"

"Of course—put him there. You can go back to your station."

The man who had brought him in went out.

"What news, Sam?"

"The military are coming in from all sides, though we got possession of the railways early on."

"I heard that they're marching in."

"We worked it out that they'd come from Kingstown by Mount Street because it's the shortest route—the Manual says they must always follow the shortest route and so they did—and several of our fellows held them up for hours at Mount Street Bridge. There's been a big battle at Phibsborough, too, and Heuston held out until today at the Mendicity Institute. No one knows how he did it with only twenty men. I'm afraid they got a bad time of it when they surrendered. Have you any new of how the people are taking it?"

"The separation women were furious. I can guess they won't like it in Rathgar and Merrion Square either. Have you seen Fergal?"

"He's at Boland's Mills with de Valera. Denis is there, too."

Sam's brother Denis, solidly like old Blake, the mill accountant, his grandfather, but with a sense of humor.

"Have you heard how they're doing?"

"They're holding out well. They've been able to send men to find out what's happening in the College of Surgeons. Crossing the river is not so easy, with Trinity College full of soldiers and the O.T.C. snipers on the roof. They have big guns there now and the Army seems to be using it as a sort of headquarters for this side of the city. We don't know how many of the stories are true but the whole picture is clear—it's a war, not a few peasants in a field surrounded by machine guns. It can't be kept quiet. We've broadcast the news on the wireless since yesterday morning, so the Americans will know that we've got going at last. How are things in the Four Courts?"

"I met Ned Daly. He was very cheerful—he told me to tell that in the Post Office."

"They're all cheerful. There's a new breath of spring in the air. Does Grandmama know where you are?"

"My snipers sent out a man to tell Johnny to take the motorcar home and tell her what's happening but I didn't hear what came of it because the man never came back. She'll guess where I am."

Of course she would, and he should get back to her at once.

Sam said, "I'm afraid you won't be able to get home. If you were at the other side of the river it wouldn't be so bad, but from tonight onward, it will be dangerous to try to cross any of the bridges. Can you get back to that place on the corner where you've been? It's as good as any other."

"Of course I'm going back. I promised to bring them some bread."

69

At eight o'clock the next morning, Wednesday, they heard the thunder of shells falling on Liberty Hall and soon afterward the big guns from Trinity College firing into Sackville Street. Others were placed at the Parnell Monument, and all day long Morgan saw with mounting horror the precision with which they were able to land their missiles in the Post Office and the other buildings. At night the center of the city was lit up with flaring orange and red patches that came and went as the fires spread from one house to the next.

During Thursday night the snipers decided to abandon their position.

The Corkman said, "This is no place for a minister's son. Tomorrow will finish it. Ah, come on now, Auntie, don't upset yourself. You can come with us."

She looked around in despair and then said, "A good job I never kept a cat."

They hurried down the stairs, the Corkman going in front, the old woman and Morgan bringing up the rear. He had to hurry to keep up with them and found that he was puffing like a steam engine by the time they rounded the corner into Henry Street, which had been raked by machine-gun fire all day. They sheltered in doorways, ran a few yards and sheltered again, then slid around the corner into Moore Street. The younger men were trotting like foxes, as if they could have gone on for hours. They darted into the house he had been in before.

It was crowded with Volunteers now. He peered around for Sam and then asked one of the young men that he remembered from his last visit, "Where is my grandson, Flaherty?"

"He's in the G.P.O.," the boy said excitedly. "They're moving over here soon. Commandant Connolly has been wounded. The whole place is on fire. Commandant Pearse has sent over a document to be printed but we haven't a hope of doing it." He took a sheaf of papers off the table, Government stationery, covered in neatly written block capitals. "Here, read it. No one will stop you."

By the light of the candle on the table Morgan read slowly. It was addressed from the Headquarters of the Army of the

Irish Republic, General Post Office, Dublin, with the date of April 28, 1916, at 9:30 A.M. It was to have been issued tomorrow.

"The forces of the Irish Republic, which was proclaimed in Dublin on Easter Monday, 24th April, have been in possession of the central part of the Capital since 12 noon on that day. Up to yesterday afternoon headquarters was in touch with all the main outlying positions, and despite furious and almost continuous assault by the British Forces all those positions were then still being held, and the Commandants in charge were confident of their ability to hold them for a long time.

"During the course of yesterday afternoon and evening, the enemy succeeded in cutting our communications with our other positions in the City, and Headquarters is today isolated.

"The enemy has burned down whole blocks of houses, apparently with the object of giving themselves a clear field for the play of Artillery and Field Guns against us. We have been bombarded during the evening and night by Shrapnel and Machine Gun fire, but without material damage to our position, which is of great strength.

"We are busy completing arrangements for the final defense of Headquarters and are determined to hold it while the buildings last. I desire now, lest I may not have an opportunity later, to pay homage to the gallantry of the Soldiers of Irish Freedom who have during the past four days been writing with fire and steel the most glorious chapter of the later history of Ireland. Justice can never be done to their heroism, to their discipline, to their gay and unconquerable spirit, in the midst of peril and death.

"Let me, who have led them into this, speak in my own and in my fellow commanders' names and in the name of Ireland present and to come, their praise, and ask those who come after them to remember them.

"For four days they have fought and toiled, almost without cessation, almost without sleep, and in the intervals of fighting they have sung songs of the freedom of Ireland. No man has complained, no man has asked 'why?' Each individual has spent himself, happy to pour out his strength for Ireland and for freedom. If they do not win this fight, they will at least have deserved to win it. But win it they will, although they may win it in death. Already they have won a great thing. They have redeemed Dublin from many shames and made her name splendid among the names of Cities.

"If I were to mention names of individuals my list would be a long one. I will name only that of Commandant General

James Connolly, commanding the Dublin Division. He lies wounded, but is still the guiding brain of our resistance."

A wave of sudden activity by the door made Morgan hurry to the end of the document.

"For my part, as to anything I have done in this, I am not afraid to face either the judgment of God or the judgment of posterity.

P. H. Pearse, Commandant General, Commanding-in-Chief the Army of the Irish Republic and President of the Provisional Government."

As he placed the document carefully on the table he could almost feel the ghosts of John O'Leary and O'Donovan Rossa and Michael Davitt and Parnell reading over his shoulder. He stood up as Sam came hurrying toward him.

"Grandpapa! Oh, my God! You're still here!"

"I couldn't get away but I'm all right. It doesn't matter about me anymore. Things are bad over there?"

"Yes, but we're holding out still. You're worse off here than you were before."

"It doesn't matter, I tell you. Forget about me. I've been in much tighter corners in my day."

"You can go to a house a few doors away, where we're sending all the civilians in this part of the street. It's been well worth it, remember that. I've heard people have changed during the week—everything will be changed after this—remember that."

"I'll remember."

How could this boy tell him, at eighty-seven years of age, to remember?

Sam was smiling, saying, "And you'll see that Molly gets a memento of me. Here, I'll give you this."

He was pulling his twenty-first birthday watch on its long gold chain out of his breeches pocket. Morgan put out his hand slowly and took it without speaking. Then Samuel turned away and went outside again.

A few minutes later, Morgan and Auntie Ellen and the two families who lived on the upper floors of the building were being escorted down the street. Morgan hoped he could pass for one of them by now, his dark-gray suit wrinkled and dusty, his white shirt grubby, his boots stained, probably even his face dirty, since he had had no chance to wash. In his pocket he fingered the watch. He was to survive all this, to take it to Sam's Molly, as good a reason as any other for not insisting on remaining. They wouldn't have let him—they were far too efficient for anything as foolish as that.

Their new quarters were in a flat over a huckster's shop, filled with a powerful smell of rotting vegetables from the yard below, where old cabbages and potatoes had decayed immemorially. The owner was a small, stooped man with a long, anxious, ratlike face. He had pulled his trousers on over his nightshirt but his feet were bare. He was very sympathetic to Morgan because of his age, placing him carefully in the best chair in the parlor and squatting beside him on the floor to comfort him.

"God help you, to be turned out of your house at this hour of your life." He looked more closely at Morgan. "I don't know you. You don't live in Moore Street?"

"No. I was caught in town on Monday. I couldn't get home since."

"You're from the west?"

"How do you know?"

"I'd know the accent anywhere. I'm from Tuam myself but I'm nearly fifty years in Dublin."

"You must have come as a boy."

Morgan was diverted in spite of himself.

"Yes. The granny had the shop and it was cheaper than going to America. I walked it from Tuam in ten days and never went back. Do you go back?"

"Yes. I have a place there—Moycullen, outside Galway."

"Well for you. I'd like to go back some time but you can never leave a shop, day or night. What's your name, sir?"

"Connolly. Morgan Connolly."

"The Fenian?"

"Yes."

A ratlike paw seized his hand and shook it agitatedly. Then he said, "I'll have to tell the missus who we have in the house. She'd kill me if I didn't tell her."

He weaved his way through the mass of his guests and came back dragging by the hand a little fat woman with tightly screwed-up hair and round, good-humored eyes. She was clutching an old shawl around her over her nightdress.

She knelt on the floor beside his knees, saying in a low voice, with a strong Dublin accent, "Don't get up, sir. Aren't you fine there? You're very welcome to our house. It's poor hospitality, all pushing and shoving together. Mickey was telling me you're the Fenian Connolly—we're honored, that's what we are. Wait a while now and I'll have a bed for you. The chiselers can move out."

"No, please—"

"Why wouldn't they? It's all they can do for you. I'll rouse you if there's need."

She left him then and came back soon to lead him away to a cubbyhole on the half-landing where there was a double bed newly made up with clean sheets. He lay down gratefully, in his clothes, as he had always done when he was on the run. The sound of the guns was muffled here and he slept a little, waking in a sweat now and then, with the idea that the house was burning down.

All day Friday they were not allowed to go out. The children of the displaced families were crotchety and whined a lot, especially the older ones of nine and ten who felt angry at being confined. In the late afternoon, Morgan collected them from their frantic mothers and sat them around him in the parlor while he tried to entertain them with stories.

"Once there was a king, the king of all Ireland, and his name was Conor MacNessa."

At first they fidgeted but soon they were listening to the Three Sorrows of Storytelling, long, leisurely, sad stories, meant to occupy each a week of winter nights. It was the way in which he used to amuse Julia's children, and Anna's, and later Fergal's, and he chose the stories now because he knew them so well. Then he wished he had begun on something more cheerful but it was too late to change. When they began to slide to the floor in sleep, gradually he stopped speaking, leaning his head against the tall back of the chair.

Another weary night in the dark little room was an intolerable prospect. Morgan said he would rather sit in the kitchen with Mickey and hear the news as it came in, since they would not let him go out into the street. The Post Office was a ruin and the garrison had moved into the other end of Moore Street. Many had been killed crossing Henry Street and the rest had had to tunnel their way through the walls of the houses.

On Saturday morning Mickey went out early and came back white-faced and stuttering. The soldiers were going wild up in North King Street, breaking into the houses and shooting any men they found. Some had buried the corpses in the backyards and covered them over with debris to hide the places. The garrison at Boland's Mills was holding out, according to a Volunteer he had spoken to, and so were the College of Surgeons and the Four Courts.

"But there's talk of surrender," Mickey said. "Commandant Pearse says the people musn't suffer any more. That's all he's thinking of—the people." He rocked up and down, his head in his hands. "Will we never be free? Will it go on until the end of the world?"

"This time it's different," Morgan said.

When they heard that Pearse had surrendered, he and Mickey went out through the yard into a narrow lane at the back of the house. The shooting seemed to have stopped in the center of the city but they could hear occasional rifle fire from the direction of the river. A small, worried man with bandy legs was trotting along the lane, going to feed his horses, he said anxiously. He was a dray driver and hadn't been able to get out to them for two days. Mickey led the way along the lane for a few yards, then through the kitchens of a hotel, into another lane, and out onto Sackville Street. A wave of nausea made Morgan reel against a wall but he recovered at once. Mickey was gazing around him, dazed, and had noticed nothing. They had come out near the Parnell Monument where a group of soldiers was standing. People were pouring out of the side streets into Sackville Street. They were keeping near the remaining walls and were rather subdued. It was cold, and the recent rain seemed to have strengthened the sour stench of the burned houses.

They moved along to join a small group of Mickey's neighbors from Moore Street who were standing at the corner opposite the Rotunda Hospital. Some of them had been out earlier and were anxious to tell how they had actually seen Commandant Pearse hand over his sword and pistol to the English general. They had seen him driven away in a motorcar and no one knew where he was now. The soldiers had said that they would all be shot. The voices buzzed vaguely in Morgan's ears. Above all things he wanted to find Sam. Fergal might have to die with Pearse but Sam—Samuel—was too innocent to be caught up in violence. That was the other Samuel, the one whom everyone had loved. Why all this blood, generation after generation?

A voice shouted, "Here they come!"

Out into Sackville Street a small column of Volunteers was marching in perfect formation, their rifles on their shoulders, their faces deathly tired, but singing as they marched. A scattered cheer went up from both sides of the street, then angry jeers and booing, then more cheering. Morgan could scarcely believe it; the Volunteers were singing:

> "'O wrap the green flag round me, boys—
> To die were far more sweet

He saw Ned Daly out in front. The marched to the Monument, where Parnell looked proudly down, and they laid their arms at his feet before lining up at the opposite side of the street. Twenty minutes later, the Moore Street men appeared. As they came closer to the Monument, a group of women rushed out from the sidewalk and screamed insults at them. Some threw bottles and stones but missed their mark, they flung so wildly.

Other women went out to pull them back but they knelt in the street and would not move, raising their hands high to curse as they had done on the first day, spitting and calling out, "Yez pack of bowsies! Murderers! Ah, the devil take the whole lot of yez!"

Among the Volunteers, Morgan saw Sam.

After that, nothing more mattered. Throughout the night, the men lay on the wet grass with machine guns trained on them, while a half-crazy British officer darted here and there, yelling at them, threatening to shoot them dead if they moved, preventing them from urinating by kicking them or knocking them down with a rifle butt. The hysterical foreign voices yapped like the bark of foxes.

"Which are the Shinners or the Germans the worse, boys?"

"The Shinners, sir!"

"Then what should we do with these swine?"

"Shoot them, sir!"

"Aye, and shoot them we will!"

The officer lit a match and held it close to the prisoners' faces, yelling, "Who wants to come over and see the animals? Beautiful specimens, Irish soldiers, grandfathers, cripples, a magnificent army!"

After a long time, Morgan felt himself being pulled away. Like a sleepwalker he followed Mickey, hardly aware that he was placing one foot in front of another. He had seen something that he had never thought to see in this life, a strange, terrible experience: he had seen the proof of victory in the eyes of an ancient enemy. Now at last he could go home.

GLOSSARY

Agrá Literally "My love." A term of endearment commonly used when speaking either Irish or English.

American wake The party given before someone emigrated, called a wake because the emigrants were as unlikely to return as the dead.

Ashplants Sticks cut from an ash tree, very strong and supple.

Bawneen Undyed white tweed cloth.

Bianconi car Named after the Italian Bianconi who came to Ireland about 1830 to sell religious prints and later set up in business with horse-drawn transport between small towns in Tipperary. His business eventually extended to the whole country. The cars were drawn by four horses and were long, uncovered, with the passengers sitting facing outward, back to back. Bianconi owned inns and stables throughout the country and became very wealthy.

Boreen A lane.

Bothán A hut.

Bowsies Low, ignorant, rough people—slang word used only in Dublin.

The Castle Dublin Castle, official seat of Lords Lieutenant of Ireland and therefore administrative center of British Government in Ireland from 1565 to 1922.

Currach A light boat covered with tarred canvas, used for inshore fishing.

Draughts The game known in America as checkers.

Eaveshoots Gutters which carry off roof water.

Gombeen man One who exacts a high rate of interest or sells to poor people at high prices, especially in hard times. A small merchant.

Haggard The enclosure for the farm buildings, also containing hay and corn stacks.

Hedge schools Open-air schools. The term was used of any school held in a barn or shed during the times when education was forbidden to Catholics in Ireland.

Hob A built-in fireside made of stone.

Jennet A cross between a female donkey and a horse.

Long car Same as Bianconi car.

Loy A spade with a heavy-tipped blade and one lug, used very much in Connacht, especially for cultivating potatoes.

Outside car The usual Irish name for what is known in America as a jaunting car. It is drawn by one horse, with the driver on a low box and the four passengers facing outward, back to back, as with the Bianconi car.

Peelers Derisive name for policemen in Ireland, because the force was set up during the Secretaryship of Sir Robert Peel.

Pilch A triangular piece of flannel, tied with tape at the waist and pinned between the legs, worn over a baby's diapers.

Poteen Illicit whiskey.

Quarter day The day when the rent was due, usually every three months—that is, every quarter year. Sometimes called the gale day.

Rackrent Excessive rent exacted for land.

Ribbonmen An agrarian association whose members wore a colored ribbon at nightly meetings.

Segoshioners Cronies.

Shebeen An unlicensed house selling alcoholic drink.

Slanes Implements resembling long-handled, narrow-bladed spades, used for cutting turf out of the bog.

Sleeveen A sly-mannered person, a schemer, a trickster. One who curries favor through cowardice.

Sloe Small, bluish-black wild plum, the fruit of the blackthorn.

Sold the pass Betrayed the people.

Solly Cohen A typical Jewish moneylender's name.

Sponging house A bailiff's house for temporary lodging of arrested debtors.

Squireen A derisive term to designate an upstart who is putting on the airs of a landowner or squire.

Stooleens Small stools.

Tallyhoes Followers of the hunt—from the huntsman's cry of "Tallyho!" to the hounds when the fox is viewed.

On the tapis Literally, "on the carpet"—in the picture.

Whiteboys Same as Ribbonmen, the insigne in this case being a white shirt.